301
CIRCUITS

Elektor Electronics (Publishing)
P.O. Box 1414
Dorchester DT2 8YH
England

The publishers have used their best efforts in ensuring the correctness of the information contained in this book. They do not assume, and hereby disclaim, any liability to any party for any loss or damage caused by errors or omissions in this book, whether such errors or omissions result from negligence, accident or any other cause

British Library Cataloguing in Publication Data
   A catalogue record for this book is available from
   the British Library

ISBN 0 905705 12 2

First published in the United Kingdom 1983
Reprinted 1983, 1984 (with corrections), 1987, 1992, 1994

© Elektuur BV

Printed in the Netherlands by Bariet BV, Ruinen

704125 £9·95.
621.38153

WARNING: electricity is dangerous

The projects in this book are, to the best of the Publisher's knowledge and belief, both accurately described and safe. None the less, great care must always be taken when assembling electronic circuits that carry mains voltages: the Publishers cannot accept responsibility for any accidents that may occur.

Because electricity is dangerous, its use, application and transmission are subject to rules, regulations and guidance. These are laid down in numerous laws, Electricity Generating Board regulations, British Standards and recommendations of the Institution of Electrical Engineers (IEE). Some of these may be obtained from your local electricity showroom, but most, if not all, should be available for reference in your local library.

decoder

Semiconductor types

Very often, a large number of equivalent semiconductors exist with different type numbers. For this reason, 'abbreviated' type numbers are used in Elektor wherever possible:

- '741' stand for μA 741, LM 741, MC 741, MIC 741, RM 741, SN 72741, etc.
- 'TUP' or 'TUN' (Transistor, Universal, PNP or NPN respectively) stand for any low frequency silicon transistor that meets the following specifications:

UCEO, max	20 V
IC, max	100 mA
hfe, min	100
Ptot, max	100 mW
fT, min	100 MHz

Some 'TUN's are: BC 107, BC 108 and BC 109 families; 2N3856A, 2N3859, 2N3860, 2N3904, 2N3947, 2N4124. Some 'TUP's are: BC 177 and BC 178 families; BC 179 family with the possible exception of BC 159 and BC 179; 2N2412, 2N3251, 2N3906, 2N4126, 2N4291.

- 'DUS' or 'DUG' (Diode Universal, Silicon or Germanium respectively) stands for any diode that meets the following specifications:

	DUS	DUG
UR, max	25 V	20 V
IF, max	100 mA	35 mA
IR, max	1 μA	100 μA
Ptot, max	250 mW	250 mW
CD, max	5 pF	10 pF

Some 'DUS's are: BA 127, BA 217, BA 218, BA 221, BA 222, BA 317, BA 318, BAX 13, BAY 61, 1N914, 1N4148.

Some 'DUG's are: OA 85, OA 91, OA 95, AA 116.

- 'BC 107B', 'BC 237B', 'BC 547B' all refer to the same 'family' of almost identical better-quality silicon transistors. In general, any other member of the same family can be used instead.

BC 107 (-8, -9) families
BC 107 (-8, -9), BC 147 (-8, -9), BC 207 (-8, -9), BC 237 (-8, -9), BC 317 (-8, -9), BC 347 (-8, -9), BC 547 (-8, -9), BC 171 (-2, -3), BC 182 (-3, -4), BC 382 (-3, -4), BC 437 (-8, -9), BC 414

BC 177 (-8, -9) families
BC 177 (-8, -9), BC 157 (-8, -9), BC 204 (-5, -6), BC 307 (-8, -9), BC 320 (-1, -2), BC 350 (-1, -2), BC 557 (-8, -9), BC 251 (-2, -3), BC 212 (-3, -4), BC 512 (-3, -4), BC 261 (-2, -3), BC 416.

Resistor and capacitor values

When giving component values, decimal points and large numbers of zeros are avoided wherever possible. The decimal point is usually replaced by one of the following abbreviations:

p	(pico-)	= 10^{-12}
n	(nano-)	= 10^{-9}
μ	(micro-)	= 10^{-6}
m	(milli-)	= 10^{-3}
k	(kilo-)	= 10^3
M	(mega-)	= 10^6
G	(giga-)	= 10^9

A few examples:
Resistance value 2k7: 2700 Ω.
Resistance value 470: 470 Ω,
Capacitance value 4p7: 4.7 pF,
or 0.000 000 000 004 7 F . . .
Capacitance value 10 n: this is the international way of writin writing 10,000 pF or .01 μF, since 1 n is 10^{-9} farads or 1000 pF.

Resistors are ¼ Watt 5% carbon types, unless otherwise specified. The DC working voltage of capacitors (other than electrolytics) is normally assumed to be at least 60 V. As a rule of thumb, a safe value is usually approximately twice the DC supply voltage.

Test voltages
The DC test voltages shown are measured with a 20 kΩ/V instrument, unless otherwise specified.

U, not V
The international letter symbol 'U' for voltage is often used instead of the ambiguous 'V'. 'V' is normally reserved for 'volts'. For instance: U_b = 10 V, not V_b = 10 V.

Mains voltages
No mains (power line) voltages are listed in Elektor circuits. It is assumed that our readers know what voltage is standard in their part of the world!
Readers in countries that use 60 Hz should note that Elektor circuits are designed for 50 Hz operation. This will not normally be a problem; however, in cases where the mains frequency is used for synchronisation some modification may be required.

contents

22, Voltmeter

1 Automatic emergency lighting unit

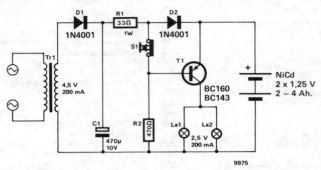

This unit charges a nickel-cadmium battery from the mains to provide a standby power supply for emergency lighting in the event of a mains failure. When the mains supply drops out, the lighting is switched on automatically.

The circuit of the unit is extremely simple. Tr1, D1 and C1 provide a halfwave rectified and smoothed DC supply of approx. 6 V, which is used to continuously charge the Ni-Cad battery at about 100 mA via R1 and D2. A 2 Ah Ni-Cad can safely be charged at this rate.

The voltage drop across D2 reverse-biases the base-emitter junction of T1, so that this transistor is turned off and the lamps are not lit. When the mains supply fails, however, T1 is supplied with base current via R2; the transistor therefore turns on and the lamps are lit. As soon as the mains supply is restored, T1 will turn off, the lamps are extinguished and the battery is once more charged via R1 and D2.

The unit can be mounted wherever emergency lighting will be required in the event of a power failure. An obvious example is in that infamous dark cupboard under the stairs, so that, should a fuse blow, a replacement can be easily found and fitted.

A transformer with a slightly higher secondary voltage can be used, provided that R1 is uprated to limit the current through this resistor to 100 mA.

2 Pseudo random running lamp

If a number of the outputs of a shift register are fed back in a certain fashion via an EXOR gate to the data input, then the Q outputs of the register will run through the maximum possible number of mutually different logic states. By using the Q outputs to drive LEDs a visual representation of the truth table for a shift register with EXOR feedback is obtained. At each clock pulse a logic '1' (LED lights up) or '0' moves up one place, so that the net result is a running light.

In this circuit the Q outputs of the shift register (IC2), which is seven bits long, are routed via an EXOR gate (N1...N4) back to pin 7, the data input, of the register. The clock signal is provided by IC1. The clock frequency, and hence the speed of the running light, can be altered by means of P1. R4...R17 and T1...T7 are included to drive the LEDs. R18, R19, C3 and D8 ensure that when the circuit is switched on, a logic '1' appears at the data input, which means that the register output state can never be all zeroes.

The circuit can be extended for use as a light organ. The LEDs are replaced by opto-couplers which, via the necessary hardware (triac etc.) control incandescent lamps.

A rectified version of the audio signal is fed via R3 to the control input of IC1, where it is used to modulate the clock frequency of the register and

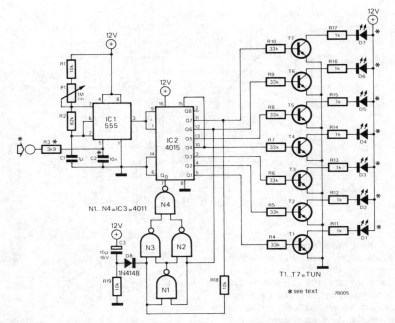

hence the speed of the running light. Capacitor C2 may then be omitted. Varying the control voltage between 0 and 15 V will result in the clock frequency being varied between 50 and 150% of the value obtained with the control input left floating.

3 Phaser

In contrast to lowpass or highpass filters, the gain of an all-pass filter remains constant over the range of frequencies at which it is used, but it does introduce a frequency-dependent phase shift. A number of all-pass filters may be cascaded to produce a phasing unit for use in electronic music. The phasing effect is produced by phase-shifting a signal and then summing the original and phase-shifted versions of the signal.

Figure 1 shows the basic circuit of a first order all-pass filter. The phase-shift is dependent on the relative values of R and C and on the input frequency. At low frequencies C has a very high impedance and the circuit simply functions as an inverting amplifier, so the phase-shift is 180°. At high frequencies the impedance of C is low and the circuit functions as a non-inverting amplifier with zero phase-shift.

The gain of the filter depends on the relative values of R1 and R2. In this case R1 and R2 are chosen equal so that the gain is unity. The graph shows the phase-shift v. frequency curve for the filter.

The complete circuit of a phasing unit using all-pass filters is shown in figure 2. Six all-pass filter stages are cascaded, so the total phase-shift at low frequencies can be up to 1080°! The use of a total of ten op-amps in the circuit may seem rather excessive, but as eight of these are LM324 quad op-amps the total package count is only four ICs.

IC1a functions as a unity gain input buffer and IC1b to IC2c are the six filter stages. The direct and phase-shifted signals are summed by IC2d. The proportion of phase-shifted signal and hence the depth of phasing can be adjusted by means of P4.

The degree of phase-shift at a particular frequency can be varied by FETs T1 to T6, which function as voltage controlled resistors. By vary-

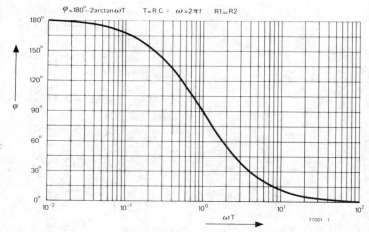

$$\varphi = 180° - 2\arctan\omega T \qquad T = R.C \; ; \quad \omega = 2\pi f \qquad R1 = R2$$

77001 1

ing the gate voltage the drain-source resistance can be increased or decreased, thus altering the effective value of 'R' in each all-pass filter and hence varying the phase-shift. This may be controlled either manually by means of P3 or may be swept up and down automatically by the output of the triangular wave generator consisting of IC3 and IC4. As the gate voltage of the FETs must always be negative the output of this oscillator swings between −2 and −6 V.
The oscillator frequency may be varied by means of P1, and the best phasing effect occurs at fre-

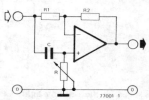

77001 1

quencies between 0.5 Hz and 1 Hz. At higher frequencies (around 4 Hz) the phasing effect is lost but a vibrato effect is obtained instead.

2

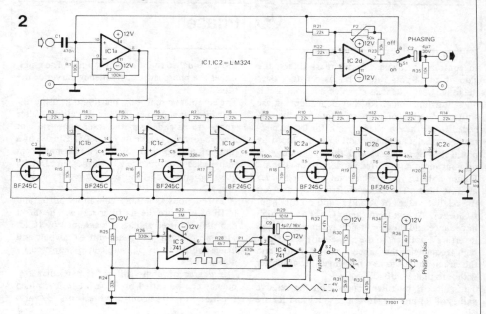

77001 2

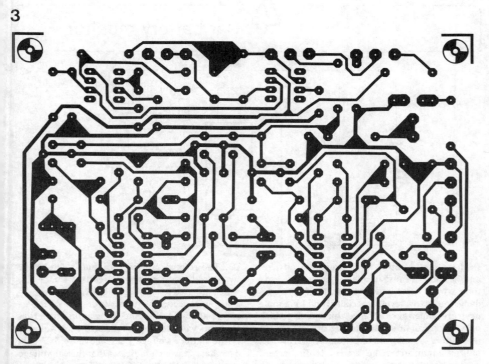

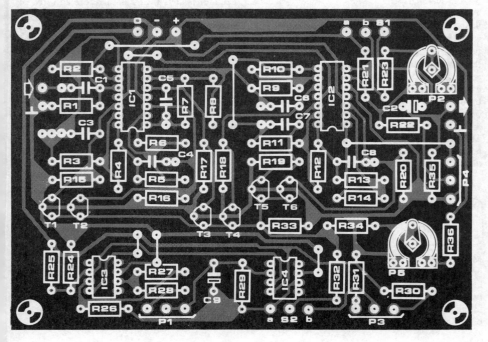

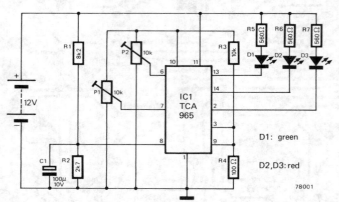

D1: green

D2,D3: red

78001

In the winter months, when starting is difficult and headlamps must frequently be used, it is all too easy for a car battery to be discharged to a dangerously low level, especially if no long journeys are undertaken. Hence this circuit, which provides continuous monitoring of the state of the battery, should prove extremely useful. The unit will indicate if the battery is discharged, o.k. or overcharged.

The circuit is based on the Siemens IC type TCA 965. This IC is a complete window comparator, which will indicate whether the input voltage lies between two preset reference voltages, is below the low reference voltage or above the high reference voltage. These three conditions are indicated by three LEDs, which are driven directly by the IC. The IC also has a reference voltage output, which can be used to derive the upper and lower thresholds of the 'window'.

The circuit is powered from the 12 V car battery, and the battery voltage is also fed, via potential divider R1/R2, to the monitoring input of the

IC. The reference voltage output is fed to the two threshold inputs via presets P1 and P2, which are used to calibrate the circuit.

The lowest acceptable voltage for a 12 V battery is about 11.5 V, and P1 is adjusted so that D1 lights when the input falls below this voltage. If the battery voltage rises above 14.5 V it is overcharged, which indicates that the car voltage regulator is at fault. P2 is therefore adjusted so that D3 is lit for input voltages above 14.5 V. Between 11.5 V and 14.5 V the green LED should light, indicating that the condition of the battery is satisfactory.

It will be noticed that the LEDs do not light and extinguish at exactly the same voltage. This is due to a hysteresis of 60 mV which is incorporated into the IC to prevent the LEDs flickering when the battery voltage is close to the threshold levels.

Siemens Application Note

TAP-tip

Many circuits for TAPs (Touch Activated Programme switches) have previously been published. However, all of these required the use of two pairs of touch contacts, one to set the TAP to the 'on' position and one to reset it to the 'off' position. The novel feature of this circuit is that it requires only one touch contact. Touching the contact once sets the TAP; touching it a second time resets the TAP.

N1 and N2 form a flip-flop (bistable multivibrator). Assume that initially the output of N2 is low. The inputs of N1 are also pulled low via R2,

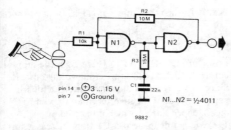

pin 14 = ⊕ 3 ... 15 V
pin 7 = ⊙ Ground

C1 22n

N1...N2 = ½ 4011

9882

so the output of N1 is high. The inputs of N2 are thus high, which satisfies the criterion for the output to be low, which was the original assumption. C1 is charged to logic high through R3 from the high output of N1. If the touch contacts are now bridged by a finger, the logic high on C1 will be applied to the inputs of N1 through R1 and the skin resistance. The output of N1 will

go low, so the output of N2 will go high, holding the inputs of N1 high even if the finger is removed. The TAP is now set.

Once the finger is removed, C1 will discharge through R3 into the low output of N1. If the touch contacts are subsequently bridged, the inputs of N1 will be pulled low by C1 (since it is now discharged). The output of N1 will thus go high and the output of N2 low, which will hold the inputs of N1 low even after the finger has been removed. The TAP is now reset to its original state. C1 will charge to logic high through R3 from the output of N1, ready for the contact to be touched again.

The only constraint on the operation of the circuit is that the interval between successive operations of the switch must be at least half a second to allow C1 time to charge and discharge.

CMOS function generator

Using only one inexpensive CMOS IC and a handful of discrete components, it is possible to build a versatile function generator that will provide a choice of three waveforms over the entire audio spectrum and beyond.

The aim of this project was to produce a simple, cost-effective, general purpose audio generator, which was easy to build and use. This aim has certainly been achieved, since the circuit offers a choice of sine, square and triangle waveforms and a frequency range from about 12 Hz to 70

kHz, yet uses only one CMOS hex inverter IC and a few discrete components. Of course, the design does not offer the performance of more sophisticated circuits, particularly as regards waveform quality at higher frequencies, but it is nonetheless an extremely useful instrument for audio work.

Block diagram
Figure 1 illustrates the operating principles of the circuit. The heart of the generator is a triangle/squarewave generator consisting of an integrator and a Schmitt trigger. When the output of the Schmitt trigger is high, the voltage fed back from the Schmitt output to the input of the integrator causes the integrator output to ramp negative until it reaches the lower trigger threshold of the Schmitt trigger. At this point the output of the Schmitt trigger goes low, and the low voltage fed back to the integrator input causes it to ramp positive until the upper trigger threshold of the Schmitt trigger is reached. The output of the Schmitt trigger again goes high, and the integrator output ramps negative again, and so on. The positive- and negative-going sweeps of the integrator output make up a triangular waveform, whose amplitude is determined by the hysteresis of the Schmitt trigger (i.e. the difference between the upper and lower trigger thresholds). The output of the Schmitt trigger is, of

13

1

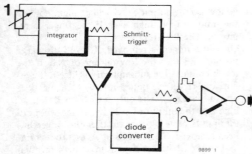

position, when the output of N3 is high a current

$$\frac{U_b - U_t}{P_1 + R_1}$$

flows through R1 and P1, where U_b is the supply voltage and U_t is the threshold voltage of N1. Since this current cannot flow into the high impedance input of the inverter, it all flows into C1 or C2 (depending on which is selected by S1). The voltage drop across C1 thus increases linearly, so the output voltage of N1 falls linearly until the lower threshold voltage of the Schmitt trigger is reached, when the output of the Schmitt trigger goes low. A current

$$\frac{-U_t}{P_1 + R_1}$$

now flows through R1 and P1. This current also flows into C1, so the output voltage of N1 rises linearly until the upper threshold voltage of the Schmitt trigger is reached, when the output of the Schmitt trigger goes high and the whole cycle repeats.

To ensure symmetry of the triangle waveform (i.e. the same slope on both positive-going and negative-going portions of the waveform) the charge and discharge currents of the capacitor must be equal, which means that $U_b - U_t$ must equal U_t. Unfortunately U_t is determined by the characteristics of the CMOS inverter and is typically 55% of supply voltage, so $U_b - U_t$ is about 2.7 V with a 6 V supply and U_t is about 3.3 V.

This difficulty is overcome by means of P2, which allows symmetry adjustment. Assume for the moment that R — is connected to the positive

course a square wave consisting of alternate high and low output states.

The triangle output is fed through a buffer amplifier to a diode shaper, which 'rounds off' the peaks and troughs of the triangle to produce an approximation to a sinewave signal.

Any one of the three waveforms may then be selected by a three-position switch and fed to an output buffer amplifier. The frequency of all three signals is varied by altering the integrator time constant, which changes the rate at which the integrator ramps, and hence the signal frequency.

Complete circuit

The practical circuit of the CMOS function generator is given in figure 2. The integrator is based on a CMOS inverter, N1, whilst the Schmitt trigger uses two inverters with positive feedback, N2 and N3.

The circuit functions as follows; assuming, for the moment, that the wiper of P2 is at its lowest

2

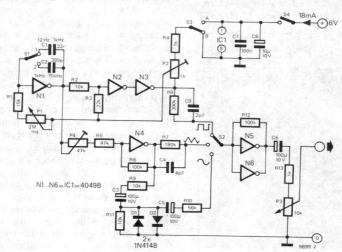

Figure 1. Block diagram of the CMOS function generator.

Figure 2. Complete circuit of the function generator.

Photos. The three output waveforms produced by the function generator.

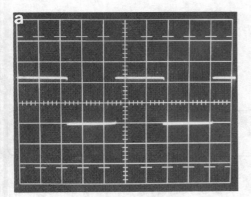

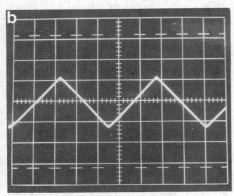

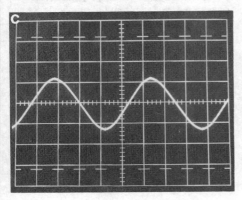

supply rail (position A). Whatever the setting of P2, the high output voltage of the Schmitt trigger is always U_b. However, when the output of N3 is low, R4 and P2 form a potential divider so that a voltage from 0 V to 3 V can be fed back to P1, depending on the wiper setting of P2. This means that the voltage across R1 and P1 is no longer $-U_t$ but $U_{P_2} - U_t$. If the slider voltage of P2 is about 0.6 V then $U_{P_2} - U_t$ will be around -2.7 V, so the charge and discharge currents will be the same. Of course, the adjustment of P2 must be carried out to suit each individual function generator, owing to the tolerance in the value of U_t. In cases where U_t is less than 50% of the supply voltage, it will be necessary to connect the top of R4 to ground (position B).

Two frequency ranges are provided, which are selected by means of S1; 12 Hz-1 kHz and 1 kHz to about 70 kHz. Fine frequency control is provided by P1 which varies the charge and discharge current of C1 or C2 and hence the rate at which the integrator ramps up and down.

The squarewave output from N3 is taken via a waveform selector switch, S2, to a buffer amplifier, which consists of two inverters (connected in parallel to boost their output current capability) biased as a linear amplifier. The triangle output is taken through a buffer amplifier N4, and thence through the selector switch to the output buffer amplifier.

The triangle output from N4 is also taken to the sine shaper, which consists of R9, R11, C3, D1 and D2. Up to about plus or minus 0.5 volts D1 and D2 draw little current, but above this voltage their dynamic resistance falls and they limit the peaks and troughs of the triangle signal logarithmically to produce an approximation to a sinewave. The sine output is fed via C5 and R10 to the output amplifier.

Sine purity is adjusted by P4, which varies the gain of N4 and thus the amplitude of the triangle signal fed to the sine shaper. Too low a signal level, and the triangle amplitude will be below the diode threshold voltage, so that it will pass without alteration; too high a signal level, and the peaks and troughs will be clipped severely, thus not giving a good sine wave.

The input resistors to the output buffer amplifier are chosen so that all three waveforms have a peak to peak output voltage of about 1.2 V maximum. The output level can be adjusted by P3.

Adjustment procedure

The adjustment procedure consists simply of adjusting the triangle symmetry and sine purity.

Triangle symmetry is actually best adjusted by observing the squarewave signal, since a symmetrical triangle is obtained when the squarewave duty-cycle is 50% (1-1 mark-space ratio). P2 is adjusted to achieve this. In cases where the symmetry improves as the wiper of P2 is turned down towards the outpu f N3 but exact symmetry cannot be obtainec he top of R4 should be connected in the alternative position.

Sine purity is adjusted by varying P4 until the waveform 'looks right' or by adjusting for minimum distortion if a distortion meter is available. Since the supply voltage alters the output voltage of the various waveforms, and hence the sine purity, the circuit should be operated from a stable

6 V supply. If batteries are used they should never be allowed to run down too far.

CMOS ICs used as linear circuits draw more current than when used in the normal switching mode, and the supply voltage should not be greater than 6 V, otherwise the IC may overheat due to excessive power dissipation.

Performance

The quality of the waveforms can be judged from the oscilloscope photographs. In all three cases the vertical sensitivity is 500 mV/div and the timebase speed 200 μ s/div.

---

7 Zener tester

This simple tester provides a reliable means of measuring zener voltages and of plotting the variation of zener voltage with zener current.

In many cases the breakdown voltage of a zener diode is printed, fairly clearly, on the case. For example, the type number of the zener family is often printed, together with the zener voltage, so a BZY88 6V8 would be a 6.8 V zener from the BZY88 family. Unfortunately, some manufacturers merely print an indecipherable code, which has to be looked up in the relevant data book in order to find the zener parameters. Furthermore, there is sometimes a requirement for testing 'job lots' of unmarked devices, or components that have been lying in the junkbox and have had their markings rubbed off. In all these cases a zener tester can prove a useful addition to the 'lab' test equipment.

The reverse characteristic of a zener diode is illustrated in figure 1. At voltages below the zener voltage the device draws very little current. Once the breakdown voltage is reached any further increase in voltage will produce a large increase in current, i.e. above its breakdown voltage the zener diode behaves as a more or less constant voltage device. However, since the zener diode possesses a finite internal resistance (known as the dynamic resistance), the zener voltage will vary slightly with current, due to the voltage dropped across this internal resistance. Because of this, manufacturers always quote zener voltage at a certain current (usually between 5 and 10

mA).

It is, of course, possible to test a zener diode using a battery, series resistor and a multimeter to measure the zener voltage. However, the current flowing through the zener will be determined by the value of the resistor and the difference between the battery voltage and the zener voltage, and will obviously be less for high-voltage zeners than for low-voltage zeners. This can lead to errors in the measurement.

The zener tester described in this article feeds a known, constant current through the zener. Furthermore, a choice of seven different zener currents is provided, which allows the zener voltage to be plotted against current.

The circuit of the zener tester, which contains only nine components, is given in figure 2. T1 and T2 function as a voltage regulator. T1 receives a bias voltage from the supply via R4 and draws current from the supply through the zener under test. However, if the emitter voltage

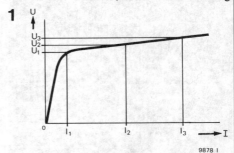

1

9878 I

2

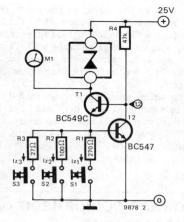

3

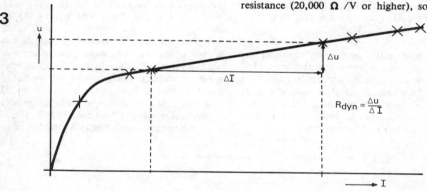

should try to rise above the 0.6 V base emitter knee voltage of T2, then T2 will draw more current, pulling down the base voltage of T1 and thus reducing the emitter voltage. Should the emitter voltage of T1 tend to fall below the base-emitter voltage of T2, then T2 will draw less current, the collector voltage will rise, and with it the emitter voltage of T1. This negative feedback system means that a constant voltage of approximately 0.6 V appears at the emitter of T1.

If one or more of the switches S1 to S3 is closed,

then a current $I = \dfrac{0.6}{\text{'R'}}$ (A, V, Ω) will flow

through one or more of the resistors R1-R3. ('R' is R1, R2, R3 or the parallel connection of two or more of these). This current will also flow through T1 and the zener. The zener voltage can then be measured by connecting a multimeter across it as shown. This should have a fairly high resistance (20,000 Ω /V or higher), so that it does not 'rob' too much current from the zener. By pressing one or more switches in different combinations a total of seven different zener currents can be obtained.

The zener currents for different combinations of the switches are shown in table 1. However, it should be noted that the actual currents obtained may vary by 10% from these figures, due to resistor tolerances and the temperature coefficient of T2.

The values of zener voltage obtained for different zener currents may be plotted on a graph of zener voltage versus zener current, as shown in figure 3. The dynamic resistance of the zener can then be calculated by dividing an increment in voltage, Δ U, by the corresponding increment in current, Δ I, i.e.

$$R_{dynamic} = \frac{\Delta\ U}{\Delta\ I}$$

Figure 1. Voltage versus current characteristic of a zener diode. Even when the breakdown voltage has been reached, the zener voltage varies slightly with current.

Figure 2. Circuit of the zener tester. Pressing S1, S2 or S3 in various combinations feeds a choice of seven different constant currents through the zener and the zener voltage is measured with a multimeter.

Figure 3. A voltage versus current curve for the zener may be plotted, from which the dynamic resistance may be found.

Table 1. The theoretical currents for the various combinations of S1, S2 and S3. These may vary in practice by 10%, due to component tolerances.

Switch	U_b	I_2
S1	25 V	2 22 mA
S2	25 V	6 mA
S3	25 V	22.2 mA
S1 + S2	25 V	8.2 mA
S1 + S3	25 V	24.4 mA
S2 + S3	25 V	28.2 mA
S1 + S2 + S3	25 V	30 mA

With the supply voltage shown, the maximum voltage that can appear between positive supply and the collector of T1 without T1 saturating is about 23 V. The maximum zener voltage that can be measured is thus about 22 V. The circuit may be modified to test higher voltage zeners by using a higher voltage transistor for T1, but care will have to be taken not to exceed the dissipation of T1 or the zener on the higher current ranges.

As the zener current is determined exclusively by the base-emitter voltage of T2 and R1 to R3, a stabilised supply voltage is not necessary, and an 18 V/50 mA transformer, 30 V/50 mA bridge rectifier and 470 μ /35 V capacitor will make a perfectly adequate unstabilised supply.

8 Voltage comparison on a 'scope

This simple circuit allows up to four DC voltages to be measured or compared by displaying them side by side on an oscilloscope.

There is frequently a need, when experimenting with circuits, to measure or compare several DC voltages at test points etc. Since most readers are unlikely to possess more than one multimeter this can be rather tedious. Using this simple circuit, up to four voltages can be compared or measured on any oscilloscope that has a DC input and an external trigger socket. The circuit uses only three ICs, five resistors and a capacitor.

The complete circuit of the voltage comparator is given in figure 1. The four voltages to be measured are fed to the four inputs of a quad analogue switch IC, the outputs of which are linked and fed to the Y input of the 'scope. N1 to N3 and associated components form an astable multivibrator, which clocks counter IC3. This is a decade counter connected as a 0 to 3 counter

1

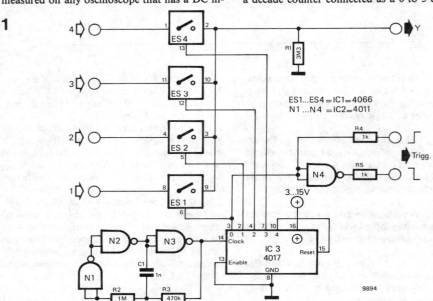

ES1...ES4 = IC1 = 4066
N1 ...N4 = IC2 = 4011

9894

Figure 1. The circuit diagram of the voltage comparator.

Figure 2. An example of 4 random voltage levels displayed simultaneously on the 'scope.

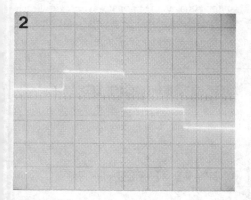

by feedback from output 4 to the reset input. Outputs 0 to 3 of the counter go high in turn, thus 'closing' each of the analogue switches in turn and feeding the input voltages to the 'scope in sequence.

Output 0 of the counter feeds a trigger pulse to the 'scope once every four clock pulses, so that for every cycle of the counter the 'scope trace makes one sweep of the screen. A positive-going trigger pulse is available via R4, or a negative-going trigger pulse is available from the output of N4 via R5. The resulting display is shown in figure 2, four different input voltages being fed to the inputs in this case. The oscilloscope timebase speed should be adjusted so that the display of the four voltage levels just occupies the whole screen width.

The supply voltage $+U_b$ may be from 3 to 15 V, but it must be noted that the input voltage should be positive with respect to the 0 V rail and not greater than $+U_b$. If voltages greater than this are to be measured then potential dividers must be used on the four inputs.

Setting up

To calibrate the circuit, simply feed a known voltage into one input and adjust the Y sensitivity of the 'scope to give a convenient deflection (for example one graticule division per volt input). The unknown voltages may then be fed in and compared against each other and against the calibration.

The circuit can easily be extended to eight inputs by adding an extra 4066 IC and connecting IC3 as a 0 to 7 counter (reset connected to output 8, pin 9).

H. Spenn

Real load resistors

When measuring and comparing the output powers of audio amplifiers (especially at the high end of the audio spectrum) it is useful to have available a 'real' load resistor, i.e. one which is a pure resistance with no parasitic inductance or capacitance. Carbon film resistors have a low self-inductance, but unfortunately are not commonly available in the high power ratings required for amplifier testing. The highest rating normally available in a carbon film resistor is 2 watts, so a load resistor for testing a 100 W amplifier would need to be made up of 50 such resistors in series/parallel combinations!

Wirewound resistors are available with high power ratings, but unfortunately such resistors are rarely wound so as to minimise self-inductance. A typical high-power wirewound resistor consists of a single layer of resistance wire

9737-1

wound helically on a cylindrical ceramic tube. This type of resistor has quite a high self-inductance, but since the usual applications of high-power wirewound resistors are DC or low-frequency AC this is not important.

For use as an amplifier load resistor some means must be found of reducing the inductance of a wirewound resistor. This can be achieved by providing the resistor with a centre tap and connecting it as shown in figure 1. Current flows in opposite directions in each half of the resistor, so the magnetic fields produced in each half (and hence the self-inductances) tend to cancel out. If the original resistor has a value R then the connection shown has a resistance R/4 since it consists of two R/2 sections in parallel.

Resistors already provided with taps, such as television H.T. dropper resistors, are suitable for this application. Presettable resistors may also be used. These consist of an exposed wire element wound on a ceramic former, and are provided with contact clips that may be fixed anywhere along the length of the element. 1 kW electric fire (heating) elements (which have a resistance of around 60 Ω) may also be used.

In order to obtain a load resistor of the desired resistance and wattage rating, several wirewound resistors may be connected in series/parallel combinations in the normal way, provided each one is first connected as shown to minimise its inductance.

10 Universal logic tester

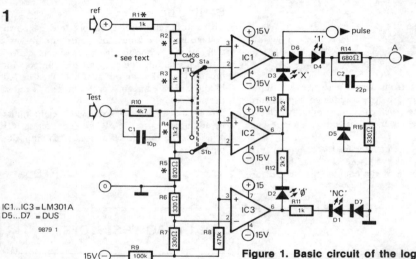

Figure 1. Basic circuit of the logic tester, which can detect high, low and undefined logic levels, and open-circuits.

Figure 2. A 'pulse stretcher' monostable.

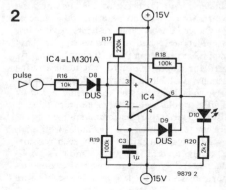

This logic tester can be used with both TTL and CMOS circuits as well as other logic families which exhibit similar characteristics. In addition to providing the usual logic 0 and logic 1 indications it will also indicate an undefined logic level and open circuit connections.

In TTL circuits a voltage less than 0.8 V is defined as logic 0 or 'low', and a voltage greater than 2 V is defined as logic 1 or 'high'. A voltage between these two is referred to as an undefined logic level. CMOS logic is capable of operating over a much wider supply range than TTL, typically 3 - 18 V. The logic levels for CMOS are not defined as absolute voltages but as percentages of supply voltage. A high logic level is defined as greater than 60% of supply voltage, and a low level is defined as less than 40% of supply volt-

20

age. Levels between these limits are undefined. A logic probe must be capable of distinguishing between low, high and undefined logic levels. There is also the possibility that an open-circuit may be encountered when using a logic tester. This could be due to the test probe not making good contact; or due to a circuit fault. Also, sometimes pins are intentionally not connected to anything (known as NC or No Connection in manufacturers' data). A logic tester must be capable of distinguishing an open-circuit from any of the other logic levels.

The circuit of the logic tester is shown in figure 1. Three voltage comparators are used to detect the four possible input conditions. The 'ref +' (reference) and '0' terminals of the tester are connected to the supply lines of the logic circuit under test. With a 5 V supply and S1 set to the 'TTL' position, 2 V will be present at the inverting input of IC1 and 0.8 V at the inverting input of IC2. With S1 set to the CMOS position the reference voltages will be respectively 60% and 40% of the supply voltage of the circuit being tested.

The inverting input of IC3 receives a potential of about −50 mV via R9, R7 and R6 from the negative rail of the tester's own (± 15 V) supply. When the 'test' input is open-circuit, the non-inverting inputs of the three comparators will be pulled down to about −100 mV via R8. The outputs of all three comparators will be negative, so LED D1 will be lit. If the test input is connected to a voltage between zero volts and the logic 0 level the output of comparator IC3 will swing positive and D2 will light due to current flowing through it from the output of IC3 into the output of IC2, thus indicating 'logic 0'.

For voltages between the logic 0 and logic 1 levels the output of IC2 will also swing positive. D2 will extinguish and D3 will light due to current flowing through it from the output of IC2 to the output of IC1. This LED indicates the undefined logic state 'X'. When the logic 1 threshold is exceeded the output of IC1 will swing positive. D3 will extinguish and D4 will light, thus indicating 'logic 1'.

Pulse indication

So far the discussion has been confined to the indication of static logic levels. However, pulses and pulse trains are frequently encountered in logic circuits. Pulse trains with a duty-cycle near 50% will cause both D2 and D4 to glow with reduced brightness. However, if the duty-cycle of a pulse train is very large or very small it will appear that one LED is lit continuously.

Also, short single pulses will be missed completely. To overcome this problem a 'pulse stretcher' circuit may be used, see figure 2. The pulse stretcher is a one-shot multivibrator with an output pulse period of approximately 200 ms. When any pulse appears at the point in figure 1 labled 'pulse', which is connected to the input of the pulse stretcher, the one-shot will be triggered and the LED will glow for about 200 ms. This is sufficiently long for the indication to be seen. If the pulse rate is greater than 5 Hz, D10 will appear to glow continuously.

A TTL-compatible pulse output is provided (A) for simple frequency counters etc. If this is not required, C2 and D5 can be omitted and R14 and R15 are replaced by a single 1 k resistor.

J. Borgman

11 Car rip-off protection

Thefts from cars of valuable accessories such as spotlamps and foglamps are on the increase. Equipped with a spanner, and given a few minutes undisturbed, the enterprising felon can frequently make a haul worth over £100. The inexpensive alarm circuit described here will protect these valuable items, and can also be used to prevent the theft of accessories from inside the car, for example radios and cassette players.

The complete circuit of the alarm is shown in figure 1. N1 to N4 form a 5-input OR gate, but the number of inputs can easily be increased by adding extra gates. When the car is unoccupied (and the ignition is switched off) R11 holds the inputs of N5 low, so the output is high. The inputs of N1 to N4 are held low via the filaments of the lamps, etc. that are being protected. The output of N4 is thus low, the output of N6 is high, T1 is turned on, T2 is turned off and relay Re.1 is de-

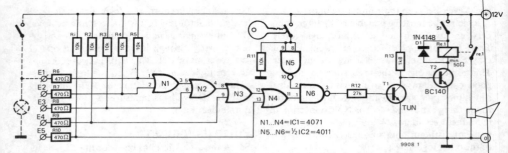

N1...N4 = IC1 = 4071
N5...N6 = ½ IC2 = 4011

9908 1

energised.

In the event of an accessory being disconnected by a thief (for example, the lamp connected to input E1), then the appropriate input to the OR gate will be pulled high by the 10 k input resistor. The output of N4 then goes high, the output of N6 goes low, T1 is turned off and T2 is turned on, energising Re.1 and sounding the car horn.

When the ignition switch is closed the output of N5 is low, which holds the output of N6 permanently high, thus disabling the alarm. This prevents the alarm from sounding when one of the accessories is switched on. Of course, the alarm will still sound if an accessory is switched on whilst the ignition is switched off. This prevents spotlamps and foglamps from accidentally being left on whilst the car is unoccupied. Alternatively, these accessories can be wired via the ignition switch so that this cannot occur.

An additional bonus is that the alarm will also sound in the event of a lamp filament failure. However, since a replacement lamp may not always be available, a secret 'cancel' switch (S1) is required...

Accessories inside the car, such as radios and cassette players, may also be protected by connecting a wire from one of the alarm inputs to the earthed case of the equipment. When the thief cuts this wire to remove the equipment then the alarm will sound. Of course, this facility should only be regarded as a backup to an alarm that prevents a thief entering the car in the first place!

Figure 1. Complete circuit of the car rip-off theft alarm.

Figure 2. Lamps connected in pairs must be isolated from one another, otherwise the alarm will not give complete protection. This can be done with a pair of diodes, as shown in figure 2a, or by double-pole switching, as shown in figure 2b.

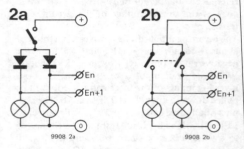

Where lamps are wired in pairs the alarm will, of course, not sound until both have been disconnected. To overcome this disadvantage a diode of suitable current rating can be wired in series with each lamp, as shown in figure 2a. Since there is a 0.7 V voltage drop across a diode, a better idea would be to use a double-pole switch for the set of lamps being protected, as shown in figure 2b.

W. Braun

 Automatic mono stereo switch

For some time now owners of stereo FM receivers will have noticed that the stereo indicator lamp stays on continuously. This is due to a decision by the BBC to transmit the 19 kHz pilot tone with all programmes, ostensibly to eliminate annoying clicks that occur when switching

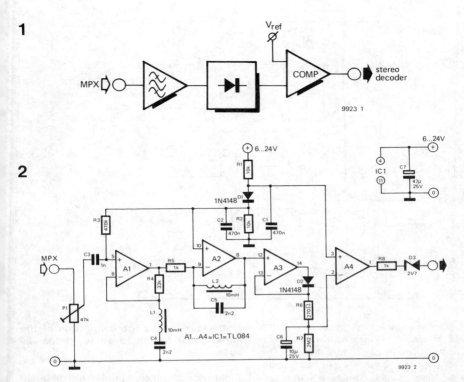

the pilot tone on and off. The commercial radio stations have, of course, followed this practice for some time.

As the mono-stereo switch in a stereo receiver operates by detecting the pilot tone, this means that such receivers are now incapable of distinguishing between mono and stereo transmissions and will be permanently switched to stereo unless the 'mono' switch is pressed. Apart from the minor annoyance of not knowing if a programme is in stereo (unless one buys the Radio Times) there is the greater inconvenience of listening to mono transmissions with the poorer signal-to-noise ratio inherent in stereo transmission. This is particularly a problem in areas of fringe reception. The circuit described in this article distinguishes between mono and stereo transmissions by detecting whether or not stereo information is present in the received signal, independent of the pilot tone.

When an FM stereo transmission has been demodulated, but before it has been decoded, it consists of two distinct channels. The left plus right (L + R) signal occupies the frequency band 0...15 kHz. This signal is essential for mono compatibility, as it is the only part of the stereo

Figure 1. Block diagram of the automatic mono-stereo switch.

Figure 2. Complete circuit of the mono-stereo switch.

signal that a mono radio can receive. The frequency band from 23...38 kHz is occupied by the lower sideband of a 38 kHz subcarrier, onto which the L − R (left minus right) signal is modulated. In principle the stereo signal is decoded by demodulating this signal, adding it to the L + R signal to get 2L, and subtracting it from the L + R signal to get 2R. Since the 23...38 kHz signal is absent during a mono transmission, a circuit which can detect this signal will be able to distinguish between mono and stereo transmissions. This is the principle of the automatic mono-stereo switch.

Block diagram

The principle of the automatic mono-stereo switch is illustrated in the block diagram of figure 1. A portion of the signal from the output of the detector stage of the tuner is fed to a selective

23

3

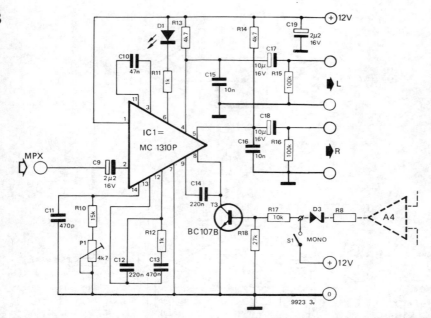

amplifier with a centre frequency of 35 kHz. If a signal is present in its passband it will be amplified, then rectified by an envelope detector. The resulting positive voltage is applied to a comparator, whose output swings negative and switches on the stereo decoder. If the transmission is mono then no signal will be fed through the selective amplifier and the comparator output will remain high, switching off the stereo decoder.

Complete circuit

The circuit of the mono-stereo switch is shown in figure 2. A1 to A4 are the four sections of a TL084 quad FET opamp. The selective amplifier is built around A1 and A2, the passband being determined by L1, L2, C4 and C5. A positive bias voltage of just less than half supply voltage is applied to the selective amplifier from the junction of R2 and D1. This is fed through the rectifier A3 to appear on capacitor C6 and hence at the inverting input of comparator A4. The non-inverting input of A4 receives a positive bias slightly higher than half supply voltage from the junction of R1 and D1. Under no-signal conditions the output of A4 is therefore positive. The output signal of the tuner is fed to the input of A1 via sensitivity control P1 and C3. If stereo information is present this will be amplified by A1 and A2 and rectified by A3,

Figure 3. Showing the connection of the mono-stereo switch to an IC stereo decoder.

Figure 4. A suggested printed circuit board design and component layout for the circuit of figure 2.

causing the voltage on C6 to rise above that at the non-inverting input of A4. The output of A4 will thus swing down to 0 V, turning on the stereo decoder.

The attack time of the rectifier is extremely short, about 2.7 ms, so the decoder will be switched to stereo immediately a stereo signal is received. However, to avoid the decoder switching back to mono during pauses in the audio signal, the decay time constant R7-C6, is made fairly long, and the circuit will not switch back to mono operation until about 20 seconds after the cessation of a stereo signal.

The mono-stereo switch can be connected to most IC stereo decoders, such as the MC1310P, as shown in figure 3. Operation of the manual mono switch which allows selection of mono operation if stereo reception is too noisy, is unaffected.

Construction

A printed circuit board and component layout

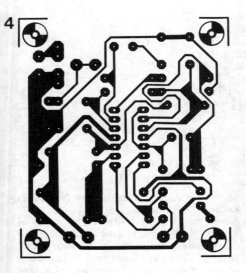

4

Parts list for figures 2 and 4

Resistors:
R1, R2 = 10 k
R3 = 470 k
R4 = 33 k
R5 = 1 k
R6 = 270 Ω
R7 = 2M2
R8 = 1 k

Capacitors:
C1, C2 = 470 n
C3 = 1 n
C4, C5 = 2n2
C6 = 10 µ /25 V
C7 = 47 µ /25 V

Semiconductors:
IC1 = TL 084
D1, D2 = 1N4148
D3 = zener 2V7

Miscellaneous:
P1 = 47 k preset
L1, L2 = 10 mH choke

for the mono-stereo switch are given in figure 4. This p.c.b. should be sufficiently compact to be built into most FM tuners, and the wide supply voltage range should allow the circuit to be powered from the supply rail of almost any tuner.

The circuit has only one adjustment, the sensitivity control P1. This should be adjusted so that the circuit operates on any stereo signal which is sufficiently strong for noise-free stereo listening. On the other hand, the sensitivity of the circuit must not be so great that it switches on spurious noise.

13 Servo polarity changer

Many model enthusiasts will be familiar with situations in which they discovered that moving a servo control in one direction prompted the model to steer in the opposite direction! The circuit described here is intended to offer a simple solution to just this problem.

The best results are usually obtained from a servo mechanism if it is mounted in the model so there are as few joints and bends in the steering rod as possible. However the direction in which the servo moves should be such that it coincides with the direction of the control knob or joystick, i.e. moving the joystick to the right causes

the model to steer to the right. However, in certain cases these two conditions prove mutually incompatible. Often the result is that the model builder has to tamper with the delicate mech-

1

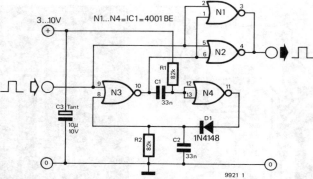

Figure 1. The circuit diagram of the servo polarity changer.

Figure 2. The finished circuit when mounted on a board occupies very little space.

Figure 3. In order to set the servo in the neutral position a pulse duration of 1.5 ms is required. The top channel shows the input signal of the circuit, whilst the bottom channel shows the output pulse. The pulse is shifted along the time axis, but this has no effect upon the operation of the servo.

Figure 4. This photo shows the output pulse obtained for an input pulse duration of 1 ms. As is apparent the duration of the output pulse is 2 ms, so that the servo will now be moved exactly the same amount (the distance corresponding to a pulse of 0.5 ms) as in the pulse of the input signal, but in the opposite direction.

2

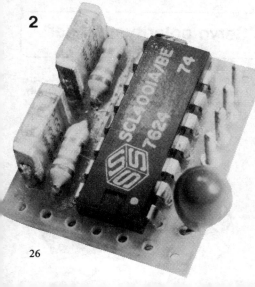

anics of the steering system or with the finnicky electronics of the servo.

Servos are generally controlled by means of pulse width modulation; a pulse width of 1.5 ms corresponds to the neutral or 'straight ahead' position, whilst 1 and 2 ms represent the extreme settings of the control. The polarity of a servo can simply be reversed, so that a pulse width of 1 ms causes the servo control to assume the position that was previously adopted with a pulse width of 2 ms, and vice versa, by modifying the width of the control pulses.

Since in both cases the neutral position of the control will correspond to a pulse width of 1.5 ms, it is possible to calculate the pulse width for all other positions on the basis of this figure. This can be done quite simply by subtracting the original pulse width from 3 ms in order to obtain its counterpart in the opposite direction. Thus in order to reverse the polarity of the servo one simply arranges for the control pulses to be subtracted from a reference pulse of 3 ms.

There are two different types of servo which are currently available, namely those which operate with positive going control pulses, and those which require a negative going pulse. The circuit described here can only be used with servos which use positive going pulses, however this represents the large majority of commercially available devices. The finished circuit occupies very little space (see figure 2) and hence there should be no problems mounting it in whatever model is under construction.

The circuit

N3 and N4 along with C1, C2, R1, R2 and D1 form a monostable with a pulse duration of approx. 3 ms. This monostable is triggered by the control signal, which is also fed to one of the inputs of N1 and N2. The other inputs of these two gates receive negative going pulses of approx. 3

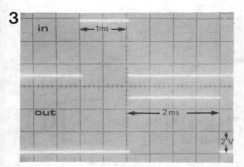

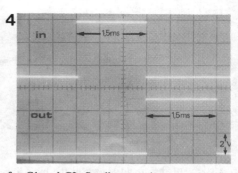

ms duration from the output of N3. Since N1 and N2 (like N3 and N4) are NOR gates, their output will produce a positive going pulse, the duration of which is equal to the difference between 3 ms and the original control pulse. N2 is connected in parallel with N1 to increase the fanout of the circuit.

The oscilloscope photos show the result before and after a pulse has been processed by the circuit. In the prototype model the duration of the monostable pulse was 3.15 ms. In most applications where the servo is permanently built into the model, allowance for slight tolerances in pulse width can be made at the transmitter. However, if a pulse duration of exactly 3 ms is required, then a value of 27 n should be chosen

for C1 and C2. Smaller capacitors can then be connected in parallel with these until a pulse of precisely 3 ms is obtained on the scope. Without a scope the pulse width can still be accurately set by altering the value of C1 and C2 in the above fashion until, with or without the polarity changer, the servo remains in exactly the neutral position.

The circuit consumes very little current (1 mA), and is unaffected (< 2%) by variations in the supply voltage between 3 and 10 V. In order to reduce the dimensions of the circuit to a minimum, a tantalum type is recommended for C3. As a result of the symmetrical construction (R1 = R2, C1 = C2) the circuit has a very low temperature coefficient.

14 Easy music

For those who do not have the time (or perhaps the patience) to master a musical instrument, but would nonetheless like to make their own music, this simple circuit may provide the answer. The only musical accomplishment necessary is the ability to whistle in tune.

The principle of 'Easy music' is extremely simple, as can be seen from the block diagram of figure 1. The 'musician's' whistle is picked up by a crystal microphone and amplified by opamp A1. A portion of the signal is fed to an envelope follower, which rectifies and filters it to produce a positive voltage that follows the amplitude envelope of the input signal. The signal is also fed to two limiting amplifiers, which convert the variable amplitude sinewave of the input signal into a constant amplitude squarewave having the same frequency as the input signal. This square-

wave is used to clock a binary counter whose division ratio can be set to 2, 4, 8 etc., so that the output is one, two, three etc. octaves below the input signal.

The counter output is used to switch transistor T1 on and off, and the collector signal of T1 is fed to the output amplifier A4. Since the collector resistor of T1 receives its supply from the output of the envelope follower, the amplitude of the collector signal, and hence of the output signal, varies in sympathy with the amplitude of the original input signal.

The output is therefore a squarewave whose frequency may be one or more octaves lower than the input signal and whose amplitude dynamics follow the amplitude of the input signal.

Complete circuit

The complete circuit is given in figure 2, and the

1

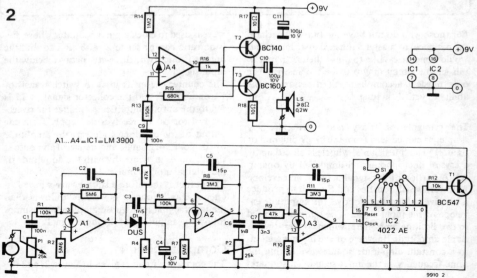

sections of the circuit shown in the block diagram are easily identified. The output of the crystal microphone is fed to P1, which functions as a sensitivity control. A1 is connected as a linear amplifier with a gain of approximately 56. A portion of the output signal from A1 is rectified by D1 and the resulting peak positive voltage is stored on C4. The output signal from A1 is further amplified by A2 and A3, the combined gain of A1 to A3 being sufficient to cause limiting at the output of A3, even with very small input signals. P2 is used to adjust the gain of the limiting amplifier so that limiting just occurs with the smallest input signal, this avoiding limiting caused by extraneous noises.

The output of A3 is used to clock a CMOS binary counter, whose division ratio may be set by means of S1. The output of IC2 switches transistor T1 on and off. Since the collector resistor of T1 (R6) receives its supply voltage from C4, the amplitude of the collector signal varies in sym-

pathy with the input signal. This signal is amplified by a small audio power amplifier built around A4, which drives a small loudspeaker.

Additions to the basic circuit

However, the possibilities do not end there. The more ambitious constructor may wish to add filters and other circuits to produce different output waveforms which will extend the tonal possibilities of the instrument. Such variations on the basic design are, however, beyond the scope of this short article, and are left to the ingenuity of the individual reader.

P.J. Tyrrell

Figure 1. Block diagram of 'Easy music'.

Figure 2. Complete circuit diagram.

2

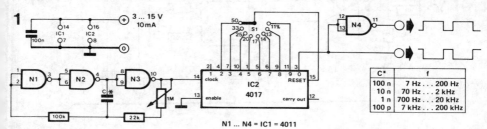

15 duty-cycles at the turn of a switch

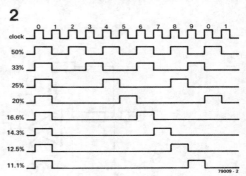

C*	f
100 n	7 Hz ... 200 Hz
10 n	70 Hz ... 2 kHz
1 n	700 Hz ... 20 kHz
100 p	7 kHz ... 200 kHz

N1 ... N4 = IC1 = 4011

79009 · 1

Only two CMOS-ICs are used in the generator described here, but in spite of its simplicity it offers a selection of 15 precisely determined duty-cycles without any need for calibration. It is a useful item of test gear, especially for calibrating other instruments that are designed to measure duty-cycles in one form or another – dwell meters, for instance.

The outputs of a divide-by-ten counter, the CD4017, are connected to an 8-position switch. One of the outputs is selected and fed back to the reset input of the IC. The result is a divider stage that can be set at any division ratio between 2 and 9. If the output is taken from the '0' output of the divider, both the frequency and the duty-cycle of the input frequency will be 'divided' by the preset ratio. Furthermore, the duty-cycle of the output signal will be independent of the input frequency: it is determined only by the setting of the selector switch.

To complete the unit, a clock generator is included (N1...N3). The 'clock' frequency is determined by the value of the capacitor, C, and by the setting of the 1 M potentiometer. The Table lists frequency ranges for a few capacitor values. The duty-cycle at the output (pin 3 of IC2) is equal to the division ratio times 100%. For instance, if output '5' (pin 1) of IC2 is selected, the division ratio is 1:5 and the duty-cycle is

$$\frac{100}{5} = 20\%.$$

Figure 1. Only two IC's are required for this little generator. The Table lists frequency ranges for a few capacitor values.

Figure 2. The duty-cycle at the output is determined by the division ratio.

No calibration required! As can be derived from figure 2, eight duty-cycles between 50% and 11.1% can be selected. N4 inverts the output signal, providing eight duty-cycles varying from 50% up to 88.9%. Since 50% is 50% no matter which way you look at it, the total number of duty-cycles available is fifteen.

The amplitude of the output signal is equal to the supply voltage, i.e. anywhere between 3 and 15 volts.

16 Analogue delay line

There are numerous applications requiring the use of an audio delay line, for example phasing and vibrato units, echo and reverberation units, and sophisticated loudspeakers with active time-

1

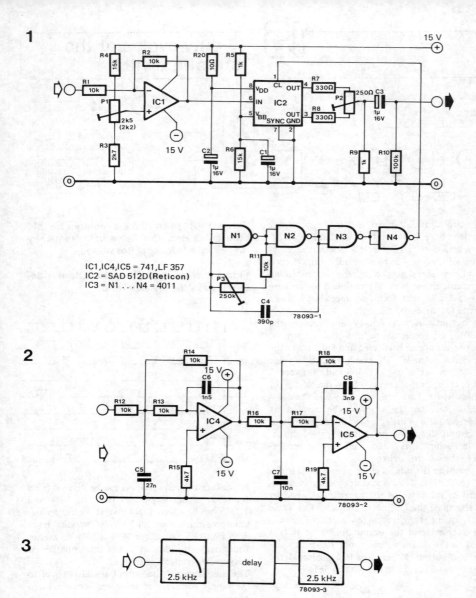

IC1,IC4,IC5 = 741,LF 357
IC2 = SAD 512D(Reticon)
IC3 = N1 ... N4 = 4011

78093-1

2

78093-2

3

2.5 kHz   delay   2.5 kHz

78093-3

delay compensation. One of the simplest ways to achieve this electronically is to use an analogue (bucket brigade) shift register. There are various types on the market and a particularly interesting one is the Reticon SAD 512, which has 512 stages and a built-in clock buffer. The clock buffer enables it to be driven from a simple, single-phase clock circuit such as a CMOS multivibrator.

Figure 1 shows a delay line utilising the SAD 512. Input signals to the device must be positive with respect to the 0 V pin, so the AF input signal is first fed to an inverting amplifier, IC2, which has a positive DC offset adjustable by P1. The clock generator is an astable multivibrator using CMOS NAND gates (N1 and N2) and its frequency may be varied between 10 kHz and 100 kHz by means of P3. The clock buffer of the

SAD 512 divides the clock input frequency by two, so the sampling frequency, f_c, of the SAD512, varies between 5 kHz and 50 kHz. The delay produced by the circuit is $n/2f_c$, where n is the number of stages in the IC. The delay may therefore be varied between 5.12 ms and 51.2 ms. To obtain longer delays several SAD 512s may, of course, be cascaded very easily, since no special clock drive circuit is required.

To minimise clock noise the outputs from the final and penultimate stages of the IC are summed by R7, R8 and P2. However, if the circuit is to be used with the minimum clock frequency then clock noise will still be audible, and the lowpass filter circuit shown in figure 2 should be connected to the output. This consists of a fourth-order Butterworth filter with a turnover frequency of 2.5 kHz and an ultimate slope of -24 dB/octave.

Of course, if low clock frequencies are to be employed then the maximum frequency of the input signal must be restricted to half the sampling frequency. This can be achieved by connecting the filter circuit of figure 2 at the input of the delay line, as shown in figure 3.

To set up the circuit the clock frequency is lowered until it becomes audible. P2 is then adjusted until clock noise is at a minimum. The clock frequency is then raised and a signal fed in. The signal level is increased until distortion becomes apparent, whereupon P1 is adjusted to minimise distortion. This procedure (increasing the signal level and adjusting P1) is repeated until no further improvement is obtained. Alternatively, if an oscilloscope is available, P1 may be adjusted so that the waveform clips symmetrically when the circuit is overloaded by a large signal.

17 Supply failure indicator

Many circuits, especially digital systems such as random access memories and digital clocks, must have a continuous power supply to ensure correct operation. If the supply to a RAM is interrupted then the stored information is lost, as is the time in the case of a digital clock.

The supply failure indicator described here will sense the interruption of the power supply and will light a LED when the supply is restored, thus informing the microprocessor user that the information stored in RAM is garbage and must be re-entered, and telling the digital clock owner that his clock must be reset to the correct time. When the supply is initially switched on the inverting input of IC1 is held at 0.6 V below positive supply by D1. Pressing the reset button takes the non-inverting input of IC1 to positive supply potential, so the output of IC1 swings high, holding the non-inverting input high even when the reset button is released. LED D2 is therefore not lit.

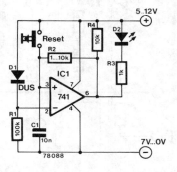

When the supply is interrupted all voltages, of course, fall to zero. Upon restoration of the supply the inverting input of IC1 is immediately pulled up to its previous potential via D1. However, C1 is uncharged and holds the non-inverting input low, so the output of IC1 remains low and D2 lights.

18 Amplifier for low-Z headphones

Stereo headphones are usually connected to the loudspeaker outputs of the power amp via an attenuator. Although this represents the cheapest solution, it does suffer from two significant drawbacks: if the loudspeakers are also switched on whilst the headphones are being used, it is impossible to vary the signal level of the headphones independently of the loudspeakers; secondly, as a result of the output impedance of the attenuator, the damping factor of the system is reduced, which adversely affects the bass reproduction of the headphones. These problems can be solved however, by using this stereo output amp, which is connected via a stereo potentiometer (P1, P1') to the tape

output of the power amp. The tone controls will then have no effect upon the headphones, but in the case of better quality 'phones that is hardly an inconvenience.

The amplifier has an output power in excess of 1 Watt. The gain, which is determined by R4 and R5, is 11 (this can be varied, if so desired, by altering the value of R4). By means of P2 the voltage at the junction of R12 and R14 is adjusted to half supply. The quiescent current is 50 to 100 mA; this can be varied by altering R8.

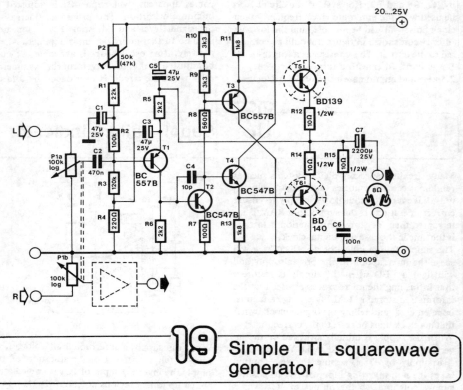

⎰⎱ Simple TTL squarewave generator

Using only a small number of TTL gates it is not difficult to construct a squarewave generator which can be used in a wide range of possible applications (e.g. as clock generator). The accompanying diagram represents the basic universal design for such a generator. The circuit is not critical, can be used over a wide range of frequencies, has no starting problems and is sufficiently stable for most applications. The frequency in not affected by supply voltage variations.

The oscillator frequency is determined by the RC

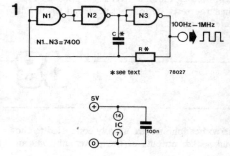

network and the propagation time of the inverters (in this case three NANDs with their inputs connected in parallel). Since the propagation delay time of the IC is, in general, strongly influenced by the temperature and supply voltage, care must be taken to ensure that the propagation times have as little effect as possible upon the oscillator frequency. The output of each gate changes state twice per period of the oscillation signal, which means that, in all, one must account for double the propagation time of all three gates. To ensure that the oscillator frequency f_O be more or less independent of variations in the temperature of the circuit and in the supply voltage, one must ensure that f_O is small compared to

$$\frac{1}{2 \cdot t_p \cdot n},$$

where t_p is the propagation time and n the number of inverters connected in series. In the case of the circuit shown here, t_p = approx. 10 ns and n = 3, so that as far as the oscillator frequency f_O is concerned:

$$f_O \ll \frac{1}{2 \cdot t_p \cdot n} = \frac{1}{2 \cdot 10 \cdot 3} = 16.6 \text{ MHz.}$$

The accompanying nomogram shows how f_O changes with R. The value of the resistor R must not be smaller than that shown in the nomogram; for example, for C = 100 nF, R must not be less than 100 Ω . A variable squarewave oscillator can be obtained by

replacing R with a 2.5 k potentiometer in series with a fixed resistor of the minimum permitted value.
A universal squarewave generator of this type can also be constructed using Low Power Schottky TTL or CMOS ICs; both these possibilities are discussed below.

---

20 Simple LS TTL squarewave generator

The design of this squarewave generator is identical to that of the circuit described above, with the exception that it employs an IC from the increasingly popular Low Power Schottky (LS) TTL series, rather than a conventional TTL IC. Since the electrical characteristics of LS TTL devices differ from those of standard TTL ICs, the relationship between the oscillator frequency and the values of R and C will also be difficult, whilst an extra resistor is required for the circuit to function satisfactorily.
The circuit will generate a squarewave with a

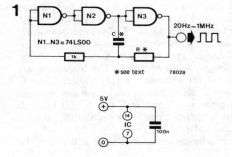

2

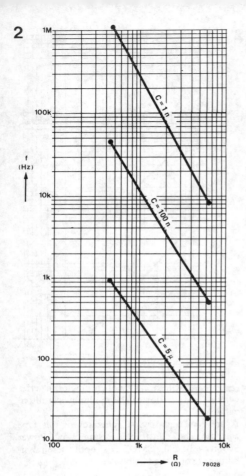

frequency between 20 Hz and 1 MHz. The nomogram once again shows the frequencies obtained for various values of R and C. As was the case in the above circuit, there is a minimum permissible value for R (680 Ω). To obtain a variable squarewave generator, R should be replaced by a 5 or 10 k potentiometer in series with a fixed resistor of 680 Ω.

21 Simple CMOS squarewave generator

In addition to standard- and Low Power Schottky TTL devices, there is, of course, no objection to using a CMOS IC in the basic squarewave generator circuit. The revised graph of frequency against R and C is shown in the accompanying nomogram. The frequencies are plotted for a nominal supply voltage of 12 V, however, this voltage is not critical, and a supply of between 5 V and 15 V may in fact be used. The frequency range of the circuit runs from 0.5 Hz to 1 MHz.

The minimum permissible value of R is 22 k. To

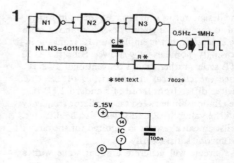

2

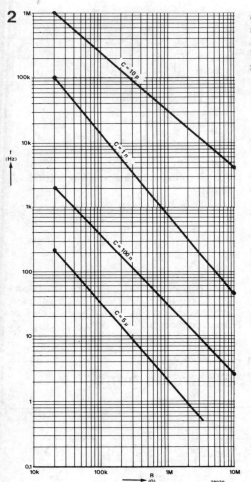

obtain a variable squarewave oscillator, R should be replaced by a fixed value resistor of 22 k in series with a 1 M potentiometer. Both the buffered and unbuffered versions of the 4011 may be used.

22 Automotive voltmeter

Although vital for satisfactory operation of the vehicle, the car battery is often taken for granted and rarely receives adequate maintenance. As a battery ages, its ability to store charge for long periods gradually decreases. The inevitable result is that one morning (usually in the depths of winter) the car fails to start.

The solid-state voltmeter described in this article allows continuous monitoring of the battery voltage so that incipient failure can be spotted at

an early stage. The circuit will also indicate any fault in the car voltage regulator which may lead to overcharging and damage to the battery. Battery voltage can, of course, be measured using a conventional moving-coil voltmeter. However, as only the voltage range from about 9 to 15 V is of interest, only the top third of the scale of a 15 V meter would be used, unless a 'suppressed zero' facility was added. Moving coil meters are also fairly delicate mechanically.

A better solution is to use a solidstate voltmeter which will indicate the voltage on a column of LEDs. Various ICs are available which perform this function. However, the 12 or 16 LED display offered by ICs such as the Siemens UAA 180 and UAA 170 is not required in this application, so an IC was chosen which will drive only five LEDs, the Texas SN 16889P. This IC provides a thermometer-type indication.

The complete circuit of the voltmeter uses only this IC and a handful of other components, since the IC will drive the LEDs directly. Diodes D1 and D2 provide protection against reverse polarity and transients on the supply line, whilst D8 offsets the zero of the meter so that it only begins to read above about 9.5 V. The circuit is calibrated using P1 so that the LEDs extinguish at the voltages shown in the accompanying table. LED D7 will be extinguished below about 15 V. If this LED is lit when the circuit is fitted in the car then the charging voltage is too high and the car voltage regulator is at fault. A red LED should be used for D7. D6 indicates that the battery is fully charged, and a green LED should be used for this component.

D5 indicates that the battery voltage is fairly

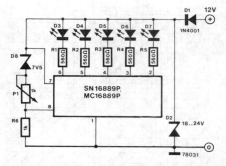

Table. Voltages below which the LEDs extinguish

D7	15 V
D6	13.5 V
D5	12 V
D4	11 V
D3	9.5 V

o.k., but the battery is not fully charged – a cautionary yellow LED can be used here. D4 and D3 indicate that the battery voltage is unacceptably low, and red LEDs should again be used for these components.

23 Electronic gong

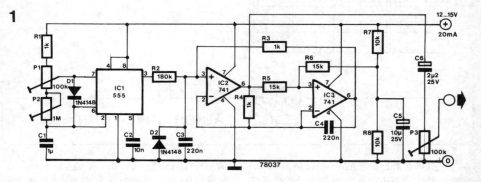

This circuit will simulate the sound of a bell or gong and may be used as a replacement for conventional bells in such applications as doorchimes, clocks etc.

The circuit consists of a resonant filter built around IC2 and IC3 which will ring at its resonant frequency when a short pulse is fed to the input. In this circuit the trigger pulses are pro-

vided by a 555 timer connected as an astable multivibrator, but other trigger sources may be used depending on the application.

The character of the sound is influenced by two factors; the Q of the filter, which may be varied by changing the value of R2, and the duration of the trigger pulse, which may be adjusted using P1. The repetition rate of the trigger pulses, i.e.

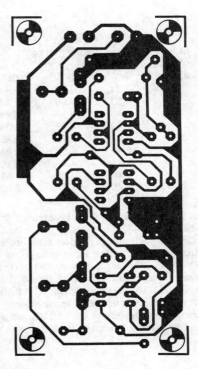

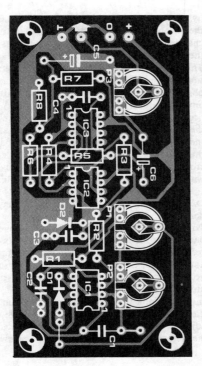

the rate at which the gong is 'struck', may be varied using P2. In order to drive a loudspeaker the output of the circuit must be fed through an audio amplifier. The output level may be varied from zero to about 5 V by means of P3.

24 Zero crossing detector

This circuit will detect precisely the negative-going zero-crossing point of an AC waveform, but requires only a single supply voltage, unlike zero crossing detectors using op-amps. N1 and N2 are Schmitt triggers connected to form a monostable multivibrator with a period of about 15 ms. P1 is adjusted so that when the input voltage falls to zero the voltage at the input of N1 is equal to the low-going threshold of the Schmitt trigger. The output of N1 thus goes high and the output of N2 goes low. C1 holds the second input of N1 below its positive-going threshold for about 15 ms, during which time the output of the circuit will remain low, even if noise pulses on the input waveform should take the first input of N1 high.

When the input signal goes positive the first input of N1 is taken above its positive-going threshold. Note that this occurs after the positive-going zero-crossing point due to the

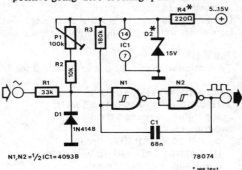

37

hysteresis of the Schmitt trigger. Subsequently the second input of N1 goes high due to C1 charging through R3. The circuit then resets and the output of N2 goes high.

The output of N2 is thus an asymmetrical squarewave whose negative-going edge occurs on the negative-going zero-crossing point of the input waveform and whose positive-going edge occurs sometime during the positive half-cycle of the input waveform. The negative-going edge of the waveform is independent of the amplitude of the input signal and occurs always at the zero-crossing point. However, it does vary slightly with supply voltage, so this should be stabilised. If a higher supply than 15 V is used then R4 and D2 must be included, otherwise the IC may be damaged.

To calibrate the circuit an oscilloscope is desirable so that P1 may be set exactly for the zero-crossing point. Alternatively, if a 'scope is not available, C1 should be temporarily disconnected and the output of N2 monitored on a multimeter.

In table 1 look up the voltage corresponding to the RMS input voltage and supply voltage and adjust P1 until this voltage registers on the meter, e.g. with a 10 V supply and a sinewave

Table 1

Input voltage (RMS sine)	Supply voltage		
	5 V	10 V	15 V
2 V	2.24	3.49	——
3 V	2.33	4.09	5.18
4 V	2.37	4.33	5.91
5 V	2.40	4.47	6.26
6 V	2.42	4.56	6.48
7 V	2.43	4.63	6.64
8 V	2.44	4.67	6.75
9 V	2.44	4.71	6.83
10 V	2.45	4.74	6.90

input of 5 V RMS P1 should be adjusted until the meter reads 4.47 V.

R1, D1 and the input protection diodes of N1 protect the circuit against input voltages up to 220 V (RMS, sinewave input). At this level the maximum permissible current of 10 mA flows into N1 and 1.5 W are dissipated in R1. If higher input voltages are to be used or less dissipation is desirable then the values of R1, R2 and P1 should be increased, keeping them in the same ratio.

25 Wideband RF amplifier

This design for an RF amplifier has a large bandwidth and dynamic range, which makes it eminently suitable for use in the front end of a shortwave receiver. The design operates without negative feedback since, if an amplifier with feedback overloads, distortion products can be fed back to the (aerial) input via the feedback loop and re-radiated.

However, good linearity is achieved by employing a device which has an inherently linear trans-

Table 1
Typical characteristics of the RF amplifier

gain: approximately 10 dB
3 dB bandwidth: 4 MHz to 55 MHz
noise figure: less than 5 dB
two-tone test:
    output power for third order
    IM distortion at −40 dB with respect to
    one tone: +22 dBm/tone

fer characteristic, in this case a dual-gate MOSFET with both gates linked. With the 3N211 used in this circuit the transconductance of the device is constant at about 14 mA/V pro-

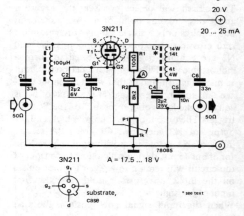

vided the drain current is greater than approximately 12.5 mA.

The MOSFET is used in a commongate configuration, with P1 used to set the drain current at around 20 mA. One home-made inductor is employed in the circuit, L2, which is wound on a Philips/Mullard type 4312-020-31521, two-hole ferrite bead, sometimes referred to as a 'pig's nose ferrite bead'. 14 turns of 31 SWG (0.3 mm)

enamelled copper wire are wound through one hole of the bead and four turns are wound through the other hole, one end of each winding being joined to form the tap which connects to C6.

P1 should be adjusted so that the voltage at the test point shown in figure 1 is between 17.5 V and 18 V.

26 Super-simple touch switch

Although there is a plethora of designs for touch switches, it is always a challenge to come up with a design that is simpler than previous versions. While most latching touch switches use a pair of NAND gates connected as a flip-flop, this circuit uses only one non-inverting CMOS buffer, one capacitor and a resistor. When the input of N1 is taken low by bridging the lower pair of touch contacts with a finger, the output of N1 goes low. When the contacts are released the input of N1 is held low by the output via R1, so the output remains low indefinitely. When the upper pair of contacts is bridged the input of N1 is taken high, so the output goes high. When the

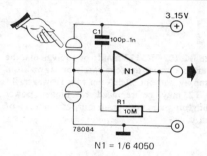

contacts are released the input is still held high via R1, so the output remains high.

27 Symmetrical ± 15 V/50 mA supply

Although IC voltage regulators have now largely displaced discrete component designs, this circuit offers a considerable cost advantage over an IC regulator.

Operation of the circuit is extremely simple. The centre-tapped transformer, bridge rectifier and reservoir capacitors C1 and C2 provide an unregulated supply of about ± 20 V. The positive and negative regulators function in an identical manner except for polarity, so only the positive regulator will be described in detail.

The positive supply current flows through a series regulator transistor T1. 15 V is dropped across zener diode D5, the upper end being at about + 15 V and the lower end at 0 V. Should the output voltage of the regulator tend to fall then the lower end of D5 will fall below 0 V and

transistor T3 will draw more current. This will supply T1 with more base current, turning it on harder so that the output voltage of the regulator will rise. If the output voltage of the regulator is too high then the reverse will happen. The potential at the lower end of D5 will rise and T3 will draw less current. T1 in turn will tend to turn off and the supply voltage will fall. The negative supply functions in a similar manner. Since D5 and D6 receive their bias from the output of the supply, R5, R6 and D7 must be included to make the circuit self-starting. An initial bias of about 10 V from the unregulated supply is provided by these components. Once the output voltage of the supply has risen to its normal value D7 is reverse-biased, which prevents ripple from the unregulated supply appearing on the output. Using inexpensive small-signal transistors such

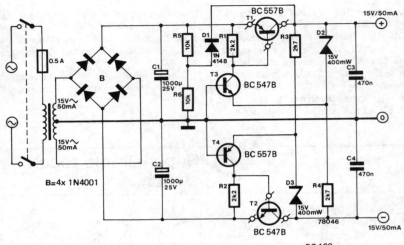

as the BC 107/BC 177 family or equivalents, the maximum current that can safely be drawn from the supply is about 50 mA per rail. However, T1 and T2 may be replaced by higher power Darlington pairs to obtain output currents of 500 mA.

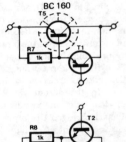

28 Improved 723 supply

The 723 is a very widely used IC regulator. Hence the following circuit, which is intended to reduce power dissipation when the 723 is used with an external transistor, should prove very popular. According to the manufacturer's specification the supply voltage to the 723 should always be at least 8.5 V to ensure satisfactory operation of the internal 7.5 V reference and of the IC's internal differential amplifier.

Using the 723 in a low-voltage high-current supply, with an external series transistor operating from the same supply rail as the 723, invariably results in excessive dissipation in the series transistor. For example, in a 5 V 2 A

supply for TTL about 3.5 V would be dropped across the series transistor and 7 W would be dissipated in it at full load current. Furthermore, the reservoir capacitor must be larger than necessary to prevent the supply to the 723 falling below 8.5 V in the ripple troughs.

In fact the supply voltage to the series transistor need be no more than 0.5 V above the regulated output voltage, to allow for its saturation voltage.

The solution is to use a separate 8.5 V supply for the 723 and a lower voltage supply for the external transistor. Rather than using separate transformer windings for the two supplies, the supply

40

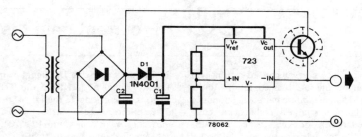

to the 723 is simply tapped off using a peak rectifier D1/C1. Since the 723 takes only a small current C1 will charge up to virtually the peak voltage from the bridge rectifier, 1.414 times the RMS voltage of the transformer minus the voltage drop of the bridge. The transformer voltage thus needs to be at least 7 V to give an 8.5 V supply to the 723.

However, by suitable choice of reservoir capacitor C2 the ripple on the main unregulated supply can be made such that the voltage falls to about 0.5 V above the regulated output voltage in the ripple troughs. The average voltage fed to the series transistor will thus be less than 8.5 V and the dissipation will be greatly reduced.

The value of C1 is determined by the maximum base current that the 723 must supply to the

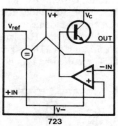

series output transistor. As a rule of thumb allow about 10 μF per mA. The base current can be found by dividing the maximum output current by the gain of the transistor. A suitable value for the main reservoir capacitor C2 is between 1500 and 2200 μF per amp of output current.

---

29 Squarewave-staircase converter

This circuit can be used to generate an up-down staircase waveform with a total of 512 steps per cycle. IC1 and IC2 are two four-bit up-down counters connected as an 8-bit counter, with an R-2R D-A ladder network connected to the outputs to convert the binary output codes to a staircase waveform.

When a squarewave is fed to the clock input the circuit will count up until the counter reaches 255, when the carry output will go low and clock FF1. The circuit will then count down until zero is reached, when the carry output will again clock FF1 and so on.

To ensure that the staircase steps are of equal height 1% tolerance resistors should be used for R1 to R23.

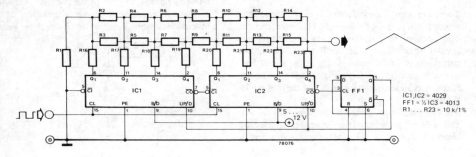

30 HF current gain tester

The high-frequency current gain of a transistor is dependent on the DC bias conditions under which it operates, maximum gain being obtained at only one particular value of collector current.

This simple circuit is designed to determine the optimum collector current for any NPN RF transistor. The transistor under test (TUT) is inserted into an amplifier stage which is fed with a constant amplitude 100 MHz signal from an oscillator built around T1. This signal is amplified by the TUT, rectified by D1 and filtered by R10 and C9 to give a DC signal proportional to the RF signal output from the TUT. This, in turn, is proportional to the gain of the TUT.

The collector current through the TUT can be varied between 1 mA and 10 mA by means of P1, which should be fitted with a scale marked out linearly between these values. It is then a simple matter to adjust P1 until the maximum output voltage is obtained on the meter, whereupon the optimum collector current can be read off from the scale of P1.

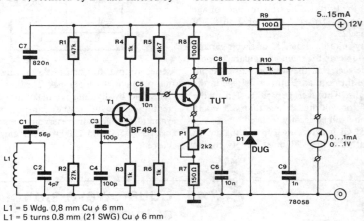

L1 = 5 Wdg. 0,8 mm Cu φ 6 mm
L1 = 5 turns 0.8 mm (21 SWG) Cu φ 6 mm

31 Hum filter

using electronically simulated inductor

There are many cases where it is useful to be able to get rid of spurious mains (50 Hz) interference. The simplest way of doing this is to employ a special filter which rejects only the 50 Hz signal components whilst passing the other signal frequencies unaffected, i.e. a highly selective notch filter. A typical circuit for such a filter is given in figure 1.

Since a filter with a notch frequency of 50 Hz and a Q of 10 would require an inductance of almost 150 Henrys, the most obvious solution is to synthesise the required inductance electronically (see figure 2).

The two opamps, together with R2...R5, C2 and P1, provide an almost perfect simulation of a conventional wound inductor situated between

1

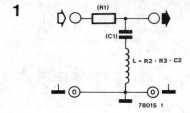

2

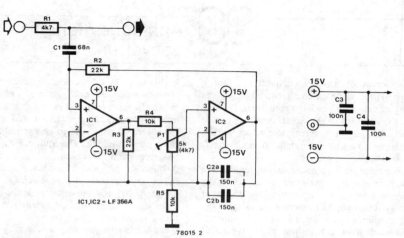

78015 2

pin 3 of IC1 and earth. The value of inductance thereby obtained is equal to the product of the values of R2, R3 and C2 (i.e. L = R2 x R3 x C2). For tuning purposes this value can be varied slightly by means of P1. If the circuit is correctly adjusted, the attenuation of 50 Hz signals is 45 to 50 dB. The circuit can be used as it stands as a hum rejection filter in harmonic distortion meters or as a hum filter for TV sound signals.

32 Voltage mirror

There are a number of different ways of using a transformer with only one secondary winding to obtain both a positive and a negative supply voltage. This design is a contribution towards such a discussion.

The circuit uses a second bridge rectifier (D1...D4) which, via C1 and C2, is capacitively-coupled to the transformer. Since the resultant voltage is DC-isolated from the transformer, to which the other rectifier (D5...D8) is connected, the positive terminal of C3 can be linked directly to the 0 V rail to give a symmetrical ± supply.

Since (because of C1 and C2) C3 is charged from a higher impedance than C4, this capacitor should have a higher value than C4, otherwise the internal impedance and ripple voltage of the negative supply will differ significantly from it's positive counterpart.

The working voltages of the capacitors should at least equal the peak value of the transformer voltage. With the values given in the diagram the circuit will supply approx. 0.1 A for a transformer voltage of 15 V and a ripple voltage of 1 V.

Naturally enough all the capacitance values can

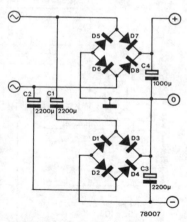

78007

be increased by the same factor in order to reduce the ripple voltage.

As far as the bridge rectifiers are concerned, these should be adequately rated to withstand the peak transformer voltage and the maximum load current.

H. Springer

33 Analogue-digital converter

Construction of an A/D converter is not a simple matter, since the circuit often requires the use of a number of precision components. However, the accuracy of the circuit described here is independent of component tolerances and is determined solely by the stability of a single reference voltage.

IC1 functions as a comparator. So long as the voltage on its inverting input is less than the analogue input voltage on its non-inverting input the output is high. FF1 receives pulses from the clock oscillator constructed around N1 and N2. Whilst its D input is held high by the output of IC1 its Q output remains high. CMOS switch S1

is closed, while S2 is open, so C2 charges from the reference voltage (U_{ref}) via S1 and R2.

When the voltage on C2 equals that at the non-inverting input the output of IC1 goes low. However, C2 continues to charge until the next clock pulse, when the Q output of FF1 goes low, S1 opens and S2 closes. C2 now discharges through R2, R5 and S2 until the voltage on it falls below the analogue input voltage, when the output of IC1 again goes high. On the next clock pulse the Q output of FF1 again goes high and the cycle repeats.

Since C2 is charging and discharging exponentially it follows that the higher the analogue

1

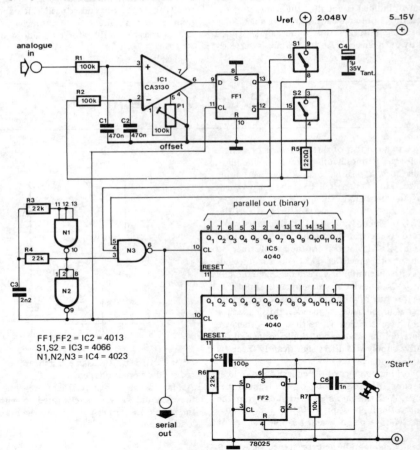

2

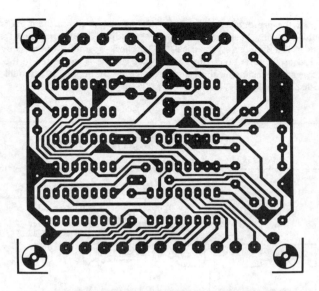

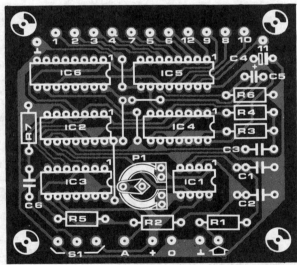

input voltage the longer will be the charge periods of C2 and the smaller will be the discharge periods. The result is that the output of IC1 is a squarewave whose duty-cycle is proportional to the analogue input voltage. Note that this only applies once the circuit has reached equilibrium. It does not apply during the initial phase when C2 is charging from zero.

When the 'start conversion' switch is closed flip-flop FF2 is set. This enables counters IC5 and

IC6. Both count clock pulses, but while IC6 counts every clock pulse IC5 counts clock pulses only whilst the Q output of FF1 is high. When the Q_{12} output of IC6 goes high FF2 is reset and the conversion ceases. The count which IC5 has reached is thus proportional to the duty-cycle of the Q output of FF1, which is proportional to the analogue input level.

If the reference voltage is exactly 2.048 V then the count of IC5 will be 1000 for an input of 1 volt. The linearity of the prototype circuit was 1%, but this could probably be improved by using an LF 357 for IC1, although a symmetrical supply will then be required. It is also possible to vary the clock frequency by changing the value of C3 (minimum 390 p for 50 kHz).

To set up the circuit the input is grounded and P1 is adjusted until the count from IC5 is zero. To check operation of the converter the reference voltage is connected to the analogue input when all outputs of IC5 should be high (count 2047).

34 Signal injector

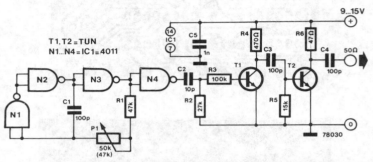

This simple signal injector should find many uses in trouble shooting and alignment applications. It produces an output with a fundamental frequency of 100 kHz and harmonics extending up to 200 MHz and has an output impedance of 50 ohms.

N1, N2 and N3 form an astable multivibrator with a virtually symmetrical squarewave output and a frequency of approximately 100 kHz. The output of the oscillator is buffered by a fourth NAND gate N4. Since the squarewave is symmetrical it contains only odd harmonics of the fundamental frequency, the higher harmonics being fairly weak due to the relatively slow rise time of the CMOS devices employed. As it is necessary for the higher harmonics to be at a reasonable level if the circuit is to prove useful at high frequencies, the output of N4 is fed to a differentiating network R2/C2. This attenuates

the fundamental relative to the harmonics, producing a needle-pulse waveform which is then amplified by T1 and T2. This is rich in harmonics and, due to the extremely small duty-cycle of the waveform, the power consumed by the output stage, T2, is fairly small. The output frequency of the signal injector can be adjusted by means of P1. If an accurate output frequency is required then the signal injector can be adjusted by beating its second harmonic with the 200 kHz Droitwich broadcast transmitter. The frequency stability of the circuit is largely determined by the construction. To minimise hand capacitance effects the unit should be housed in a metal box for screening, with the only output connection being the signal probe. If desired, a 1 k preset may be included in series with P1 to allow easier fine tuning.

35 Flasher bleeper

Although extremely useful, the selfcancelling devices fitted to car direction indicators are not infallible. For example, they will not operate

when only a small movement of the steering wheel is made, as when pulling out to overtake. An audible warning device to indicate that the

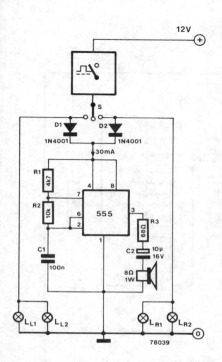

flashers have not cancelled is preferable to the visual indication normally fitted, as it is more noticeable and does not require the driver to take his eyes off the road.

The circuit consists simply of a 555 timer connected as a 1 kHz astable multivibrator. The output of the 555 is more than sufficient to drive a small loudspeaker. When the trafficator switch (S) is set to either the left or right positions, power is supplied to the multivibrator via the flasher unit and D1 or D2. The circuit thus 'beeps' with the same rhythm as the flashing of the indicators. If desired, the volume can be reduced by increasing the value of R3. The 'beep' frequency is determined by C1. For operation in positive earth cars D1 and D2 should be reversed and the multivibrator circuit turned upside-down, i.e. the C1/pin 1/loudspeaker junction is connected to the commoned anodes of the diodes and the R1/pin 4/pin 8 junction is connected to supply common.

36 IC counter timebase

A Mostek IC, the MK 5009, is a complete timebase for frequency counters and other applications. The internal block diagram of the IC is shown in figure 1. It incorporates a clock circuit (which may be used either with an external reference frequency, with an external RC circuit or with an external crystal) and a programmable divider. By applying an appropriate binary code to the programming inputs the division ratio may be varied in decade steps from 10^0 to 10^8. Other division ratios are also available, the most interesting being divide-by- 2×10^4, which gives a 50 Hz output with a 1 MHz clock frequency or a 60 Hz output with a 1.2 MHz clock frequency.

A practical circuit using the MK 5009 is shown in figure 2, whilst table 1 shows the division ratios that may be obtained for the different settings of S1 to S4. A 1 MHz crystal is used in a parallel resonant circuit and this crystal should be a 30 p parallel resonant type.

The divided down output is available at pin 1 of the IC. This output will drive CMOS circuits or

one TTL unit load directly. However, since the IC is fairly expensive it is recommended that a permanent buffer stage be connected to the output. This may take the form of a TTL or CMOS

S1	S2	S3	S4	division ratio
0	0	0	0	10^0
0	0	0	1	10^1
0	0	1	0	10^2
0	0	1	1	10^3
0	1	0	0	10^4
0	1	0	1	10^5
0	1	1	0	10^6
0	1	1	1	10^7
1	0	0	0	10^8
1	0	0	1	6×10^7
1	0	1	0	36×10^8
1	0	1	1	6×10^8
1	1	1	0	2×10^4

0 = switch closed
1 = switch open

1

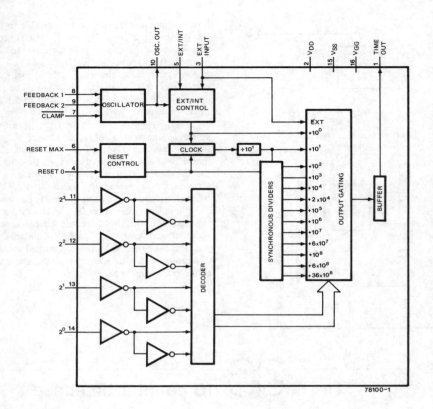

2a

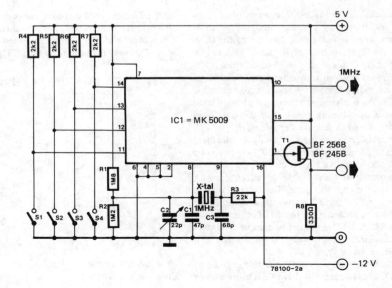

2b

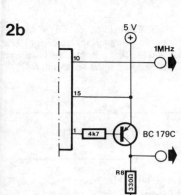

2c

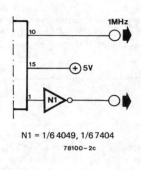

N1 = 1/6 4049, 1/6 7404

78100-2c

gate or buffer, a FET or a bipolar transistor. The 1 MHz clock frequency is available at pin 10 of the IC and must similarly be buffered if it is to be used.

Trimming of the oscillator frequency for maxi-

mum accuracy can be carried out using C2. With the division ratio set to 10, C2 can be adjusted for zero beat between the output and an accurate frequency such as the 200 kHz Droitwich transmitter.

37 Stable-Start-Stop-Squarewave

In digital circuits where parallel information must be converted into serial data, a start-stop oscillator is often used. One system is to use the oscillator to clock a counter, the output of which is compared with the parallel data. Initially the counter is reset; the external oscillator is then started, clocking the counter; when the correct

count is reached, the oscillator is stopped. The result is a (clock) pulse train, the length of which corresponds to the binary number given by the parallel data. It is not sufficient for these applications to gate the output of a free-running oscillator, since the 'enable' signal is not normally synchronised to the oscillator. The circuit de-

1

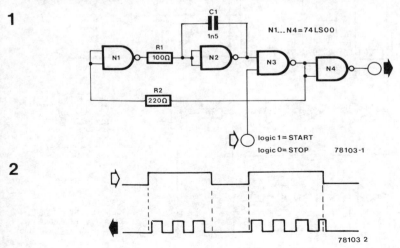

2

49

scribed here is actually turned on and off by the enable signal, and it has proved reliable and stable for output frequencies up to 10 MHz.

As long as the enable input (one input of N3) is at logic 0, the oscillator is blocked and the output of N4 is also held at logic 0. When the enable input becomes logic 1, the oscillator starts immediately and the first output pulse is delayed only by the propagation times of N3 and N4.

38 Digital audio mixer

A novel approach is employed in this circuit, which allows mixing of two audio signals and cross-fading between them. Rather than using conventional potentiometers as analogue attenuators together with a summing amplifier, the circuit functions by sampling the two signals alternately at a high frequency.

The input signals are fed to a pair of electronic switches each comprising two elements of a 4066 CMOS analogue switch IC. The use of a switch in shunt with the signal path as well as in series allows a high load impedance to be used (for low distortion) whilst at the same time maintaining good signal isolation when the switch is 'off'. The two switches are opened and closed alternately by a 100 kHz, two-phase clock constructed around N1 to N6. When S1 is closed, S2 is open and signal A is fed through to IC1. S3 however, is open and S4 closed, so signal B is blocked. When S3 is closed and S1 open then signal B is, of course, passed while A is blocked. P1 allows the duty-cycle of the clock pulses to be adjusted, i.e. the proportion of the total time for which each signal is passed. This in turn varies the amplitude of each signal. With P1 in its mid-position both signals have approximately the same amplitude whilst at the two extremes one signal is completely blocked whilst the other is passed continuously.

A lowpass filter built around IC1 removes any clock frequency components from the output. Although these are inaudible they could, if not

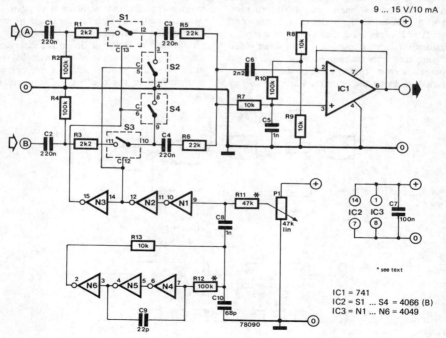

IC1 = 741
IC2 = S1 ... S4 = 4066 (B)
IC3 = N1 ... N6 = 4049

* see text

78090

filtered out, damage power amplifiers and loudspeaker tweeters or beat with the bias oscillator in a tape recorder to cause high-pitched bleeping tones.

The supply voltage, which should be stabilised and ripple-free, may lie between 9 V and 15 V. Above 15 V the CMOS ICs may be damaged and below 9 V the 741 will not function satisfactorily. The maximum input signal that the circuit will accept without distortion is about 1 V RMS.

39 Cheap crystal filter

1

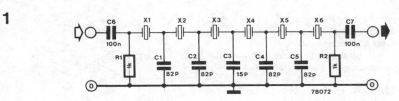

X1...X6 = 4.433618 MHz Xtal

In view of the dramatic drop in the price of crystals used in colour TV sets, they now represent an economical way of building an SSB-filter. The circuit shown in the accompanying diagram is for a filter with a − 6 dB bandwidth of roughly 2.2 kHz.
The layout for the p.c.b. indicates how such a circuit can be constructed. This type of arrangement has the advantage that the input and out-

2

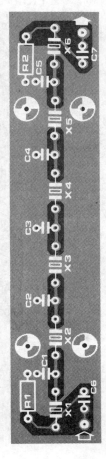

Parts list.

Resistors:
R1, R2 = 1 k

Capacitors:
C1, C2, C4, C5 = 82 p
C3 = 15 p
C6, C7 = 100 n ceramic

Miscellaneous:
X1, X2, X3, X4, X5, X6 = 4.433,618 kHz

Table.

f_0	4432,03 kHz		
$f_{-6\ dB}$ (r)	4433,06 kHz	$B_{-6\ dB}$	2,26 kHz
$f_{-6\ dB}$ (l)	4430,70 kHz		
$f_{-60\ dB}$ (r)	4435,30 kHz	$B_{-60\ dB}$	7,90 kHz
$f_{-60\ dB}$ (l)	4427,40 kHz		
slope factor (r)	1:3,17		
slope factor (l)	1:3,48		
ripple	2 dB		

put are as far as possible apart from one another, so that rejection outside the passband is at a maximum. By terminating the input and output with a 1 k resistor in parallel with an 18 p trimmer capacitor, passband ripple can be tuned down to 2 dB. The most important specs are given in the accompanying table, to which should be added that the out-of-band attenuation is 90 dB.

40 FET millivoltmeter

FET opamps have high gain, low input offset and an extremely high input impedance. These three characteristics make them eminently suitable for use in a millivoltmeter. The circuit presented here can measure both voltages and currents.

Figures 1a and 1b show the basic circuits for voltage and current measurement respectively. In figure 1a, the opamp is used in a virtual earth configuration and the gain is therefore determined by the ratio Ra/Rb and by the voltage divider circuit Rc/Rd. The exact formula is given in the diagram. The current measurement circuit, figure 1b, is also basically a virtual earth configuration; the opamp will maintain an output voltage such that the left-hand (input) end of Ra is at zero potential and, since the input current must flow through this resistor, the voltage

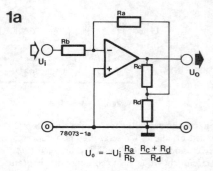

1a

$$U_o = -U_i \frac{R_a}{R_b} \frac{R_c + R_d}{R_d}$$

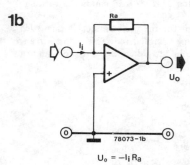

1b

$$U_o = -I_i R_a$$

drop across Ra equals I x Ra. Therefore, the output voltage must − I x Ra.

The complete circuit (figure 2) combines these two functions. The range switch S3 selects the required feedback resistor (Ra in figure 1) and the voltage divider (Rc and Rd) if the latter is required. The resulting ranges are listed in Table 1. The polarity of the meter can be reversed by means of switch S2.

A symmetrical $+/-3$ V supply is required, capable of delivering 1 mA. This low voltage and low current consumption means that the FET millivoltmeter can be battery-powered. This is a highly desirable feature, since the meter can then be used for so-called 'floating' measurement. A higher supply voltage is permissible, if it is easier

Table 1

S3	U_i (f.s.d.)	I_i (f.s.d.)
a	10 mV	1 nA
b	50 mV	5 nA
c	100 mV	10 nA
d	500 mV	50 nA
e	1 V	100 nA
f	5 V	500 nA
g	10 V	1 μA
h	50 V	5 μA
i	100 V	10 μA
j	500 V	50 μA
k	1000 V	100 μA

Table 2

S3 in position:	a	b	c
I_a (f.s.d.)	1 μA	5 μA	10 μA
I_b (f.s.d.)	10 μA	50 μA	100 μA
I_c (f.s.d.)	100 μA	500 μA	1 mA
I_d (f.s.d.)	1 mA	5 mA	10 mA
I_e (f.s.d.)	10 mA	50 mA	100 mA
I_f (f.s.d.)	100 mA	500 mA	1 A

2

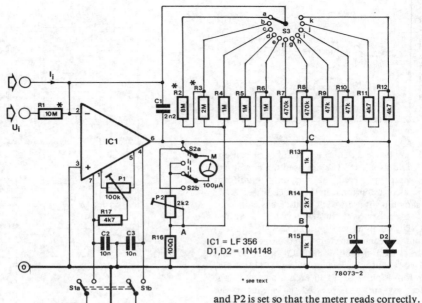

* see text

and P2 is set so that the meter reads correctly.
Figure 3 shows an optional extra: the 'universal
shunt'. This consists of nothing more than a
chain of resistors that can be connected across
the voltage input terminals of the meter. If current is passed through any one of these resistors,
a corresponding voltage drop will appear across
this resistor. Since there is no voltage drop
across any of the other resistors, this voltage will
be indicated by the meter. Table 2 lists the resulting current measurement ranges. As before, 1%
resistors should be used for the actual measuring
chain (R19...R24).

to obtain (4.5 V flat batteries, for instance); the
maximum for these opamps is a symmetrical
+/− 16 V supply.
It is advisable to use 1% resistors, and P1 and P2
should preferably by high-quality preset potentiometers. R1, R2 and R3 may prove difficult to
obtain, in which case a series-chain of 1 M resistors must be used.
Preset P1 is for offset compensation. With the
meter input shorted, this preset is adjusted until
the meter reads zero. P2 is the calibration potentiometer: a known voltage (or current) is applied

J. Borgman

3

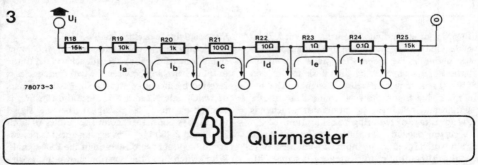

78073-3

---

41 Quizmaster

In many quiz games speed of response plays an
essential part, the contender who presses a
button first getting the first chance of answering

a question. The circuit shown here is designed to
determine and indicate which contestant is
'quickest on the draw'. The design is modular

1

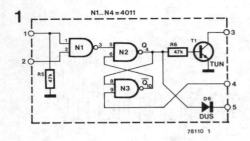

78110 1

2

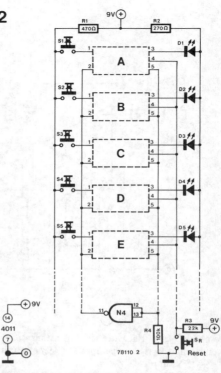

78110 2

and may be extended to any number of contestants, and as CMOS ICs are used the circuit can be battery powered, as the only significant current consumption is in the indicator LEDs.

As shown in figure 1 each module basically consists of a set-reset flip-flop N2/N3, with a NAND gate on its set input. Diodes D6 on the Q output of each flip-flop together with N4 in figure 2 form a multi-input NOR gate. So long as every Q output is low the output of N4 is high, therefore input 2 of N1 in each module is high. When any button is pressed the output of the corresponding N1 goes low and the Q output of the associated flip-flop goes high, turning on T1 and lighting the LED. Via D6 the input of N4 goes high. The output thus goes low, taking the inputs of all N1's low and inhibiting the pushbuttons so that no other flip-flop may be set.

The flip-flop which has been set may be reset ready for the next question by pushbutton S_R. By connecting additional modules as shown in figure 2 the circuit may be extended almost in-

definitely. If desired the output of N4 may be used to drive a buzzer via a buffer transistor.

P. Wendt

---

42 CMOS FSK modulator

In order to store digital information on a magnetic tape or to transmit it over long-distance (telephone) lines, use is often made of a modulator which converts the digital signal into an FSK (Frequency Shift Keyed) signal. The accompanying figure shows a circuit diagram of a simple and reliable FSK modulator which has the advantage of requiring no calibration.

A crystal oscillator supplies a reference pulse train which is fed to the input of a counter, IC1. At the Q10 output of this counter is a signal with a frequency of approx. 2,400 Hz, whilst a signal with exactly half that frequency, i.e. approx. 1,200 Hz, is available at the Q11 output. Since a crystal oscillator is used, the frequency of both

these signals is extremely stable.

Depending upon the logic level of the input signal, one of the above frequencies is fed to the output. Switching between the two frequencies is effected by means of flip-flop FF1, the outputs of which gate N3 and N4. Since the flip-flop is clocked by the 1,200 Hz signal, the FSK signal will always consist of 'complete' cycles of both 1,200 and 2,400 Hz. This arrangement is necessary to facilitate demodulation of the FSK signal. With switch S1 in the position shown in the diagram, the modulator will output data at a speed of 300 Baud (= bits per second). By changing over the position of this switch a transmission rate of 600 Baud can be obtained, in which case

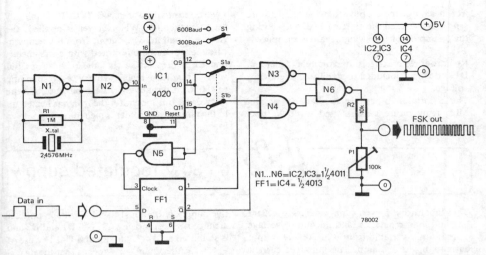

the frequencies used then become 2,400 and 4,800 Hz. Since the number of bits *per cycle* therefore remains the same, the reliability of the modulator is not affected.

The amplitude of the output signal can be varied by means of P1. If the modulator is used with a cassetterecorder, it may prove necessary to include a lowpass filter between the modulator output and the recorder. A simple RC network with a break frequency of roughly 5 kHz should do the trick.

Although it is in fact available, the crystal (2.4576 MHz) may prove difficult to track down, in which case one can, of course, experiment with other crystal values and other counter outputs.

H.W. Braun

43 Electronic soldering iron

A simple soldering iron regulator for 40 V irons can be constructed using only one opamp, a transistor and a handful of other components. The opamp is used as a comparator. The output from the temperature sensor in the iron is connected to the inverting input and compared with a reference voltage at the non-inverting input, set by P1. When the output from the temperature sensor is lower than the reference voltage, the opamp output is high and transistor T1 is turned on. The relay pulls in and power is applied to the iron. At a certain point, as the

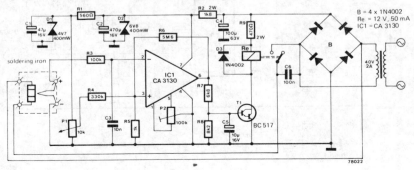

iron heats up, the output from the temperature sensor will exceed the reference voltage causing the opamp output to swing negative, turning off T1.

R6 introduces hysteresis to avoid relay 'chatter'. D1 and D2 are included to stabilise the reference voltage.

The calibration procedure is relatively simple. Most temperature sensors used in 40 V irons have a sensitivity of 5 mV/100°C. P1 is initially set to maximum. When power is applied, the relay will pull in. The output from the temperature sensor can be monitored with a mV-meter, and P2 is then set so that the relay drops out when this voltage reaches 20 mV, corresponding to 400°C. Alternatively, P2 can be set so that the relay drops out soon after the iron has heated up to the point where solder is melted readily.

44 0 - 30 V regulated supply

This laboratory power supply offers excellent line and load regulation and an output voltage continuously variable from 0 to 30 V at output currents up to one amp. The output is current limited and protected against output fault conditions such as reverse voltage or overvoltage applied to the output terminals. The circuit is based on the wellknown 723 IC regulator. As readers who have used this IC will know, the minimum output voltage normally obtainable from this IC is + 2 V relative to the V − terminal of the device (which is normally connected to 0 V). The problem can be overcome by connecting the V − pin to a negative potential of at least − 2 V, so that the output voltage can swing down to + 2 V relative to this, i.e. to zero volts. To avoid the necessity for a transformer with multiple secondary windings the auxiliary nega-

tive supply is obtained using a voltage doubler arrangement comprising C1, C2, D1 and D2 and is stabilised at − 4.7 V by R1 and D4. The use of − 4.7 V rather than − 2 V means that the differential amplifier in the 723 is still operating well within its common-mode range even when the output voltage is zero.

The main positive supply voltage is obtained from the transformer via bridge rectifier B1 and reservoir capacitor C3. The supply to the 723 is stabilised at 33 V by D3 to prevent its maximum supply rating being exceeded and a Darlington pair T2/T3 boosts the output current capability to 1 A. The current limit is continuously variable by means of P3.

The output voltage may be adjusted using P2, while preset P1 is used to set zero output voltage. The supply is protected against reverse polarity

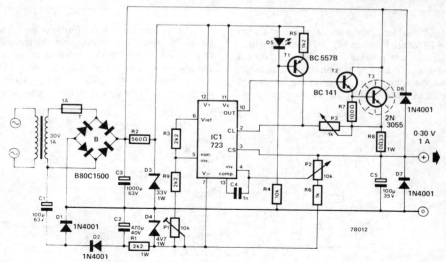

being applied to the output terminals by D7, and against overvoltages up to 63 V by D6.

To set the output voltage to zero P2 is first turned anticlockwise (wiper towards R8) and P1 is then adjusted until the output voltage is zero. With P2 turned fully clockwise the output voltage should then be approximately 30 V. If, due to component tolerance, the maximum output is less than 30 V the value of R6 may require slight reduction. When constructing the circuit particular care should be taken to ensure that the 0 V rail is of low resistance (heavy gauge wire or wide p.c.b. track) as voltage drops along this line can cause poor regulation and ripple at the output.

45 Car ammeter

A surfeit of circuits has already been published for solid-state car battery voltage monitors. However, no design for a corresponding car ammeter has so far appeared. This design remedies that omission.

Resistor R1 is a shunt across which is a voltage

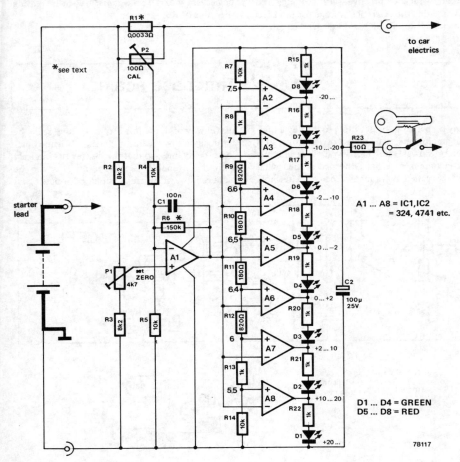

78117

proportional to the current flowing through it (max 133 mV at 40 A). The voltage drop across this shunt is amplified by differential amplifier A1 and used to drive a LED voltmeter comprising A2 to A8. With no current through the shunt, P1 is used to set the output voltage of A1 to nominally 6.5 V, so that the circuit is just on the point of switching over from D4 to D5.

When current is drawn from the battery, the right-hand end of the shunt will be at a lower potential than the left-hand end, so the output of A1 will rise, and the discharge indicating LEDs D5 to D8 will light successively as the current increases. When current flows into the battery, the converse is true, the output of A1 falls, and the charge indicating LEDs D4 to D1 light successively. Of course, variation in battery voltage will also cause the output voltage of A1 to rise and fall, which could give false readings. To overcome this the reference voltage for the LED voltmeter is not fixed but is also taken direct

from the battery, so that it rises and falls with the output of A1. This does mean that the calibration of the meter varies slightly with battery voltage, but extreme precision is not a prerequisite for a car ammeter. With the component values shown the calibration is nominally correct at a battery voltage of 13 V, but may vary by ± 15% if the battery voltage changes between 11 V and 15 V.

Several possibilities exist for R1. It can be wound using Manganin or Eureka resistance wire; alternatively the voltage drop along the lead between the battery and regulator box may be utilised by connecting one end of P2 to the positive battery terminal and the other end to the battery lead at the regulator box. P2 can then be used to calibrate the ammeter. If the voltage drop along the battery lead is insufficient it may be necessary to raise the gain of A1 by increasing the value of R6.

46 Timebase scaler

It may on occasion be desirable to display a digital or analogue signal, on an oscilloscope, at a faster or slower rate than is possible with the built-in timebase. What is needed is then what might be called a 'timebase scaler'. The most

useful way of doing this is to frequency-scale the input signal, by means of a bucket-brigade (analogue delay line), so that the display fits in nicely with the available sweep speed. This can be achieved by writing a 'chunk' of input signal

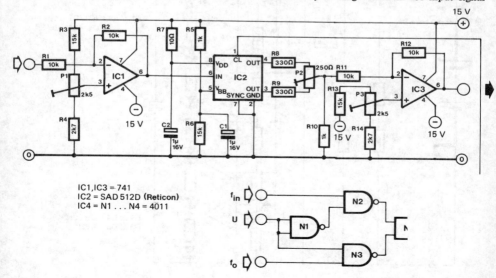

IC1,IC3 = 741
IC2 = SAD 512D (Reticon)
IC4 = N1 . . . N4 = 4011

into the memory 'buckets' at one clock rate, then reading the same chunk out at a lower or higher rate.

The simple circuit shown here will process analogue and digital signals up to 200 kHz. The total write-read cycle should not last longer than 0.1 s (at normal temperatures), otherwise too much information will be lost in the leaky buckets, giving an unacceptably attenuated output. The actual bucket brigade (IC2, Reticon type SAD 512) is preceded and followed by DC-level shifters using 741's. If the DC signal component is not of interest, the level-restorer (IC3) can be omitted and the signal taken out directly through a 100 nF capacitor.

When the control voltage U is *low,* the 'writing' clock frequency f_{in} is fed to the bucket brigade; when U is *high* the 'read' clock frequency (f_o) is applied. During the write-phase there will in general also be an (unwanted) output signal; it may be desirable to also arrange to suppress the output when U is low. If the circuit is to process a periodic signal, the control voltage should be obtained from a trigger running on the input signal, otherwise each chunk of output signal will start with a different phase. It will also be necessary to generate a number of write-periods per chunk at least equal to the number of buckets (512), to prevent 'old' information being read out.

The circuit given contains three preset potentiometers. Start by setting P1 to bring the output of IC1 to about 5 volts. Then set P2 for minimum clock noise on the output signal. Now slightly readjust P1 to achieve symmetrical clipping of an excessive signal. Finally set P3 to give the required output DC level, preferably by setting the output to 0 volts with the circuit input shorted to earth.

47 Model railway lighting

Generally speaking, the internal lighting for model railway carriages is powered direct from the voltage on the rails. However, this voltage is also used to power the locomotive and is varied to control the speed of the train. The result is that the brightness of the lighting varies with the speed of the train, and if the train is actually stopped, then the lighting will be completely extinguished. It goes without saying that such an arrangement involves a complete loss of realism. However, this problem can be resolved with the aid of the following circuit which ensures an independent supply for the carriage lighting.

The circuit utilises the fact that a DC motor will not operate off an AC supply, and that, furthermore, has a fairly high impedance if the frequency of the AC voltage is high enough. This means that if a high-frequency AC voltage is super-imposed upon the normal (DC) supply voltage for the locomotive, it will have no effect upon the speed of the train, but it can be used to power the carriage lighting. To ensure that the lighting is supplied solely by the AC voltage, each carriage is DC decoupled by means of a capacitor.

The principle behind the circuit is illustrated in figure 1. The inductor, L, prevents AC voltages from getting back into the DC power supply. Since this coil has to be able to withstand fairly large DC currents, it would be a good idea to use

1

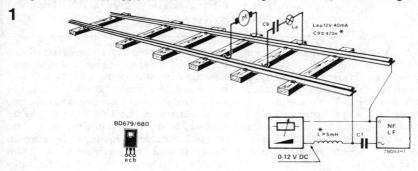

BD679/680

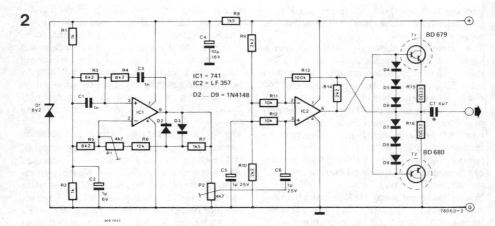

see text

the type of coil employed in loudspeaker cross-over filters.

Figure 2 shows the circuit diagram of the circuit used to supply the necessary AC voltage. The circuit actually consists of a sinewave generator followed by an amplifier which can deliver a current of approx. 1.5 A for a maximum output voltage of 10 V RMS, i.e. sufficient to supply roughly 30 lamps. The frequency of the sinewave generator round IC1 is approx. 20 kHz. The gain of IC1 is adjusted by means of P1 until a pure sinewave is obtained at the output of the IC. The amplitude of the output voltage is set by means of P2. The best results are obtained when P2 is adjusted such that, under maximum load condition (approx. 30 lamps), the output voltage exhibits minimum distortion. A polyester or polycarbonate (e.g. MKH) capacitor should be used for C7. If the value shown should prove unobtainable in a single capacitor, then several MKH (MKM) capacitors can be connected in

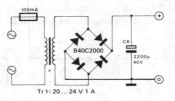

parallel. Since they cannot withstand large AC currents, the use of bipolar electrolytics is unsatisfactory. For every carriage lamp a series capacitance of about 0.5 µ is required. Thus, if the carriage lighting consists of two lamps, then the capacitor in series with these two lamps should have a value of approx. 1 µ F. Again, the use of MKH or MKM capacitors is recommended. Finally, it should be noted that the output of the circuit is short-circuit proof, and that transistors T1 and T2 should be provided with heat sinks.

48 Frequency synthesiser controller

In transceivers the desired frequency is often dialled into a frequency synthesiser by means of thumbwheel switches. This type of switch is not particularly cheap, so the alternative proposed here is worth considering. This circuit has the added advantage that a new frequency can be selected by means of two push-buttons which can be mounted next to the push-to-talk button on the microphone – a useful feature, particularly for mobile use.

The basic principle of a frequency synthesiser is fairly straightforward. The output frequency of a voltage controlled oscillator (VCO) is divided by a presettable number. The result is compared with a fixed reference frequency, and some type of control system (usually a PLL) adjusts the frequency of the VCO so that the result of the division has the same frequency as the reference. The net result is that the output of the VCO is equal to the reference frequency multiplied by the division ratio, so that it can be easily and accurately tuned in a succession of fixed steps by altering this division ratio.

In the circuit described here, the VCO output (f_{VCO}) is divided by IC3, IC4 and IC5. These counters are set in the decimal down-count mode. Each time they reach zero (000) the carry-out pulse of IC5 is fed through N10 to the preset-enable inputs of these three ICs. IC3 and IC4 are then preset to the decimal number determined by two further divide-by-ten counters, IC1 and IC2, and IC5 is preset to 1111. The same pulse is fed to one input of the PLL, where it is compared with the reference frequency. The output frequency of the pulses from N10 must therefore be equal to the reference frequency and, since the VCO output is used to clock the counters, the output frequency of the VCO must therefore be equal to the reference frequency multiplied by a number '9XY', where X and Y are the 'preset' values stored in IC2 and IC1 respectively. As an example, if the reference frequency is 1 kHz the tuning range will be from 900 to 999 kHz in 1 kHz steps. If the preset number in IC1 is 4 and the number in IC2 is 6, the output frequency in this case will be 964 kHz.

If IC1 and IC2 where thumbwheel switches, the circuit would be fairly conventional. However, they aren't. As noted earlier, these ICs are decimal counters and they will only 'store' a number as long as they do not receive count pulses. S1 and S2 are used to set up the required count, S1 causing them to count up and S2 resulting in count-down. If either of these buttons is pressed briefly, the count will change by one. However, if the button is held down the count will continue to change in the direction determined by the choice of pushbutton (S1 increasing the count and S2 decreasing it), whereby the rate at which new values occur increases if the button is held down for any length of time.

Starting from the pushbuttons, this part of the circuit operates as follows. N6 and N7 suppress contact bounce for S1; similarly N8 and N9 clean up the output from S2. When either of the buttons is operated the corresponding output (from N6 or N8) goes low, so the output of N5 goes high and N3 is enabled. This gate will now pass the output of the voltage-controlled square-wave generator, consisting of N1 and N2, to the

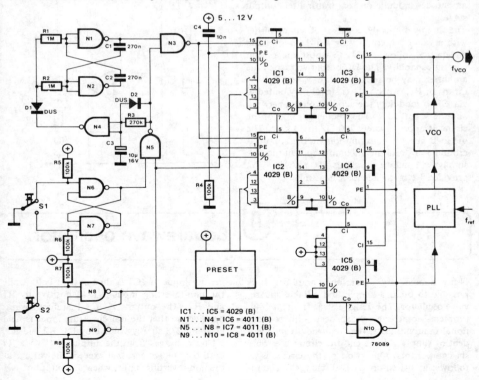

clock inputs of IC1 and IC2. The clock frequency from N1 and N2 depends on the output state of N4: If this output is high the clock frequency is low and vice versa.

Initially, C3 is discharged, the output of N4 is high, and the clock frequency is low. However, if a pushbutton is held down the output of N5 will remain high, charging C3 through R3. After a short time C3 will have charged sufficiently for the output of N4 to change state and the clock frequency will increase. As soon as the button is released C3 will discharge rapidly through D2 and N5. When S1 is operated, the output of N6 is low and the output of N8 is high, so IC1 and

IC2 are in the up-count mode. When S2 is operated, the output of N6 is high but the output of N8 is low; this output state switches both counters into the down-count mode.

Both IC1 and IC2 can be preset at initial switch-on of the circuit. To this end C4 and R4 are included; these components enable the preset inputs of these counters briefly when power is first applied. Any desired initial setting can be programmed (in BCD) by connecting the preset inputs of IC1 and IC2 to positive supply or supply common. This possibility is symbolised in the circuit by the rectangle labelled 'preset'.

49 Modulatable power supply

This DC power supply, whose output voltage can be modulated by an audio-frequency or other LF signal, is intended for such applications as modulation of Gunn-diode oscillators and amplitude modulation of transmitter output stages.

The supply basically consists of an amplifier with a gain of 2, comprising a 741 op-amp and an emitter follower, T2, to boost the output current capability. The DC output voltage of the amplifier may be set between 6 V and 8 V by means of P1, whilst an AC signal may be fed in via C1 to modulate the supply voltage between about 3 V and 10 V. The frequency range of the circuit is approximately 200 Hz to 30 kHz. The off-load current consumption of the supply is around 5 mA and the maximum current that the supply will deliver is about 800 mA at 6 V, provided T2 has an adequate heatsink.

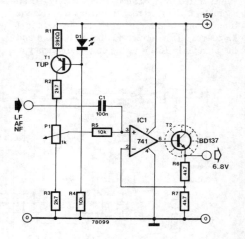

50 Squarewave oscillator

Using almost any operational amplifier it is possible to build a simple and reliable squarewave oscillator. The design is free from latch-up problems sometimes experienced with conventional multivibrators, the frequency is independent of supply voltage and the circuit uses only six components. Operation of the circuit is as follows: at switch-on C1 is discharged. The inverting input of IC1 is thus at zero volts while the non-inverting input is held positive by R1 and R2. The output of IC1 therefore swings positive, so that the non-inverting input is held at about 2/3 supply voltage by R1, R2 and R3. C1 now charges from the output of IC1 via R4 until the voltage across it exceeds the voltage at the non-inverting input, when the output of IC1

1

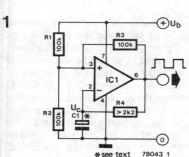

* see text 78043 1

Table 1.

Op-amp	lowest supply voltage	highest supply voltage	highest frequency
709	5 V	36 V	325 kHz
741	3.5 V	36 V	100 kHz (triangular output above 30 kHz due to slew-rate limiting)
CA3130	3 V	16 V	275 kHz
CA3140	5 V	36 V	200 kHz
CA3100	8.5 V	36 V	275 kHz
LF357	3 V	36 V	325 kHz
LM301	3 V	36 V	325 kHz

swings down to about zero volts. The exact positive- and negative-going output swing achieved depends on the type of opamp used. The non-inverting input of IC1 is now at 1/3 supply voltage.

C1 now discharges through R4 into the output of IC1 until its voltage falls below that on the non-inverting input, when the output of IC1 again swings positive and the cycle repeats. Since variations in supply voltage equally affect the charging of C1 and the threshold levels at which the opamp output changes state, these two effects cancel and the oscillation frequency is independent of supply voltage.

The frequency of oscillation is given

$$\text{by } f = \frac{1}{(1.4)\,R_4 C_1}$$

where f is in Hertz
R4 is in Ohms
C1 is in Farads

Alternatively, if R4 is in kilohms and C1 is in microfarads then f will be in kilohertz.

Practically any opamp may be used in this circuit and table 1 lists several popular opamps, together with the supply voltage range over which each may be used and the maximum oscillation frequency which is typically obtainable. The duty-cycle of the squarewave should be

2

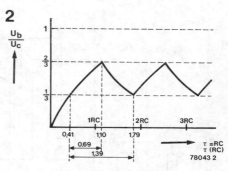

50%, but due to slight asymmetry in the output stages of the opamps this will not be the case. The only opamp amongst those listed which will give a duty-cycle of exactly 50% is the CA 3130. At low supply voltages it may also be found that the frequency changes with supply voltage due to variations in the output characteristics of the op-amps. However, with supply voltages greater than 10 V this should not be a problem.

The working voltage of C1 must be at least 2/3 of the supply voltage.

---

51 Temperature-compensated

The popular 723 IC regulator has an on-chip reference voltage with a fairly low temperature coefficient. By using a simple gimmick the 723 can be used as an 'oven' to maintain itself (and hence the reference voltage) at a virtually constant temperature, thus practically eliminating the temperature dependence of the reference voltage. The 723 is connected as a unity-gain non-inverting amplifier, to whose input is fed a voltage

$$\frac{U_{ref} \times R_4}{R_3 + R_4}$$

This causes a current to flow through load resistor R5 via T1 and T2, the output transistors of the 723. The power dissipated in these transistors causes the chip temperature to rise. The temperature of the IC is between 60 and 70°C, i.e. just bearable to the touch. The adjustment procedure may take some time as it will be necessary below the value set by P1 then T3 will turn on, cutting off the output current until the chip temperature has fallen sufficiently for T3 to turn off again.

The result is that the chip, and hence the reference voltage, is held at a virtually constant temperature. Obviously the chip temperature must be maintained considerably higher than ambient for correct operation (since the circuit cannot cool the chip to a temperature below ambient) and P1 is provided to adjust the chip temperature. P1 should be adjusted until the case temperature of the IC is between 60 and 70°C, i.e. just bearable to the touch. the adjustment procedure may take some time as it will be necessary to allow the chip temperature to stabilise after each adjustment of P1. The best procedure is to turn the wiper of P1 towards R1, switch on and allow to stabilise, measure the temperature, readjust P1, allow to stabilise etc.

The value of R5 is dependent on the supply voltage used and should be 33 ohms for voltages between 9 V and 15 V, 68 ohms for 15 V to 25 V and 100 ohms for 25 V to 35 V.

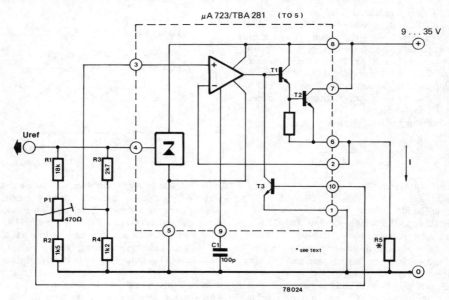

μA 723/TBA 281 (TO 5)

52 Frequency synthesiser

The output frequency of this squarewave generator can be programmed in 1 kHz steps from 1 kHz to 999 kHz. The heart of the circuit is a 4046 CMOS phase-locked loop which has an extremely wide capture range.

The output of a 1 kHz clock generator, N1/N2, is divided down by FF1 to give a symmetrical 500 Hz squarewave output, which is fed to one of the phase comparator inputs of the 4046 (IC6). The Voltage Controlled Oscillator (VCO) output of IC6 is fed to the second input of the phase comparator via a programmable frequency divider (IC3-IC5) and FF2.

The VCO output frequency of the PLL adjusts

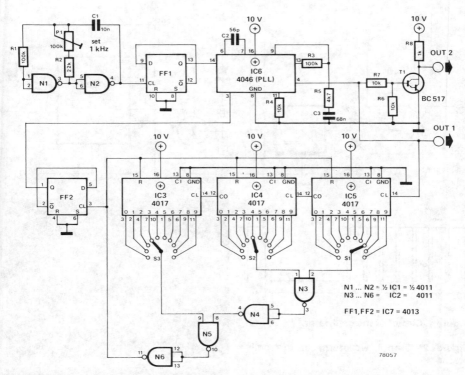

itself until the output of FF2 has the same frequency and phase as the clock output from FF1. If the division ratio set on switches S1 to S3 is n then the VCO frequency must obviously be n times the 1 kHz clock frequency. Setting a number n on switches S1 to S3 therefore gives an output frequency of n kHz. The VCO output from pin 4 may be used to drive CMOS circuits direct, however, for other applications a transistor buffer may be required.

If greater frequency accuracy is required then the clock oscillator may be replaced by a more stable 1 kHz reference frequency such as the divide-by-10^3 output of the IC counter timebase described elsewhere in this book.

53 Scope calibrator

It is comforting to believe in the infallible accuracy of one's test instruments, especially when there are no other standards around to contradict them. However, instruments, and particularly complex ones such as oscilloscopes, tend to drift with age, and if more than a year or so old can be highly inaccurate. This simple calibrator will check the gain and bandwidth of the Y amplifiers and attenuators and the frequency calibration of the timebase. It is so compact that it can be built into virtually any oscilloscope, making regular calibration a simple procedure. Since the Y attenuators and timing capacitors in an oscilloscope are usually fairly stable components most of the drift generally takes place in the X and Y amplifiers and the rest of the timebase circuitry. Thus an oscilloscope will frequently agree with itself between different Y sensitivity and timebase ranges, even though the calibration may be wildly inaccurate with reference to an external standard. Gross discrepancies between ranges usually occur only in the

1

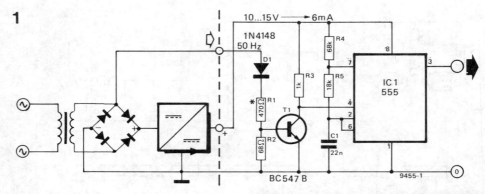

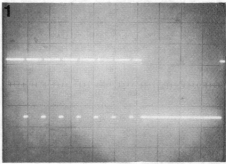

2

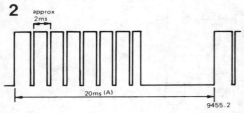

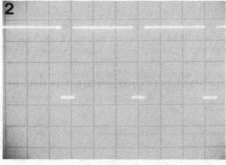

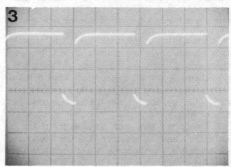

Figure 1. Circuit of the calibrator.

Figure 2. Output waveform of the calibrator.

Figure 3. Printed circuit board and component layout for the calibrator.

Photo 1. Oscillograph of the calibrator output waveform.

Photo 2. An expanded view of a portion of the waveform as seen on a correctly calibrated oscilloscope.

Photo 3. The waveform of photo 2 seen on an oscilloscope with poor h.f. response.

event of a fault in the circuit and a drift in the overall calibration may go unnoticed for some time.

The simple circuit of the calibrator is given in figure 1. It consists of a 555 timer connected as an astable multivibrator with a period of 1.5...2 ms. This is gated on and off by T1, which is driven by a 50 Hz signal. The complete output waveform, shown in figure 2, comprises a burst of pulses (approx. 2 ms) followed by a 10 ms gap, followed by a further burst of pulses and so on. The time from the start of one burst of

3

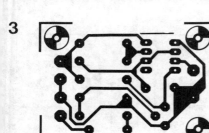

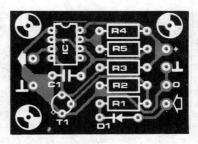

Parts List

Resistors:
R1 = 470 Ω *
R2 = 68 Ω *
R3 = 1 k
R4 = 68 k
R5 = 18 k
* see text

Capacitors:
C1 = 22 n

Semiconductors:
D1 = 1N4148
T1 = BC547B, BC107B
IC1 = 555 timer

pulses to the start of the next burst is equal to the period of the 50 Hz waveform i.e. 20 ms. This can be used to calibrate the oscilloscope timebase. The amplitude of the calibration signal is approximately equal to the supply voltage, which can be measured with a multimeter. The amplitude of the waveform can then be used to calibrate the Y amplifiers.

The 2 ms pulses are useful for checking the bandwidth of the Y amplifiers and the compensation of the Y attenuators and also for calibrating oscilloscope probes. Photo 1 shows an oscillograph of the complete test waveform, while photo 2 shows the pulses as seen on a correctly calibrated oscilloscope. Photo 3 shows the effect of poor highfrequency response due to in-

correct adjustment of the compensation trimmers in the Y attenuator.

Construction

A printed circuit board and component layout for the calibrator are given in figure 3. This is very compact and can easily be mounted inside most oscilloscopes. It is assumed that the necessary supply voltage can be derived from the oscilloscope power supplies. With modern transistor oscilloscopes this should be no problem, the supply can probably be derived from one of the low-voltage supplies in the oscilloscope either-direct or via a simple zener stabilizer.

The anode of D1 is simply connected to one of the low voltage secondaries of the oscilloscope mains transformer. The values of R1 and R2 depend on the secondary voltage: R1 = 470 Ω up to 8 V; R1 = 680 Ω from 8 V to 11 V; R1 = 1 k from 11 V to 16 V; R1 = 1k5 from 16 V to 23 V; R1 = 3k9/½ W and R2 = 150 Ω from 23 V to 40 V. R2 = 68 Ω , as shown, up to 23 V.

Installation in older, valve-type oscilloscopes may pose a problem and it may be preferable to instal a separate power supply for the calibrator using a miniature mains transformer and a simple zener stabilized supply. Care should then be taken that the magnetic field of the transformer does not affect the performance of the oscilloscope.

The output of the calibrator can be brought out to a socket on the front panel of the oscilloscope so that the calibration can easily be checked by inserting a probe into the socket.

 Electronic open fire

Many electric fires are equipped with a special coal- or log- effect to simulate the appearance of

an open fire. This effect is sometimes spoilt, however, by the fact that the lamp provides a constant rather than a flickering light. The circuit described here is intended to remedy that defect.

There is no doubt that most people find the sight of an open fire pleasing. There seems to be something soothing in watching the flames flicker and play about the coals. On the other hand, coal fires are difficult to light, slow in producing heat, and also extremely messy to clean out. For this reason many people prefer the convenience and speed of an electric fire, and reluctantly relinquish the pleasures of a hearth fire. Manufacturers of electric fires have realised this fact, and attempted to entice the consumer to buy electric by fitting the front of their fires with a coal- or log effect. Unfortunately, the lamps which are used to illuminate these fronts sometimes provide only a constant light, thereby considerably diminishing the realism of the effect. However, using only a handful of components from the junk-box, it is possible to construct a small circuit to restore the 'flicker' in your fire.

The way the circuit functions is quite simple. When power is applied capacitor C1 is charged via the lamp, resistor R2 and diode D1. After several half cycles of the mains supply, the voltage across this capacitor exceeds the trigger voltage of diac Di1. This diac in turn triggers thyristor Th1, with the result that capacitor C2 charges up rapidly through this thyristor and D1. However, when the mains voltage next crosses zero, this thyristor turns off. Capacitor C3, which is part of the trigger circuit of Tri1, is now charged rapidly by capacitor C2 via resistor R3. This 'DC bias' on C3 decreases as capacitor

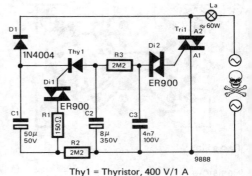

Thy1 = Thyristor, 400 V/1 A

Tri 1 = Triac, 400 V/ 4 A

C2 discharges. This in turn results in a gradual change in the triggering angle of the triac, causing the lamp La to flicker. Once C1 has again reached the trigger voltage of the diac, the entire cycle repeats itself.

As far as component values are concerned, care should be taken to ensure that the maximum current taken by the triac is at least twice the maximum current drawn by the lamp La. For a normal sized fire a 4 A type should prove sufficient. The triac must also be able to withstand the peak mains voltage i.e. approx. 400 V. A 400 V (1 A) thyristor should also prove suitable. D1 may be any commonly available 600 V rectifier diode.

During construction it should be remembered that the full mains voltage may appear across any point in the circuit. For this reason it should be well insulated.

S. Kaul

55 Common-base virtual-earth mixer

The most usual form of virtual-earth mixer consists of an inverting amplifier with the inputs to be mixed (or more accurately summed) being fed via resistors to the virtual-earth point at the inverting input. However this unusual circuit utilises a single transistor operated in common-base configuration, and does not invert the input signals.

T1 receives a constant base bias voltage from R1, D1 and D2, and thus the emitter voltage is also held constant at about 0.6 V. A constant

current of $\frac{0.6}{R2}$ thus flows through R2. Assuming, for simplicity, that the mixer is dealing with AC input signals, under quiescent (no signal) conditions the DC current through R2 is almost entirely supplied by T1 and is almost equal to the collector current.

If an AC signal is applied to one of the input resistors R5 then an AC current $\frac{Un}{R5}$ will flow through R2. Since the total current through R2 remains constant the proportion of that current supplied by T1 will vary in sympathy with the input signal and an AC output signal will appear at the collector of T1. The gain of the mixer is $\frac{R3}{R5}$ so, assuming all the R5's are the same, the output voltage $U_0 = \frac{R3}{R5} (U_1 + U_2 + U_3 + \ldots\ldots + U_n)$.

As the emitter of T1 remains at constant voltage it is an almost perfect virtual-earth summing point. The distortion factor of the mixer is determined almost exclusively by the linearity of the current gain in the common-base configuration, which is $\frac{hfe}{1 + hfe}$.

If a high-gain transistor (large hfe) is used then the current gain will be almost unity and variations in hfe will have little effect, so the distortion will be low.

The input resistance of the circuit is equal to R5, so R5 must obviously be made equal to the desired input resistance. R3 is chosen equal to $\frac{R5}{n}$, where n is the number of inputs.

Finally, for optimum results R2 should be made

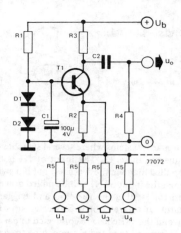

equal to $\frac{1.2 \times R3}{Ub}$. This fixes the DC collector current of T1 and sets the collector voltage to around half supply.

As an example, if R5 is 33 k and there are four inputs the value of R3 is 8k2. With a supply voltage of 15 V R2 is thus 680 Ω (these are nearest preferred resistors to actual values).

56 CMOS alarm circuits

Because of their low cost, high input resistance, good noise immunity and wide supply voltage range CMOS logic circuits lend themselves to the construction of cheap and reliable alarm circuits for various applications.

Figure 1 shows a basic alarm oscillator constructed around two CMOS NAND gates. As long as input Q is low the circuit remains inactive. When input Q goes high the circuit begins to oscillate, switching T1 and T2 on and off and producing an alarm signal from the loudspeaker.

Figure 2 shows a circuit for triggering the alarm after a preset time delay that can be varied between one second and one minute. On switch-on the input of N2 is briefly held low by C2, so the flip-flop is reset and the Q output is low. C1 now charges via P1 so that the input voltage of N1 falls until the flip-flop is set and the Q output goes high.

Figure 3 is an alarm circuit that is triggered when a circuit is broken, this is particularly useful in

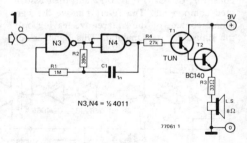

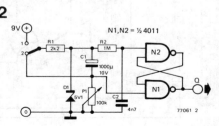

3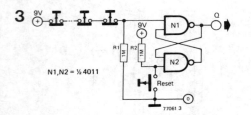

4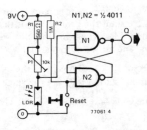

burglar alarm systems where several switches can be connected in series. The input of N1 is normally pulled high via the switches, but if a switch is opened the input of N1 will be pulled down by the resistor, setting the flip-flop and triggering the alarm. If the resistor is connected up to + supply and the switches are connected in parallel down to ground then the alarm can be triggered by closing a switch.

Figure 4 shows an alarm circuit that responds to light. In darkness the resistance of the LDR is high and the input of N1 is pulled high by R1 and P1. If light falls on the LDR the resistance falls and the input of N1 is pulled down, setting the flip-flop and triggering the alarm.

57 Spot-frequency sinewave generator

This circuit employs an unusual method of producing a sinewave signal and, unlike most sinewave generators, requires no amplitude stabilising components such as thermistors or FETs. N1 and N2 are connected as a Schmitt trigger at whose output appears a squarewave (how this happens will become apparent). The squarewave signal is fed into two cascaded selective filters consisting of IC2/T1, IC3/T2 and their associated components. The filters remove the harmonic content of the squarewave leaving only the sinusoidal fundamental. This signal is fed

back via C1 to the input of the Schmitt trigger. At each zero-crossing of the sinewave the Schmitt trigger changes state, thus producing the original squarewave that is fed to the input of IC2. P1 adjusts the trigger point of the Schmitt trigger, which varies the duty-cycle of the squarewave and hence the sinewave purity. By suitable adjustment of P1 distortion levels of 0.15% to 0.2% can be achieved. With the ICs used lower figures are not possible due to the distortion introduced by IC3 and T2.

N3 and N4 also function as a Schmitt trigger,

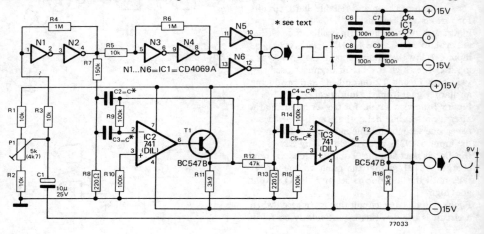

which further speeds up the leading and trailing edges of the squarewave from N2. A squarewave signal with short rise and fall times, synchronised to the sinewave signal, is available at the outputs of N5 and N6. The value of C for a particular frequency f_0 is given by $C\ (\mu F) = \dfrac{0.34}{f_0\ (Hz)}$.

58 Signal injector

1

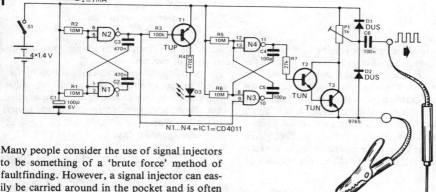

Many people consider the use of signal injectors to be something of a 'brute force' method of faultfinding. However, a signal injector can easily be carried around in the pocket and is often the service engineer's 'first line of defence' when undertaking repairs in the customer's home. Certainly a signal injector is much more portable than an array of sophisticated signal generators.

Most of the cheap signal injectors on the market produce a squarewave output at about 1 kHz. Since the squarewave is rich in harmonics extending up into the Megahertz region these are useful for testing r.f. circuits, as well as using the fundamental for audio testing.

The signal generator described here differs slightly in that the 1 kHz squarewave is keyed on and off at about 0.2 Hz, which makes it easier to trace.

Figure 1 shows the complete circuit of the signal injector. The keying oscillator consists of an astable multivibrator built around two CMOS NAND gates N1 and N2. This switches on and off T1, which drives a LED to indicate when the signal is on. The 1 kHz squarewave generator also consists of an astable multivibrator, which utilises the two remaining NAND gates in the 4011 package. This astable is gated on and off by the first astable. The output of the 1 kHz oscillator is buffered by transistors T2 and T3, the output being taken from the collector of T3 via a potentiometer P1 which serves to adjust the output level. The maximum output is approximately equal to the supply voltage (5.6 V). Diodes D1 and D2 provide some protection for T2 and T3 from external transients, and C6 isolates the circuit from any DC voltage in the circuit under

2

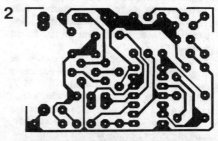

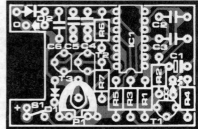

Parts List

Resistors:
R1, R2, R5, R6 = 10 M
R3 = 100 k
R4 = 470 Ω
R7 = 27 k
P1 = 1 k preset

Capacitors:
C1 = 100 μ /6 V
C2, C3 = 470 n

C4, C5 = 100 p
C6 = 100 n/250 V (see text)

Semiconductors:
IC1 = 4011
T1 = TUP
T2, T3 = TUN
D1, D2 = DUS (see text)
D3 = LED (e.g. TIL209)

Miscellaneous:
S1 = SPST switch
4 x 1.4 V mercury batteries

test. If the signal injector is to be used to test circuits having high voltages present, especially mains (e.g. television sets) then C6 should be rated at 1000 V working, in which case it will be too large to mount direct on the p.c. board, the layout for which is given in figure 2. It is also a good idea to mount the complete circuit inside a box made of insulating material, especially when working on live chassis equipment such as a television set. D1 and D2 should be types capable of handling any transient voltages and currents likely to be encountered.
Power for the circuit can be provided by four 1.4 V mercury batteries. The exact type of battery chosen is up to the individual constructor, but should neither be so small that the battery life is too short, nor so large that the complete instrument is too bulky.

J.W. van Beek

 Precision V to f converter

Although this Voltage Controlled Oscillator uses only two CA3130 opamps the linearity of its voltage/frequency transfer characteristic is better than 0.5% and its temperature coefficient less than 0.01%/°C.
The circuit operates as follows: IC1 functions as a voltage controlled multivibrator. Assuming that the output voltage of IC1 is initially + 15 V, C1 will charge via D3, R4 and P1 with a time constant (R4 + P1) C1 until the voltage on the inverting input of IC1 exceeds that on the non-inverting input. Neglecting D1 and D2 for a moment this is approximately 10 V, set by the potential divider R1, R3 and R2. The output of IC1 will now swing down to zero and the voltage on the non-inverting input will fall to about 5 V due to the hysteresis introduced by R3.
C1 will now discharge into the output of IC2 at a rate determined by R7 and the output voltage of IC2 until the voltage on the inverting input of IC1 falls below 5 V, when the output of IC1 will swing up to + 15 V again and the cycle will repeat. The output waveform of IC1 thus consists of a series of positive pulses whose duration (T2) is a constant and whose spacing (T1) depends on the output voltage of IC2.
The output voltage of IC1 is filtered by R6 and C3 to give a DC voltage (V2) equal to the average value of the IC1 waveform i.e.

$$V_2 = 15 \times \frac{T_2}{T_1}.$$

Since T2 is constant V2 is proportional to 1/T1 i.e. proportional to the output frequency of IC1. The input voltage V1 is applied to the inverting input of IC2, which functions as an integrating comparator. If V1 is less than V2 the output of IC2 will ramp positive. C1 will thus discharge at a slower rate, making the interval T1 longer and reducing V2. If V1 is greater than V2 then the output of IC2 will ramp negative (i.e. towards zero) making C1 discharge more quickly and reducing T1. When V1 and V2 are equal the output voltage of IC2 will remain constant.
The circuit will thus always reach equilibrium with V1 = V2. However, since V2 and the output

72

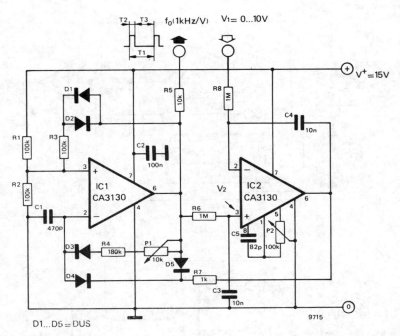

frequency of IC1 are proportional then the output frequency of IC1 is also proportional to the input voltage V_1, since V_1 and V_2 are equal.

A few small refinements are added to improve the temperature stability of the circuit. The temperature coefficients of D3 and D4 could introduce errors by varying the charge and discharge times of C1, so these are compensated by including identical diodes in series with R3 to produce

a similar variation in the reference voltage at the non-inverting input of IC1.

P2 is included to null the offset voltage of IC2 which would otherwise cause a zero error.

P1 provides fine adjustment of the conversion ratio, which with the values given is about 1 kHz/volt.

Lit.: RCA Application Notes

60 Monitor switching for two tape decks

Although modern audio amplifiers frequently sport an abundance of (seldom-used?) gimmicks, very few amplifiers possess comprehensive tape switching and monitoring facilities. Most have only a single tape socket, with facilities for making a recording onto one tape deck and monitoring that recording, and have no provision for a second tape deck.

The simple switching circuits described here will allow recording from disc or other sources onto two tape recorders, either one at a time or simultaneously, with monitoring of both recordings. In addition, transcription from either tape re-

corder to the other is possible, while at the same time a totally different source (disc, tuner, etc.) can be played through the amplifier.

The switching circuit is shown in figure 1. The function selector switch of the amplifier (disc, tuner, aux, etc.) is represented by S1. S2 and S3 are part of the switching unit. With S3 in its centre position a signal can be taken from the source to the record inputs of both tape recorders. With S1 in position 1 → 2 the playback output of one tape deck is fed to the record input of the second, while in the 2 → 1 position the playback output of the second deck is fed to the

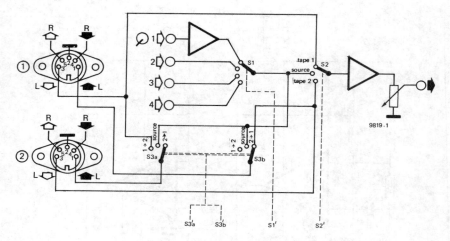

1

9819-1

2

9819-2

record input of the first.

Whatever the position of S3, monitoring of tape 1, source, or tape 2 is possible by means of S2. Therefore, with S3 in position 1 ➔ 2 or 2 ➔ 1 it is still possible to listen to disc, tuner, etc. by setting S2 to its centre position. For clarity only the left channel is shown, but the right channel is identical.

The circuit may be incorporated into the amplifier by inserting it between the output of the function switch and the input of the next stage of the amplifier. The original tape monitor switch (if fitted) can be discarded and replaced by S2, while an extra hole must be drilled in the front panel for S3.

Alternatively the switching unit can be mounted in its own box and can be connected to the

amplifier via the existing tape socket. The output to the unit is simply taken from the record pin of the tape socket, and the input back to the amplifier from the rotor of S2 is taken to the replay pin of the tape socket. The amplifier must then be operated with the tape monitor switch depressed.

A slight modification to the circuit, shown in figure 2, allows recording from disc while listening to a different source. With S4 in the left-hand position the output of the disc preamp can be tapped off and fed to the tape decks, while S1 can be in any of its four positions, thus allowing disc or some other source to be listened to at the same time. The recording may also still be monitored by setting S2 to 'tape 1' or 'tape 2'.

AM/FM alignment generator

This circuit can be used to align IF strips with a frequency of 455 kHz. The generator produces a 455 kHz signal which, depending upon the position of switches S1 and S2, is either amplitude- or frequency modulated.

The actual oscillator is built round FET T1. A conventional IF transformer is used to determine the frequency. The alignment generator is tuned to the correct frequency by passing the output signal through a ceramic IF filter. After rectification the signal can be measured on a voltmeter to ascertain at which setting of the IF transformer coil the amplitude of the signal is greatest. The frequency of the generator should then coincide with the desired value of 455 kHz.

The circuit is provided with the possibility of AM and FM modulation. When the generator is being aligned, switch S1 should be open, thereby

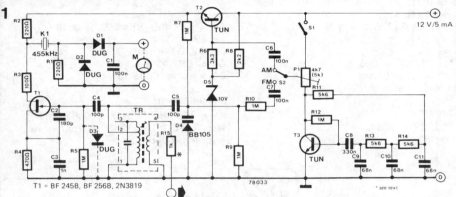

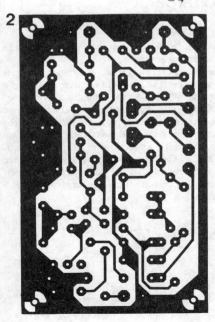

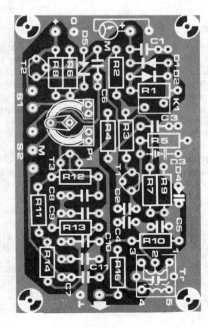

75

preventing modulation of the output signal. The modulation signal is generated by the low frequency oscillator round T3.

Amplitude modulation is realised by modulating the supply voltage of T1 via T2. S2 should then be in the 'AM' position. Frequency modulation (S2 in the 'FM' position) is obtained by means of the varicap diode, D4. In both cases the modulation depth can be varied by means of P1.

The output signal of the alignment generator is taken from the secondary winding of the IF transformer. Depending upon the desired output voltage and impedance, the series output resistor, R15, can have any value above $100\,\Omega$. In most cases a value of 1 k should prove sufficient.

Parts list

Resistors:
R1, R2 = 220 Ω
R3 = 100 Ω
R4 = 470 Ω
R5, R7, R9, R10, R12 = 1 M
R6 = 3k3
R8 = 2k2
R11, R13, R14 = 5k6
P1 = 4k7 (5 k) preset
   potentiometer

Capacitors:
C1, C6, C7 = 100 n
C2 = 180 p

C3 = 1 n
C4, C5 = 100 p
C8 = 330 n
C9, C10, C11 = 68 n

Semiconductors:
T1 = BF 245B, BF 256B, 2N3819
T2, T3 = TUN
D1, D2, D3 = DUG
D4 = BB 105
D5 = zener diode 10 V

Miscellaneous:
K1 = 455 kHz (Murata) ceramic filter
Tr = Toko 11100, 12374 IF transformer
   (or equivalent)

---

⑥② Poltergeist

The title of this article should really be 'remote-controlled poltergeist-imitator'. By operating a miniature ultrasonic transmitter concealed for example in one's jacket pocket, a receiver hidden somewhere in the room will simulate the sound of a poltergeist loose in the house. Should the authentic poltergeist then fail to put in an appearance, the ambitious ghost-hunter can ensure success by virtue of his electronic stand-in.

The idea behind this article is not to put the poltergeist out of a job, but rather to provide a little innocent fun for those of our readers inclined to practical jokes.

The miniature ultrasonic transmitter which is concealed on the person of the user consists of a handful of components, and the current consumption is negligible (approx. 0.3 mA). When the receiver, which is hidden somewhere in the same room, picks up the ultrasonic signals from the transmitter an audio generator is activated. A loudspeaker then audibly signals the presence of our noisy visitor, the poltergeist. The maximum transmission range is approx. 4 to 5 metres.

1

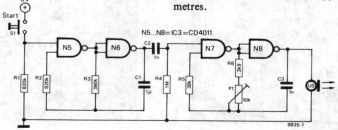

2a

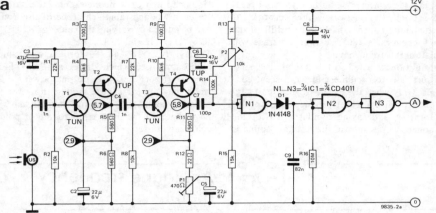

The transmitter

As is apparent from figure 1, the ultrasonic transmitter requires little more than one IC type 4011 and an ultrasonic transducer.

The four gates of the IC are used to form two astable multivibrators; the frequency of the first (N5, N6) is approx. 1 Hz, whilst that of the second (N7, N8) is roughly 40 kHz. Closing S1 starts the first AMV, which triggers the second AMV at 1 second intervals. This second AMV then produces a burst of 40 kHz ultrasonic signal, lasting only a few milliseconds. As a glance at the circuit diagram makes clear, the circuit is ideally suited for miniaturisation; as already mentioned, the current consumption is so small as to be negligible.

The receiver

Figures 2a, 2b and 2c show the circuit diagram of the receiver. The input signal is fed to a two-stage amplifier, each stage consisting of a pair of DC-coupled transistors. The gain of the second stage (T3/T4) is preset by means of P1. The total gain should not be set higher than is necessary to ensure good reception, otherwise the receiver becomes oversensitive and prone to interference.

To prevent the circuit being triggered by spurious pulses, the amplifier is followed by a voltage comparator with an adjustable threshold (R13/R15/P2 and N1). The trigger threshold may be varied by means of P2, and the best setting for this potentiometer should be determined experimentally.

Once the signal has passed the trigger stage it is rectified, then buffered by N2 and N3, before being fed to the audio generator N4 (figure 2b).

2b

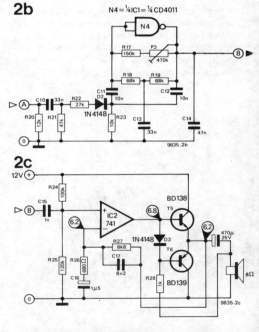

Figure 1. The circuit diagram of the poltergeist-transmitter. The frequency of the ultrasonic signals can be adjusted by means of potentiometer P1, to find the greatest transmission range.

Figure 2. The circuit diagram of the receiver. Both Valvo and Murata ultrasonic transducers are suitable for the transmitter and receiver.

This gate is connected as an inverter, and feedback is applied via a twin-T filter network. At the resonant frequency f_0 the phase shift of the twin-T network is 180°, so that the stage will oscillate at this frequency.

P3 should be adjusted so that the audio generator just fails to oscillate under quiescent conditions. Only when the oscillator receives a trigger pulse from N3 will it produce an output in the form of a decaying oscillation. With the component values shown, the resultant sound is similar to that of someone rapping their knuckles on a wooden table. The tone of this sound can be altered by varying the values of R18, R19, R23, C11, C12 and C13.

Finally, IC2, T5 and T6 form a very simple audio amplifier which drives an 8 Ω loudspeaker (figure 2c). The output power of 2-3 watts may appear a little modest, however the resulting sound will bear full comparison with anything even the most troublesome of poltergeists can muster.

⑥③ Analogue frequency meter

A true 'universal meter' should be able to read not only voltage, current and resistance – but also other quantities. The usual multimeter will only do this when used as a 'mainframe' in conjunction with 'plug-ins', that convert the input quantity into a form suitable for feeding into the actual meter. This circuit is for a 'frequency

plug-in' that will enable any multimeter (or voltmeter) to read frequencies between 10 Hz and 10 kHz.

To measure frequency one does not immediately have to 'go digital'. The analogue approach will invariably prove simpler and cheaper, in particular when the analogue readout (the multimeter) is already to hand. All that is needed is a plug-in device, a 'translator', that will give the meter an input it can 'understand'. This design is based upon an integrated frequency-to-voltage converter, the Raytheon 4151. The device is actually described as a voltage-to-frequency converter; but it becomes clear from the application notes that there is more to it than just that. The linearity of the converter IC is about 1%, so that a reasonably good multimeter will enable quite accurate frequency measurements to be made.

Because the 4151 is a little fussy about the waveform and amplitude of its input signal, the input stage of this design is a limiter-amplifier (comparator). This stage will process a signal of any shape, that has an amplitude of at least 50 mV, into a form suitable for feeding to the 4151. The input of this stage is protected (by diodes) against voltages up to 400 V p-p. The drive to the

A few specifications:

frequency range:	10 Hz...10 kHz
input impedance:	>560 k
sensitivity:	50 mV p-p
max input voltage:	400 V peak
minimum load on output:	
	5 k (if 10 V out required)

1

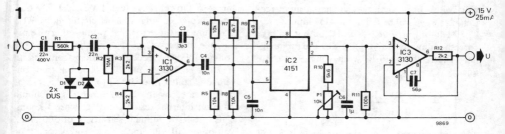

multimeter is provided by a short-circuit-proof unity-gain amplifier.

The circuit

Figure 1 gives the complete circuit of the frequency plug-in. The input is safe for 400 V p-p AC inputs only when the DC blocking capacitor is suitably rated. The diodes prevent excessive drive voltages from reaching the input of the comparator IC1. The inputs of this IC are biased to half the supply voltage by the divider R3/R4. The bias current flowing in R2 will cause the output of IC1 to saturate in the negative direction. An input signal of sufficient amplitude to over-

Figure 1. The input frequency is passed via a comparator (limiter) IC1 to a frequency-to-voltage converter (IC2, 4151), that delivers a DC voltage via buffer IC3 to a normal multimeter.

Figure 2. Printed circuit board and component layout for the frequency 'add-on'

come this offset will cause the output to change state, the actual switchover being speeded up by the positive feedback through C3. On the opposite excursion of the input signal the comparator

2

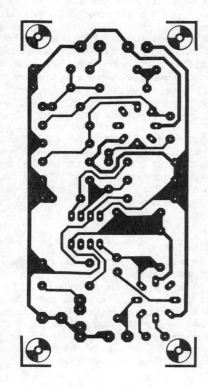

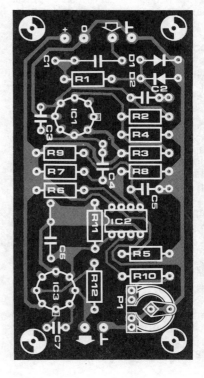

will switch back again — so that a large rectangular wave will be fed to the 4151 input.

The 4151 will now deliver a DC output voltage corresponding to the frequency of the input signal. The relationship between voltage and frequency is given by:

$$\frac{U}{f} = \frac{R_9 \cdot R_{11} \cdot C_5}{0.486 \, (R_{10} + P_1)} \quad (V/Hz)$$

The circuit values have been chosen to give 1 V per kHz. This means that a 10 volts f.s.d. will correspond to 10 kHz. Meters with a different full scale deflection, for example 6 volts, can, however, also be used. There are two possibilities: either one uses the existing scale calibrations to read off frequencies to 6 kHz, or one sets P1 to achieve a 6 volt output (i.e. full scale in our example) when the frequency is 10 kHz. The latter choise of course implies that every reading will require a little mental gymnastics! With some meters it may be necessary to modify the values of P1 and/or R10; the value of R10 + P1 must however always be greater than 500 Ω . The output is buffered by another 3130 (IC3). The circuit is an accurate voltage follower, so that low frequencies can be more easily read off (without loss of accuracy) by setting the multi-meter to a lower range (e.g. 1 V f.s.d.). The output is protected against short-circuiting by R12. To eliminate the error that would otherwise occur due to the voltage drop in this resistor, the voltage follower feedback is taken from behind R12. To enable the full 10 volt output to be obtained in spite of the drop in R12 (that has to be compensated by the IC) the meter used should have an internal resistance of at least 5 kohm. This implies a nominal sensitivity of 500 ohm/volt on the 10 volt range. There surely cannot be many meters with a sensitivity lower than that. If one has a separate moving coil milliameter available, it can be fitted with a series resistor that makes its internal resistance up to the value required of a voltmeter giving f.s.d. at 10 volt input. This alternative makes the frequency meter independent of the multimeter, so that it can be used to monitor the output of a generator that for some reason may have a dubious scale- or knob-calibration.

Construction

No trouble is to be anticipated if the circuit is built up using the PC board layout given in figure 2. Bear in mind that the human body will not necessarily survive contact with input voltages that may not damage the adequately-rated input blocking capacitor. If one contemplates measuring the frequency of such high voltages the circuit should be assembled in a well-insulated box!

The power supply does not need to be regulated, so it can be kept very simple. A transformer secondary of 12 volts, a bridge rectifier and a 470 μ /25 V reservoir electrolytic will do the job nicely. Although a circuit that draws 25 mA is not too well suited to battery supply, one may need or wish to do this. In this case the battery should be bridged by a low-leakage (e.g. tantalum) 10 μ /25 V capacitor to provide a low AC source impedance.

Parts list for figures 1 and 2.

Resistors:
R1 = 560 k
R2 = 10 M
R3, R4, R12 = 2k2
R5, R6, R8 = 10 k
R7 = 4k7
R9 = 6k8
R10 = 5k6
R11 = 100 k
P1 = 10 k preset

Capacitors:
C1 = 22 n/400 V
C2 = 22 n
C3 = 3p3
C4, C5 = 10 n
C6 = 1 μ low leakage
C7 = 56 p

Semiconductors:
D1, D2 = DUS
IC1, IC3 = 3130
IC2 = 4151

Calibration

The calibration can really only be done with an accurate generator.

A 10 kHz signal is fed to the input and P1 is set to bring the multimeter to full scale deflection (e.g. 10 V). That completes the calibration — although it is wise to check that the circuit is operating correctly by using lower input frequencies and observing whether the meter reading is also (proportionately) lower.

64 Electret microphone preamplifier

This compact, low-noise, battery powered preamplifier can be used to boost the signal from electret and low impedance dynamic microphones.

Microphones frequently have to be connected to amplification and/or recording equipment via several metres of screened cable. Since the output of a microphone is very small (typically a few millivolts) there is often significant signal loss, and microphonic noise may also be generated by the cable. This article describes the construction of a good-quality microphone with built-in preamplifier, using a commercial electret or moving coil capsule. The built-in preamplifier boosts the output level to several hundred millivolts, which allows the signal to be fed direct to the 'auxiliary' or 'line' inputs of amplifiers or tape decks. If a mixer is being used the need for microphone preamps on each mixer input is dispensed with.

Readers are probably familiar with the principle of the moving coil, dynamic microphone, which basically operates like a loudspeaker in reverse. A diaphragm is coupled to a cylindrical coil, which is suspended in the field of a powerful permanent magnet. Sound pressure waves deflect the diaphragm, and hence the coil, which cuts the magnetic flux lines and generates an output current and voltage that is an electrical analogue of the acoustic signal.

The electret microphone, which has become very popular in recent years, operates in a similar manner to a capacitor microphone, but is cheaper and less bulky. The diaphragm of the microphone is made of the electret material. This is a thin insulating plastic film, which has been polarised with a permanent electric charge (this is usually done by heating the film and placing it in a strong electric field). The diaphragm forms one plate of a capacitor, the other plate of which is a fixed metal backplate. Since the diaphragm is charged a potential difference exists between the diaphragm and the backplate, which is related to the charge on the diaphragm and the capacitance of the microphone capsule by the equation

$$U = \frac{Q}{C},$$

Parts list for figures 1 and 2

Resistors:
R1 = 2k2
R2 = 10 k
R3 = 47 Ω
R4 = 6k8
R5, R6 = 39 k
R7 = 4k7
R8 = 8k2
R9 = 120 k

Capacitors:
C1, C2, C5 = 2 µ2/40 V
C3, C4 = 47 µ /25 V

Semiconductors:
T1 = BC 549C or equivalent
T2 = BC 559C or equivalent

Miscellaneous:
Microphone capsule = Philips
    LBC 1055/00 or similar
9 V battery
S1 = SPST switch (see text)
Plastic or aluminium tubing for
microphone housing.

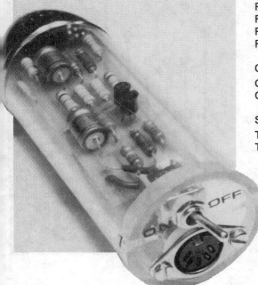

1

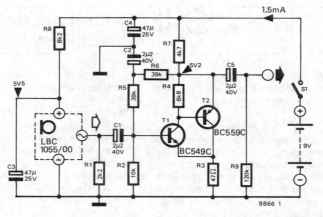

where U is voltage, Q is charge, and C is capacitance. C is related to the distance between the plates of the capacitor by the equation

$$C = \frac{k}{d}$$

where k is a constant. Therefore

$$U = \frac{Qd}{k}.$$

When sound pressure waves deflect the diaphragm, the distance d varies, and since the charge Q is fixed the output voltage varies in sympathy with the deflection of the diaphragm.
Since the microphone capsule is effectively a very small capacitor (only a few pF), its impedance at audio frequencies is extremely high, and its output must be fed to a very high impedance buffer stage. This usually consists of a FET source-follower incorporated into the microphone capsule, which acts as an impedance transformer with an output impedance of a few hundred ohms.

Preamplifier circuit

The complete circuit of the microphone preamplifier is given in figure 1. If an electret microphone capsule is used, the built-in FET buffer will require a DC power supply. This will usually be lower than the 9 volts required by the rest of the circuit, so the voltage is dropped by R8 and decoupled by C3. The value of R8 shown is for the Philips LBC 1055/00 microphone capsule, and other capsules may require a different value.
Resistor R1 is a load for the FET buffer. Here again, 2k2 is the recommended value for the Philips electret capsule, and different values may be

Figure 1. Circuit of the microphone pre-amplifier.

Figure 2. Printed circuit board and component layout for the preamplifier (EPS 9866).

Figure 3. If the completed microphone is fitted with an output socket then a shorting link can be used to replace S1.

Photo. Completed prototype of the electret microphone with built-in preamp, which is housed in a piece of clear acrylic tube for display purposes.

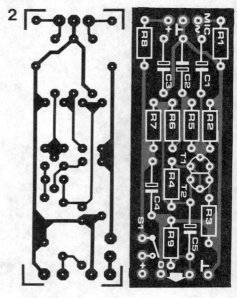

required for other capsules. If a moving coil microphone capsule is used then R1, R8 and C3 may be omitted.

The preamplifier itself consists of a two stage amplifier T1 and T2. Its input impedance is approximately 8 k, and its gain is determined by the ratio R7 : R3 – about 100 with the values shown. The current consumption of the preamp is extremely low, typically 1.5 mA.

With some microphone capsules having a higher output voltage, it may be necessary to reduce the gain of the preamp to prevent overloading. This is done by decreasing the value of R7. To restore the correct DC bias conditions it will also be necessary to reduce the value of R6, and this will result in a slight increase in current consumption. However, reducing the value of R7 does lower the output impedance of the preamp, which means that longer cables can be driven without attenuation of high frequency signals.

Performance

The output voltage of the specified electret capsule is typically 6.3 mV/Pa ('Pa' is Pascal; 1 Pascal = 1 N/m² = 10 bar). To put this figure into context, the threshold of audibility (0 dB SPL) is taken as occurring at a sound pressure level of 0.0002 bar, and the threshold of pain, 120 dB higher at 200 bar. However, overloading of the electret capsule begins at around 104 dB SPL, so the maximum output voltage that can be expected in normal use is around 20 mV, or 2 V at the preamp output.

The frequency response of the specified capsule

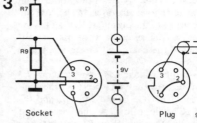

plus preamp combination is flat within 3 dB from 100 Hz to 17 kHz, which is quite good considering the modest cost of the unit.

Construction

A printed circuit board and component layout for the microphone preamplifier are given in figure 2. The circuit board is extremely compact, and the microphone capsule, board, and a small 9 V battery can easily be fitted into a length of plastic pipe or aluminium tubing. The grille that protects the microphone capsule can be made from half a 'tea-egg' infuser, as shown in the photograph, or from a wire mesh coffee strainer.

To make a really professional job the output of the preamp can be taken via a Cannon XLR or locking DIN connector socket mounted in the base of the housing. It is then possible to dispense with the on-off switch by making a shorting link in the connector plug, as shown in figure 3. When the microphone is unplugged after use the preamp is automatically switched off.

65 Long interval timer

The drawback of most analogue timers (monostable circuits) is that, in order to obtain reasonably long intervals, the RC time constant must be correspondingly large. This invariably means resistor values in excess of 1 M Ω, which can give timing errors due to stray leakage resistance in the circuit, or large electrolytic capacitors, which again can introduce timing errors due to their leakage resistance.

The circuit given here achieves timing intervals up to 100 times longer than those obtainable with standard circuits. It does this by reducing the charging current of the capacitor by a factor of 100, thus increasing the charging time, without the need for high value charging resistors.

The circuit operates as follows: when the start/reset button is pressed C1 is discharged and the output of IC1, which is connected as a voltage follower, is at zero volts. The inverting input of comparator IC2 is at a lower potential than the non-inverting input, so the output of IC2 goes high.

The voltage across R4 is approximately 120 mV, so C1 charges through R2 at a current of around 120 nA, which is 100 times lower than could be achieved if R2 were connected direct to positive supply.

Of course, if C1 were charged from a constant

120 mV it would quickly reach this voltage and would cease to charge. However, the bottom end of R4 is returned to the output of IC1, and as the voltage across C1 rises so does the output voltage and hence the charging voltage applied to R2.

When the output voltage has risen to about 7.5 volts it will exceed the voltage set on the non-inverting input of IC2 by R6 and R7, and the output of IC2 will go low. A small amount of positive feedback provided by R8 prevents any noise present on the output of IC1 from being amplified by IC2 as it passes through the trigger point, as this could otherwise give rise to spuri-ous output pulses.

The timing interval is given by the equation:

$$T = R_2 C_1 \left(1 + \frac{R_5}{R_4} + \frac{R_5}{R_2}\right) \ln \left(1 + \frac{R_7}{R_6}\right)$$

This may seem a little complicated, but with the component values given the interval is $100 \cdot C_1$, where C1 is in *microfarads*, e.g. if C1 is 1 µ the interval is 100 seconds. It is evident from the equation that the timing interval can be varied linearly by replacing R2 with a 1 M potentiometer, or logarithmically by replacing R6 and R7 with, say, a 10 k potentiometer.

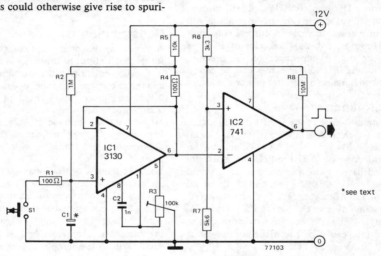

66 Temperature-to-voltage converter

This circuit provides a simple means of constructing an electronic thermometer that will operate over the range 0 to 24°C (32 to 75°F). The circuit produces an output of approximately 500 mV/°C, which can be read off on a voltmeter suitably calibrated in degrees.

In order that the circuit should be kept simple the temperature sensing element is a negative temperature coefficient thermistor (NTC). This has the advantage that the temperature coefficient of resistance is fairly large, but unfortunately it has the disadvantage that the temperature coefficient is not constant and the temperature-voltage output of the circuit is thus non-linear. However, over the range 0 to 24°C the

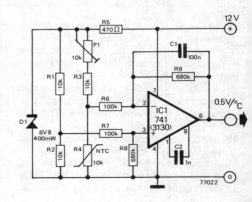

84

linearity is sufficiently good for a simple thermometer.

Op-amp IC1 is connected as a differential amplifier whose inputs are fed from a bridge circuit consisting of R1 to R4. R1, R2, R3 and P1 form the fixed arms of the bridge, while R4 forms the variable arm. The voltage at the junction of R1 and R2 is about 3.4 volts. With the NTC at 0°C P1 is adjusted so that the output from the op-amp is zero, when the voltage at the junction of R3 and R4 will also be 3.4 V. With increasing temperature the resistance of the NTC decreases and the voltage across it falls, so the output of the op-amp increases. If the output is not exactly 0.5 V/°C then the values of R8 and R9 may be increased or decreased accordingly, but they should both be the same value.

The IC can be a general purpose op-amp such as a 741, 3130 or 3140. The compensation capacitor C2 is not required if a 741 is used since this IC is internally compensated. Almost any 10 k NTC thermistor may be used for R4, but the smaller types will obviously give a faster response since they have a lower thermal inertia. 5 k or 15 k types could also be used, but the values of P1 and R3 would have to be altered in proportion.

---

67 Super zener

This circuit is intended primarily to produce a stable reference voltage in battery operated equipment designed for minimum current consumption. Despite the fact that only 1 mA flows through the zener the output voltage showed a fluctuation of less than 1 mV for supply voltage variations of 10 to 30 volts.

The reference voltage from the zener is applied to the non-inverting input of a 741 op-amp, and the output voltage is the zener voltage multiplied by the op-amp gain i.e.

$$V_O = V_Z \times \frac{R_2 + R_3}{R_3}$$

This approach has two advantages. Firstly, a low temperature coefficient zener (5.6 V) can be used to provide any desired reference voltage simply by altering the op-amp gain. Secondly, since no significant current is 'robbed' from the zener by the op-amp input, the zener need only be fed by a small current. So that the resistance of the zener does not affect the output voltage the zener current must be fairly constant. This is achieved by feeding the zener via R1 from the output of the op-amp. The zener current is

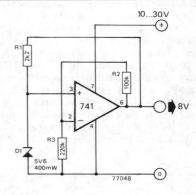

$$\frac{V_O - V_Z}{R_1},$$

so R1 should be chosen to give a zener current of about 1 mA. The reference voltage obtained from the op-amp output can supply currents of up to 15 mA.

One point to note when using this circuit is that the supply voltage must be at least 2 V greater than the output voltage of the circuit.

---

68 Simple transistor tester

This simple circuit checks the functioning and measures the current gain (h_{FE}) of PNP or NPN bipolar transistors. It operates by feeding a known constant current into the base of the transistor and measuring the collector current. Since the collector current of a non-saturated

85

transistor is h_{FE} times the base current (which is known) it is a simple matter to calculate the value of h_{FE}, and in fact the meter which measures the collector current can be calibrated directly in h_{FE}.

Since both PNP and NPN transistors must be tested, two constant current sources are required, to provide a negative base current for PNP transistors and a positive base current for NPN transistors. The voltage dropped across the LED causes a constant current to flow through the emitter resistor of the TUP and a corresponding constant collector current, which flows into the base of the NPN transistor under test. This current can be set to 10 µA by connecting a 50 µA meter between points B and E and adjusting P1.

The lower LED and TUN constitute the negative current source. Here again, this may be set to 10 µA by connecting a microammeter between the lower points B and E, and adjusting P2.

When a transistor is plugged into the appropriate socket a current of 10 µA will thus flow into the base and a current of h_{FE} times this will flow through the milliammeter. The full-scale deflection of the milliammeter depends on the maximum h_{FE} to be measured. Since the collector current is h_{FE} times the base current (which is .01 mA) a reading of 1 mA corresponds to an h_{FE} of 100, so if a 5 mA meter is to hand it can be calibrated in h_{FE} values from 0 to 500, which

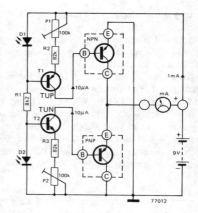

should be adequate for most run-of-the-mill transistors. However, for testing 'C' versions of small-signal transistors, which can have gains up to 800, a 10 mA meter calibrated 0 to 1000 could be used, or lower f.s.d. meter shunted to read 8 mA and calibrated 0 to 800.

Readers may have noticed that it is actually the emitter current of the PNP transistor that is measured, which is of course $1 + h_{FE}$ times the base current. However, since few transistors have gains less than 50 the worst error introduced by this is less than 2%, which is probably less than the error of the milliammeter.

69 Automatic NiCad charger

It is not generally appreciated that, if Nickel-Cadmium batteries are subjected to prolonged overcharging from chargers of the constant current type, their life may be considerably reduced.

The charger described here overcomes this problem by charging at a constant current but switching off the charger when the terminal voltage of the battery rises, which indicates a fully-charged

1

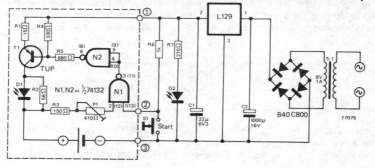

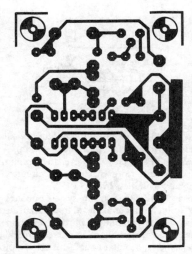

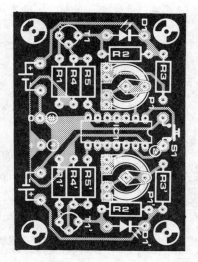

condition. The basic circuit described is intended to charge a single 500 mAh 'AA' cell at the recommended charge rate of around 50 mA, but it can easily be extended at little cost to charge more than one cell.

Power for the circuit is provided by a transformer, bridge rectifier and 5 V IC regulator. The cell is charged by a constant current source T1 which is controlled by a voltage comparator based on a TTL Schmitt trigger N1. While the cell is charging the terminal voltage remains at around 1.25 V, which is below the positive trigger threshold of N1. The output of N1 is thus high, the output of N2 is low and T1 receives a base bias voltage from the potential divider R4/R5. While the cell is being charged D1 is lit.

When the cell approaches the fully-charged state the terminal voltage rises to about 1.45 V, the positive trigger threshold of N1 is exceeded and the output of N2 goes high, turning off T1. The cell ceases to charge and D1 is extinguished.

As the positive trigger threshold of N1 is about

1.7 V and is subject to a certain tolerance, R3 and P1 are included to adjust it to 1.45 V. The negative trigger threshold of the Schmitt trigger is about 0.9 V, which is below the terminal voltage of even a fully-discharged cell, so connecting a discharged cell in circuit will not cause charging to begin automatically. For this reason a start button S1 is included which, when pressed, takes the input of N1 low.

To charge a number of cells the portion of the circuit enclosed in the dotted box must be duplicated. This has the advantage that, unlike chargers in which cells are connected in series, cells in any state of discharge may be placed on the charger and each will be individually charged to the correct level. The disadvantage is that batteries of cells cannot be charged. However, up to ten AA cells may be charged if the circuit is duplicated the appropriate number of times.

H. Knote

70 Car lights failure indicator

It is often the case that the first a motorist knows of a failure in one of his car lights is when his attention is drawn to the fact by a policeman. The circuit described here, which consists solely of a single reed-relay, one LED and one resistor, should provide a more economical warning system.

A LED is mounted in a suitable spot on the dashboard, and is extinguished as soon the lamp

1

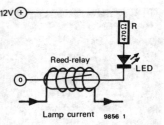

2

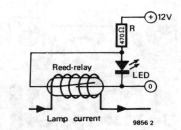

concerned ceases working. It is of course possible to use several such circuits to monitor different lamps or groups of lamps.

The circuit (figure 1) works by feeding the supply current to a lamp or group of lamps through the operating coil of a reed-relay. If a particular lamp fails, the current falls, causing the relay to drop out and the LED to turn off. The number of turns in the operating coil should be large enough to pull in the relay at the normal operating current of the lamp, yet small enough to cause the relay to drop out in the event of lamp failure.

Generally speaking, a relay requires from 30 to 100 AT (ampere turns = current x no. of turns). Thus, in view of the relatively high currents drawn by car lamps, in this particular application the operating coil need consist of only a few turns. For example, the two headlamps draw a current of approx. 7.5 A (at 12 V). A reed-relay rated at 50 AT would therefore require only 7 turns to monitor the current of both headlamps. If one of the lamps fails, then the current through the operating coil falls to about half, causing the relay to drop out and the LED on the dashboard to be extinguished. The circuit shown in figure 2 is an alternative version which makes

the LED light up when a lamp needs replacing. This provides a more prominent warning – particularly in the dark. However the circuit in figure 1 is failsafe; even electronic circuitry does not have a limitless life...

To ensure that the warning system operates satisfactorily, it is recommended that a separate reed-relay is used to monitor lamps of differing wattage, i.e. a different relay for the rear lights, brake lights, headlamps etc. It is also possible to use a single relay to monitor both right and left turning indicators by using a double winding round the coil. However, it is not advised to use one relay to monitor a circuit or combination of circuits in which more than two lamps can be 'on' simultaneously.

If the circuit of figure 2 is used then the supply to the LED should be taken from the switched side of the lamp supply. This ensures that when the relay drops out due to the lamp being switched off the LED does not light, since its supply is also disconnected.

It is important to note that the gauge of wire used to wind the relay coil should be at least as heavy as that used in the original car wiring, to minimise the voltage drop across the coil and possible overheating.

71 Two-TUN voltage doubler

This little circuit will produce a DC output that is almost twice the supply voltage. A square-wave input is required of sufficient level to turn T1 fully on and off. When T1 is conducting, C2 is charged to just under the supply voltage. When T1 is cut off, T2 starts to conduct and raises the voltage at the negative end of C2 to just under the positive supply level. This implies that the voltage at the positive end of C2 is raised to almost twice the supply voltage, so that C3 will ultimately charge to this level.

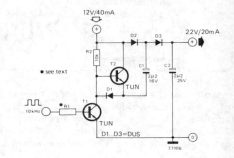

88

The circuit is remarkably efficient: the current drawn from the main supply is only marginally greater than twice the output current. In the example shown here, the efficiency is approximately 90%.

The value for R1 depends on the amplitude of the square-wave input: T1 will require a base current of 0.5...1 mA.

RCA application note

72 TTL voltage doubler

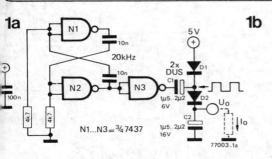

1a

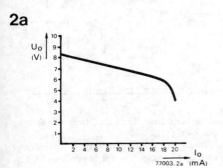

1b

This voltage doubler can be used in circuits that have only a 5 V supply rail, where a higher voltage is required at a low current.

Figure 1a shows the basic circuit, which uses three of the gates in a 7437 quad two-input NAND buffer IC. N1 and N2 are connected as a 20 kHz astable multivibrator, and the output of N2 drives N3, which acts as a buffer between the astable and the doubler circuit. When the output of N3 is low C1 charges through D1 and N3 to about +4.4 V. When the output of N3 goes high the voltage on the positive end of C1 is about 9 V, so C1 discharges through D2 into C2. If no current is drawn from C2 it will eventually charge to about +8.5 V. However, if any significant current is drawn the output voltage will quickly fall, as shown in figure 1b.

Much better regulation of the output voltage, as shown in figure 2a, can be obtained by using the push-pull circuit of figure 2b. This is driven from an identical astable to that in figure 1b. While the output of N1 is low and C1 is charging, the output of N2 is high and C2 is discharging into C3, and vice versa. Since C3 is being continually charged the regulation of the output voltage is much improved.

2a

2b

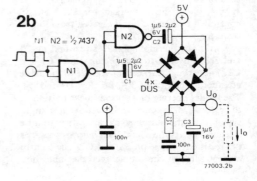

73 Stereo noise filter

The signal-to-noise ratio of an FM broadcast received in stereo is considerably worse than that of the same broadcast received in mono. This is most noticeable on weak transmissions, when switching over from stereo to mono will considerably reduce the noise level. This noise reduction occurs because the left-channel noise is largely in anti-phase to the right-channel noise. Switching to mono sums the two channels and the antiphase noise signals cancel.

By summing only the high-frequency components of the signal it is possible to eliminate the annoying high-frequency noise without destroying the stereo image since channel separation is still maintained at middle and low frequencies.

Each channel of the circuit consists of a pair of emitter followers in cascade, with highpass filters comprising R3 to R7 and C3 to C5 that allow crosstalk to occur between the two channels above about 8 kHz when switch S1 is closed. When S1 is open the two channels are isolated, but resistors R9 to R11 maintain a DC level on C3 to C5 so that switching clicks do not occur when S1 is closed.

The stereo-mono crossover frequency can be in-

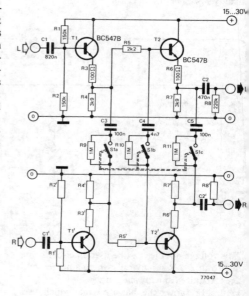

creased by lowering the values of C3 to C5 or decreased by raising them.

74 Signal powered dynamic compressor

This dynamic range compressor will provide approximately 20 dB of compression over the input voltage range 100 mV to 10 V. An unusual feature of the circuit is that it requires no power supply, the control voltage for the voltage-controlled attenuator being derived from the input signal.

A portion of the input signal is rectified by D1 and D2 and used to charge capacitors C1 and C2. These provide a control voltage to the diode attenuator comprising R3, R5, R6, D3 and D4. The diodes operate on the non-linear portion of their forward conduction curve. At low input signal levels the output signal appears with little attenuation. As the signal level increases so does the rectified voltage on C1 and C2. The control current through the diodes increases and their

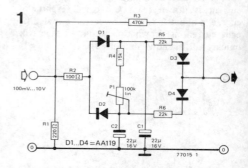

dynamic resistance decreases, thus attenuating the output signal.

The attack time of the compressor is fixed and depends on the time constant consisting of C1 or

C2, R2 and the output impedance of the circuit feeding the compressor, which should be as low as possible. The decay time of the compressor can be varied to a small extent by P1. The input impedance of the circuit that the compressor output feeds should be as high as possible.

The circuit works best with germanium diodes, since these have a low forward voltage threshold and a much smoother and more extended 'knee' than silicon types. The accompanying graph shows the response of the compressor using both silicon and germanium diodes, and it is obvious which are better!

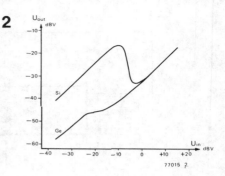

---

75 Sawtooth-CCO

This sawtooth waveform generator which is built round a current controlled oscillator is distinguished by its large sweep range. It is suitable for use in electronic music applications, and the narrow output pulse also enables the circuit to be used as a pulse-CCO for sample/hold circuits.

The circuit consists of a controllable current source (T1, T2), a trigger (N1, N2) and a switch (T3). As soon as the circuit is switched on capacitor C1 is charged by the current source. When the voltage across C1 reaches the threshold value of N1, T3 is turned on via N1 and N2, and C1 is discharged, after which the whole cycle repeats itself. The sawtooth output signal which is buffered by FET T4 has a peak-to-peak value of approx. 1.3 V.

With the component values shown in the diagram, the frequency can be adjusted from ap-

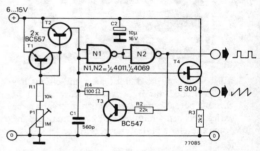

prox. 5 to 500 kHz (with P1). Although a higher output frequency is possible, there is a corresponding deterioration in the waveform. With C1 = 5n6 and R1 = 1 k, the frequency range runs from 0.5...500 kHz.

In place of NANDs inverters may be used.

---

76 Knotted handkerchief

Since the advent of paper handkerchiefs, that time-honoured method of jogging a forgetful memory, namely tying a knot in one's hanky, has been faced with practical difficulties. The circuit described here offers a modern answer to this old problem, i.e. an electronic 'knot' in the shape of an audible alarm signal which can be set to sound after an interval of up to 60 minutes.

The circuit is built round the CMOS IC CD 4060, which consists of a pulse generator and a

counter. When switch S1 is closed a reset pulse is fed to the IC via C2. At the same time the internal oscillator begins feeding pulses to the counter. After 2^{13} pulses the counter output (Q14) will go high, switching on the oscillator round T1 and T2. The result is a piercing 3 kHz signal which is made audible via an 8 ohm miniature loudspeaker or earpiece insert. The circuit is switched off by opening S1.

With the values given for R2 and C1, the 'knot'

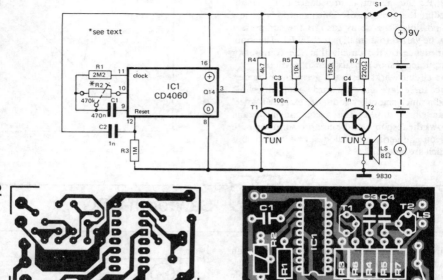

*see text

1

2

will sound approx. 1 hour after the circuit has been switched on. By replacing R2 with a 1 M variable potentiometer, the alarm interval can be varied between 5 minutes and 2¼ hours, and the potentiometer suitably calibrated.

The circuit consumes very little current (0.2 mA whilst the counter is running and 35 mA during the alarm signal) so that a 9 V battery would be assured of a long life.

77

Digital capacitance meter with 555 timer

Anyone possessing a frequency counter with a facility for period measurement can build this simple add-on unit to measure capacitance direct.

In the circuit shown the 555 is connected as an astable multivibrator, the period of which is given by $T = 0.7(R_A + 2R_B)C_x$. If the unknown capacitor is connected in the C_x position then, since R_A and R_B are fixed, the period is proportional to C_x, the unknown capacitor. The period of the multivibrator can be measured by the period meter and, if R_A and R_B are suitably chosen, this reading can be made to equal the capacitance in picofarads, nanofarads or microfarads. As an example, suppose the period meter has a maximum reading of one second and this is to be the reading for a capacitance of 1μ F. Then the total value of $R_A + 2R_B$ should be

$1.43 M\Omega$.

A slight problem exists when measuring electrolytic capacitors around the 1μ F value. As shown above, for a reading of one second the resistance required is fairly high and errors may occur due to the capacitor leakage resistance. In

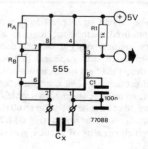

this case it is probably better to opt for a reading of 1 second = 1000 μ F, since the resistance values can be 1000 times smaller. If a seven decade counter is used that gives a reading of 1.000000 for one second = 1000 μ F, then 1 μ F will give a reading of 0.001000, which is still better than the accuracy of the circuit.

Some suitable values for R_A and R_B are given in the table. 1% metal oxide resistors should be used for these to give a reasonable accuracy. Other values can be calculated to suit personal taste and the counter used.

When using the circuit the wiring capacitance of any jigs and fixtures used to hold the capacitor should be taken into account and subtracted from the reading. For this reason, such jigs should be of rigid mechanical construction so that the capacitance does not vary. For example, in the prototype it was found that the circuit was reading consistently 36 pF high due to wiring capacitance. This was therefore noted on the test jig so that it could be subtracted from all readings. Of course, when testing large value capacitors this small error is not significant.

R_A	R_B	C_X	T
1 k	220 Ω	1000 μ F	1 s
1 M	220 k	1 μ F (non-electrolytic)	1 s

J. Borgman

78 Tremolo

Tremolo is one of the most popular effects used in electronic music. The tremolo effect is produced by amplitude modulating the music signal with a low-frequency signal of between 1 Hz and 10 Hz. The effect gives warmth and richness to the otherwise 'flat' sound of instruments such as electronic organs. The most pleasing effect is produced when the modulation waveform is sinusoidal. The music signal is buffered by emitterfollower T1 and is then fed into op-amp IC1, whose gain can be varied by means of P1. The output of IC1 is fed to the diode modulator D1/D2, the output of which is buffered by a second emitter follower T2. The sinusoidal signal is generated by an oscillator built around IC2, whose frequency can be varied between 1 Hz and 10 Hz by P2. The output level, and hence the modulation depth, can be varied by P3. Switch S1, when closed, disables the oscillator, which allows the music signal to pass unmodulated.

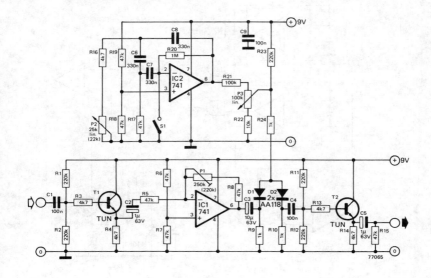

93

79 AC touchswitch

There are many designs for touchswitches around these days. However, most of these operated on skin resistance and thus required a double contact that could be bridged by a finger. Single contact operation is possible using a capacitive pickup of mains hum, but this is not very reliable, and will not work at all with battery powered equipment! The design given here overcomes these difficulties and provides a reliable single-point touch switch.

N3 and N4 form a 1 MHz oscillator. When the contact is not touched the signal from the output of N4 is fed via C2 and C3 to the input of N1, which causes the output of N1 to go high and low at a 1 MHz rate. This charges up C4 via D1, holding the input of N2 high which causes the output to remain low.

When the contact is touched, body capacitance 'shorts out' the 1 MHz signal. The input of N1 is pulled high by R3 and the output goes low. C4

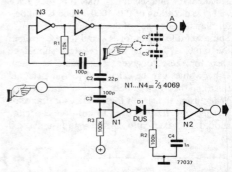

discharges through R2 and the output of N2 goes high.

One oscillator will provide a 1 MHz signal for several touch switches, which may be connected to point A.

A.M. Bosschaert

80 Audible logic probe

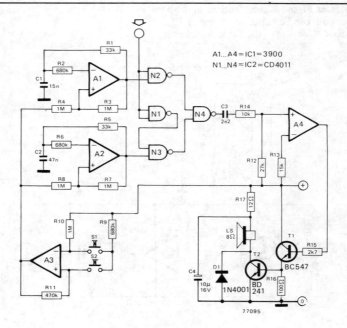

A1...A4 = IC1 = 3900
N1...N4 = IC2 = CD4011

This logic probe provides an audible rather than a visual indication of logic state by producing a high-frequency audio tone for a logic '1' state and a low-frequency tone for a logic '0' state.

The logic input signal is fed to N1 and N2. If the input is high then N2 will pass the high frequency signal from the oscillator built around A1. If the input is low then N2 will block, but the output of N1 will be high so N3 will pass the low frequency signal from the oscillator built around A2.

Depending on the input state one or other of these signals is fed through N4 to the input of a differentiator built around A4. This produces a train of short pulses from the squarewave input signal and these are fed to an audio amplifier comprising T1 and T2. The use of short pulses

ensures a high peak audio output while keeping the average current consumption low.

To avoid the annoying 'bleeping' of the circuit when measurements are not being taken both oscillators may be switched on and off by a flip-flop constructed around A3, which is controlled by two push buttons S1 and S2.

If the circuit is to be used exclusively with TTL circuits then N1 to N4 should be a 7400 IC and the supply voltage should be +5 V, which can be derived from the circuit under test. If it is to be used with CMOS ICs then N1 to N4 should be a 4011 IC, and the circuit will operate over supply voltages of 5 to 10 V at a current consumption of between 4 and 10 mA.

H. Käser

81 Level shifter

It is often necessary, particularly when experimenting with circuits, to make connection between the output of one circuit and the input of another which is at a different DC level. If the signals involved in the circuit are AC signals this is no problem, a capacitor can be used to isolate the DC levels while allowing AC signals to pass. However, when dealing with DC or very low frequency AC signals the solution is not so easy, and it is in these cases that this little gimmick will prove useful.

The circuit consists simply of an op-amp connected as a voltage follower whose quiescent output voltage can be set to any desired level within the output range of the op-amp.

Input A is connected to the output of the circuit in question while the output is connected to the input of the circuit which it is feeding. Input C is grounded, while input B is connected to a DC voltage equal to the difference between the input voltage of the second circuit and the output voltage of the first.

It can easily be proved that this works! Firstly, voltages appearing at the non-inverting input of the op-amp are amplified by a factor

$$\frac{R_3 + R_4}{R_3} = 2.$$

Secondly, suppose the output voltage of the first circuit is V_A and the input voltage of the second circuit is V_1. The voltage V_B applied to input B

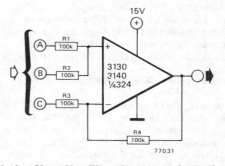

77031

is thus $V_1 - V_A$. The voltage appearing at the

junction of R1 and R2 is thus $V_A + \dfrac{V_B - V_A}{2}$.

The voltage appearing at the op-amp output is twice this, i.e. $V_A + V_B$

But since $V_B = V_1 - V_A$ this equals V_1, the input voltage of the second circuit. Obviously, if V_1 is less than V_A then V_B will be a negative voltage.

Despite the difference in input and output levels the circuit functions as a voltage follower in that any change in the voltage at input A will produce the same voltage change at the output.

The circuit can also be used as an inverter. In this case the signal is fed to input C, B is grounded and A is fed with a DC reference voltage. To see what voltage must be applied to A it

95

is simplest to treat the circuit as a unity gain differential amplifier. The output voltage V_O is equal to the difference between the voltages at the non-inverting and inverting inputs i.e. $V_O = V_A - V_C$ so $V_A = V_O + V_C$, i.e. input A must be fed with a voltage that is the sum of the voltage at C and the required output voltage. Any change in the input voltage at C will produce the same change at the output, but of opposite polarity.

Two points must be noted when using this circuit. Firstly, care must be taken not to exceed the common-mode input rating of the op-amp used, especially with a single-ended (asymmetric) supply. Secondly, the values of R1 to R4 should be at least ten times the output resistance of the circuit feeding the level shifter to avoid excessive loading of the output.

82 Complementary emitter follower

This circuit presents an interesting alternative method of constructing a low-distortion buffer or output stage for use at low output powers. The quiescent current flowing through T1 and T2 is determined solely by the value of U and of R1 and R2 respectively. This contrasts with conventional circuits where the bases of T1 and T2 are connected to one another by means of a diode network. The current supply of the diodes normally has an unfavourable influence on the input impedance (unless bootstrapping is used) causing variations in the quiescent current.

In this circuit the quiescent current through T1

equals $\dfrac{U - 0.6}{R_1}$, and that through T2 is $\dfrac{U - 0.6}{R_2}$,

assuming that the current gain of T1 and T2 are so high (or closely matched) that the voltage drop across R3 is negligible. Normally R1 is given the same value as R2. The relative values of C2, C3 and R4 determine the lowest frequency at which the circuit will function.

If T1 and T2 have the same current gain and R1 equals R2, then no DC voltage is produced across R3, and C1 may be omitted. If the circuit is fed from an op-amp then both C1 and R3 may be omitted.

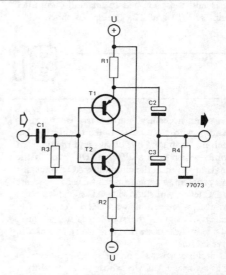

The circuit is intended as a class-A buffer or output stage. The maximum class-A output power

dissipated in R4 is I^2R4, where I is $\dfrac{U - 0.6}{R}$

assuming that R4 is smaller than $R = R1 = R2$.

83 Reaction speed tester

This circuit represents a simple design for one of the most popular types of electronic game, namely a reaction tester.

As soon as the 'start' button is pressed, IC1 feeds a train of pulses to the counter IC3, causing LEDs 1...10 to light up one after another. The sooner the 'stop' button is pressed, the smaller the number of LEDs which light up; the last LED to light up burns continuously. If the oscillator which generates the clock pulses is set so that a pulse is produced say, every 20 ms, then the reaction time of the players can be calculated quite simply by observing which LED remains lit.

A new game can be started after pressing the reset button.

With the component values given in the diagram the circuit consumes 120 mA with a 5 V stabilised supply. The oscillator frequency may be adjusted by means of P1 between 10 and 80 Hz.

If desired, an additional LED with a 220 Ω series resistor can be included between the output of N3 and positive supply. This will light up as soon as the opponent presses the 'start' button.

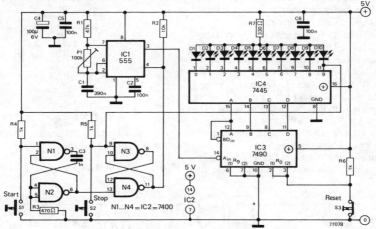

84 Non-inverting integrator

A drawback of conventional integrator circuits (figure a) is that the R-C junction is at virtual earth; this means that C appears as a capacitive load across the op-amp output, a fact that may adversely affect the stability and slew rate of the op-amp. Since the non-inverting character of an integrator is of minor importance in many applications the circuit shown in figure b offers a viable alternative to conventional arrangements.

This integrator, unlike that in figure a, is non-inverting. The time constants R_1C_1 and R_2C_2 should be equal.

If both R_1 and C_1, and R_2 and C_2 are transposed then the result is a non-inverting differentiator.

For correct offset-compensation R_1 and R_2 should have the same value.

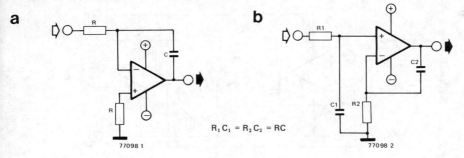

a

b

$$R_1 C_1 = R_2 C_2 = RC$$

77098 1

77098 2

97

85 Positive-triggered set-reset flip-flop

The standard set-reset flip-flop circuit consists of two cross-coupled NAND gates and is set and reset by applying a logic '0' level to the appropriate input. The circuit shown in the figure is triggered by a logic '1' and uses inverters.

Assume that initially both inputs are low and the Q output is high. The input of N1 is also pulled high via the 180 k resistor, so the Q output is low, which holds the input of N2 low. If a logic '1' is applied to the S input the $\overline{Q}$ output will go low, pulling the input of N1 low, and the Q output will go high, thus holding the input of N2 high even if the S input subsequently goes low. Applying a logic '1' to the R input will reverse the procedure and reset the flip-flop.

The circuits feeding the inputs of the flip-flop should be capable of providing a logic '1' level

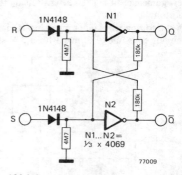

into a 180 k load, which normal CMOS circuits are capable of doing.

Reference: RCA Application Notes.

86 Auto trigger level control

Oscilloscopes, frequency counters and other instruments triggered by AC signals almost invariably have a manual trigger level control, to adjust the point on the waveform at which triggering occurs. When making measurements where the signal level varies, for example at different places in a circuit, it is tedious to have to make frequent adjustments to this control.

The circuit described here provides a trigger signal at a fixed percentage of the peak input level, irrespective of what that level is, so the frustration of having the trace disappear from an oscilloscope when the signal level falls below the

trigger level is avoided.

The circuit consists basically of a peak rectifier that provides one input of a comparator with a DC voltage equal to a fixed percentage of the peak signal level. The other input of the comparator is fed with the signal. When the signal level exceeds the DC reference level the comparator output will go low. When it falls below the reference level the comparator output will go high.

The peak rectifier consists of IC1 and T1. On positive half cycles of the signal waveform the output of IC1 will swing positive until T1 starts

1a

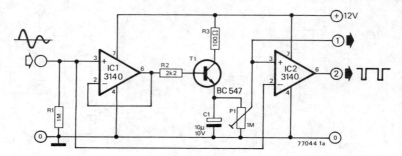

to conduct, after which IC1/T1 will act as a voltage follower, charging up C1 to the peak value of the signal.

A portion of this voltage is taken from the slider of P1 and applied to the non-inverting input of IC2, which functions as a comparator. The AC signal is fed to the inverting input. When the signal level exceeds the reference voltage the comparator output will go low; when the signal level falls below the reference level the comparator output will go high (see figure 1b).

P1 may be used to set the trigger level to any desired percentage of the signal level. The DC level at the slider of P1 may also be fed to the comparator input of an existing trigger level circuit.

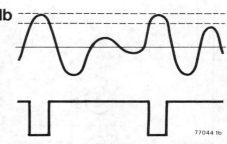

1b

In this case this circuit should have a high input impedance to avoid discharging C1. Alternatively the output from P1 can be buffered by an op-amp connected as a voltage follower.

87 LED logic flasher

The condition of the LED is determined by the logic states of the two inputs A and B. If A is low and B is high then the LED will be lit continuously. If B is low then the LED will be extinguished, irrespective of the state of A. If A and B are both high then the astable multivibrator comprising N1, N2 and N3 will start to oscillate and the LED will flash at about 3.5 Hz. Component values are given for supply voltages of 3, 10 and 15 V. At the maximum supply voltage of 15 V the current consumption is less than 25 mA.

Source: RCA CMOS Application and design ideas.

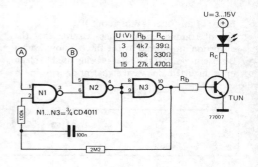

U (V)	R_b	R_c
3	4k7	39Ω
10	18k	330Ω
15	27k	470Ω

N1...N3 = ¾ CD4011

88 Complementary twin-T selective filter

This filter will pass signals at its centre frequency while attenuating signals at all other frequencies. The input signal is fed via R1 to the bases of the complementary emitter follower T1/T2. Feedback is taken from the emitters of T1 and T2, through the twin-T network to the inputs of the complementary amplifier T3/T4. At frequencies removed from the centre frequency of the twin-T network, the feedback signals will pass through the twin-T unattenuated. These signals will be amplified by T3 and T4 and will appear at T3 and T4 collectors in antiphase with the input sig-

nal. The input signal, and hence the output signal from the emitters of T1 and T2, will be greatly attenuated.

At the centre frequency of the twin-T the feedback signal will be greatly attenuated, so little antiphase signal will appear at the collectors of T3 and T4 and the input signal will pass unattenuated. The output may be taken from the emitter of either T1 or T2.

The quality factor of the filter is approximately

$\dfrac{A}{4}$, where A is the gain of the T3/T4 stage,

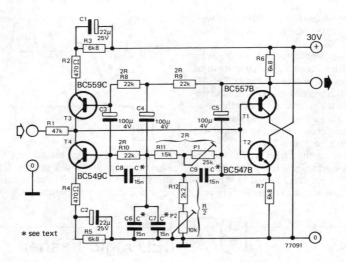

which is $\frac{2R1}{R2}$ (R2 and R4 are equal). The Q-

factor of this filter is thus about 500.

Use of complementary stages ensures that the distortion introduced by the filters is low, which is a useful point if the filter is being used to clean up a distorted sinewave signal prior to using it

for a distortion measurement.

The centre frequency of the filter is given by

$f = \frac{1}{2\pi RC}$, and with the component values

shown the centre frequency is about 1 kHz. P1 and P2 can be used to fine tune the filter for maximum output at the required frequency.

89 Negative supply from positive supply

It is sometimes necessary to provide a negative supply voltage in a circuit that otherwise uses all positive supply voltages, for example to provide a symmetrical supply for an op-amp in a circuit that is otherwise all logic ICs. Providing such a supply can be a problem, especially in battery operated equipment.

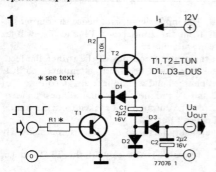

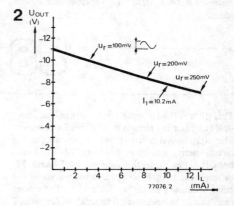

In the circuit shown here T1 is turned on and off by a squarewave signal of 50% dutycycle at approximately 10 kHz. In logic circuits it is quite conceivable that such a signal may already be available as clock pulses. Otherwise an oscillator using two NAND gates may be constructed to provide it.

When T1 is turned off, T2 is turned on and C1 charges through T2 and D2 to about 11 V. When T1 turns on, T2 turns off and the positive end of C1 is pulled down to about +0.8 V via D1. The negative end of C1 is now about 10.2 V negative so C1 discharges through D3 into C2, thus charging it. If no current is drawn from C2 it will eventually charge to around − 10 V. Of course, if a significant amount of current is drawn, the voltage across C2 will drop as shown in the graph and a 10 kHz ripple will appear on the output.

---

90 Microphone preamp

This preamp is specifically intended for use with low impedance microphones; its advantages are high output level, large bandwidth and extremely low noise figure. The maximum gain of the preamp is approx. 200. Depending upon the sensitivity of the microphone used the gain can be adjusted by altering the value of resistor R3 (for which a suitable typical value is around 22 k).

The low noise figure (virtually undetectable in the lab) is obtained by precise impedance-matching of the input. Optimal results are therefore obtained only with microphones of 500 to 600 Ω impedance. For 200 Ω microphones R4 should be reduced in value to 220 Ω , and C1 increased to 4 μ7.

Sound 'perfectionists' may wish to use metal film resistors for R3...R6 and parallel-connected MKM capacitors in place of an electrolytic capacitor for C1. Further details: with an input signal of 3.5 mV$_{pp}$ and maximum gain, an output signal of 800 mV$_{pp}$ was obtained. The maxi-

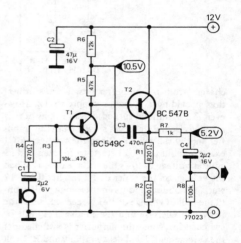

mum output level is approx. 10 V$_{pp}$ for an input of 50 mV$_{pp}$. The frequency response was flat within 3 dB from 50 Hz...100 kHz.

---

91 Loudspeaker delay circuit

Many owners of hi-fi equipment are plagued by switch-on and switch-off thumps which, while they rarely cause actual damage to the loudspeakers, are nonetheless very annoying. The simple solution is to switch the loudspeakers into circuit after the amplifier has been switched on and has settled down, and to switch them out of circuit before the amplifier is switched off.

This can be done manually, but there is always the chance that the user will forget, so an automatic switch seems the best answer. This can be achieved in a very simple manner. The circuit consists basically of a delay circuit and a relay that is energised to switch in the speakers a few seconds after the amplifier is switched on.

The DC supply to the relay has a very short time constant (much shorter than that of the amplifier power supply) so that when the amplifier is switched off the relay immediately drops out, disconnecting the speakers before a switch-off thump can occur.

The circuit functions as follows: at switch-on C2

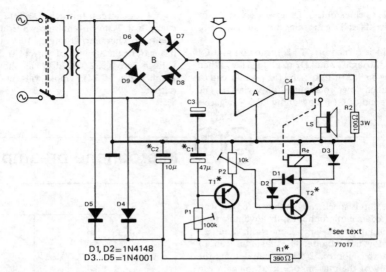

D1, D2 = 1N4148
D3...D5 = 1N4001

charges from the amplifier power transformer, thus providing a collector supply to T2. However, T2 is initially turned off and relay Re1 is not energised. C1 charges slowly from the amplifier supply rail via P1. When the voltage on C1 exceeds about 0.6 V T1 starts to conduct and its emitter voltage follows the voltage on C1. When the voltage on the slider of P2 reaches 0.6 V T2 starts to conduct and its emitter voltage rises until the pull-in voltage of Re1 is reached, when the relay will energise and the loudspeaker will be switched in. When the amplifier is switched off the voltage on C2 will decay rapidly and Re1 will drop out, disconnecting the loudspeaker before the amplifier supply voltage has decayed and thus eliminating the switch-off thump.

The switch-on delay can be set by means of P1. P2 can be used to set the final voltage across Re1 to just above its pull-in voltage. This means that the relay voltage is not critical and any relay with a pull-in voltage less than the amplifier supply voltage may be used.

If the amplifier output is capacitor coupled then a 100 Ω 3 W resistor should be connected between the normally closed contact of the relay and ground to charge the output capacitor before the loudspeaker is connected. One set of relay contacts is, of course, required for each channel of the amplifier.

The ratings of transistors T1 and T2 should be chosen to suit the amplifier supply voltage. Medium power transistors such as BC142's should be adequate in most cases.

J. Rongen

92 Voltage-controlled LED brightness

It is sometimes necessary to make the brightness of an LED vary in proportion to the magnitude of a DC control voltage, which in some cases may be less than the forward voltage drop of the LED.

The brightness of an LED is proportional to the current flowing through it, so the circuit required is a voltage/current converter which will provide a current through the LED independent of the forward voltage drop. This requirement is met by the well-known op-amp active rectifier circuit.

If a positive voltage is applied to the input in figure (a) then the output voltage will swing negative until the LED conducts. As the inverting input of the op-amp is a virtual earth point the cur-

1

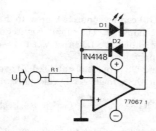

2

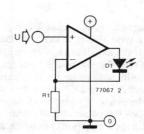

rent flowing through R1 and hence through the LED is $\dfrac{U}{R1}$. In the absence of an input the op-amp offset could cause the output to swing positive and exceed the reverse breakdown voltage of the LED. For this reason D2 is included to limit the maximum positive excursion to $+0.6$ V. Negative voltages may be used by reversing D1 and D2.

In figure (a) the input voltage must supply all the current taken by the LED, but figure (b) shows a circuit with a high input resistance that takes virtually no current from the input voltage.

The positive input voltage is applied to the non-inverting input of the op-amp, and the output voltage of the op-amp swings positive until the

voltage on the inverting input is the same. A current $\dfrac{U}{R1}$ thus flows through R1 and since it is provided by the op-amp output it also flows through D1.

The value of R1 is simply $\dfrac{U_{max}}{I_{max}}$, where these are respectively the maximum input voltage and maximum LED current required. Any op-amp capable of supplying the required current may be used.

C. Chapman

93 Clipping indicator

This circuit is designed to indicate the onset of clipping in an amplifier on both positive and negative peaks. Clipping occurs when the output of an amplifier swings up or down to its positive or negative limit, which is usually just below the supply voltage, so the circuit is designed to de-

tect this.

When the amplifier output clips positive T5 will turn off, which will cause T4 to turn off, triggering the monostable T1/T2, which will cause D2 to light for about 200 ms. If the amplifier clips negative then T3 will turn off, again triggering

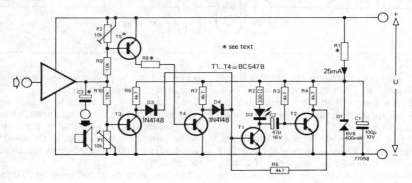

103

the monostable. If the amplifier clips briefly then just a short flicker of the LED D2 will be seen, but if the amplifier clips continuously the monostable will be continuously retriggered and the LED will appear to be permanently lit. Potentiometers P1 and P2 adjust the exact level at which the indicator operates. If the amplifier clips within 0.6 V of positive or negative supply voltage then these presets may be omitted.

If the amplifier has a single (positive) supply rail and capacitor-coupled output then the input of the circuit should be connected to the 'hot' end of this capacitor, i.e. to the top of C3 in the diagram (C3 is the output capacitor of the amplifier). The supply rails to the circuit should be connected between + supply and 0 V.

If the amplifier has a symmetrical supply and direct-coupled output then the input (junction of

R9 and R10) can be connected direct to the output of the amplifier. The supply connections to the circuit should be taken between + supply and − supply.

R1, D1 and C1 provide a stabilised low-voltage supply for the circuit. R1 is calculated by the equation: $R1 = \dfrac{Vs - 6.8}{25}$ (k Ω). R8 is chosen so that about 1 mA flows through it and is given by $R8 = \dfrac{Vs}{1}$ (k Ω). Where Vs is the total supply voltage between + and 0 or + and − rails as appropriate. For values of Vs up to 45 V T5 may be a BC157B or BC557B and for voltages up to 65 V a BC556N.

94 Using LEDs as reference diodes

Depending on type and the current flowing, the forward voltage drop of an LED may lie between 1.4 and 2 volts. The temperature coefficient of this voltage is about − 1.5 mV/°C.

As this is virtually the same as the temperature coefficient of the base-emitter voltage of a silicon transistor, it is very easy to construct a constant current source with almost zero temperature coefficient, as shown in the accompanying circuit.

The current is approximately $\dfrac{U_{LED} - U_{BE}}{R}$.

Since the temperature coefficients of the LED

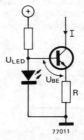

and the transistor are almost the same they cancel out and the current is almost independent of temperature.

95 CMOS PLL

As PLL (phase-locked loop) ICs are still somewhat expensive it seems reasonable to look around for a cheaper alternative, particularly for non-critical applications that do not require such high specifications.

Using two CMOS NAND gates it is possible to construct a CCO (current controlled oscillator) as described elsewhere in this book. If a 4011 quad two-input NAND gate IC is used this

leaves one gate to act as a phase comparator and another as an input amplifier.

The circuit shows a complete PLL using one 4011 and a few discrete components. Considering the simplicity and low cost of the circuit the results obtained were surprisingly good, and using a typical 4011 the following measurements were taken.

CCO frequency range (adjusted by P2): 25 kHz

– 800 kHz. Hold range: 20% of CCO free-running frequency. Output level: 45 mV measured at f_{in} = 500 kHz, deviation = ±30 kHz, modulation frequency = 1 kHz. AM suppression for 30% AM: better than 40 dB. Minimum input level: less than 2 mV from 50 Ω source.

These measurements were taken at a supply voltage of 6 V, when the current consumption was 600 μA.

Since different IC manufacturers use different processes and different chip geometries it might be expected that results would vary even when using different types of IC. The best results were obtained using ICs in which the gates had a steep transfer characteristic (better approach to an ideal switch) and lowest crosstalk between gates. In our experience, the Solid State Scientific SCL 4011 is a good example of this type of chip.

The 4011 PLL is particularly suitable for narrow-band FM demodulation, and in fact proved superior, in terms of s/n ratio and impulse noise rejection, to several monolithic PLL ICs.

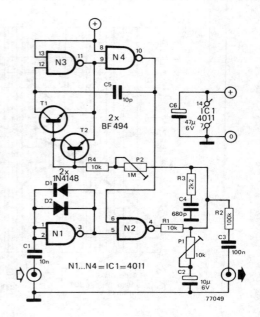

96 Guitar preamp

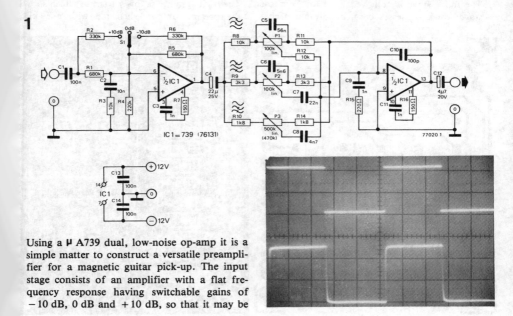

Using a μA739 dual, low-noise op-amp it is a simple matter to construct a versatile preamplifier for a magnetic guitar pick-up. The input stage consists of an amplifier with a flat frequency response having switchable gains of −10 dB, 0 dB and +10 dB, so that it may be

2

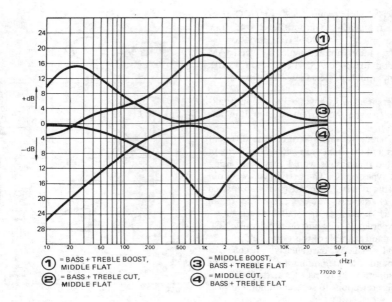

① = BASS + TREBLE BOOST, MIDDLE FLAT
② = BASS + TREBLE CUT, MIDDLE FLAT
③ = MIDDLE BOOST, BASS + TREBLE FLAT
④ = MIDDLE CUT, BASS + TREBLE FLAT

77020 2

used with pick-ups having a variety of output levels. The switchable gain also makes possible feedback when the guitar is brought close to the loudspeakers. This effect, much favoured by guitarists, can be achieved if the guitar amplifier power is around 20 watts or greater.

The input stage is followed by a tone control stage which possesses bass, middle and treble controls. As the frequency response of many guitar pick-ups is far from flat these controls can be used to compensate for any peaks or dips. The response of the tone control networks for different settings of the control pots is shown in the accompanying graph.

The oscillogram, the lower trace of which shows the preamp output when fed with a 1 kHz

3

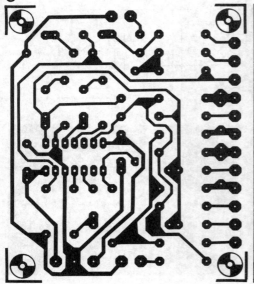
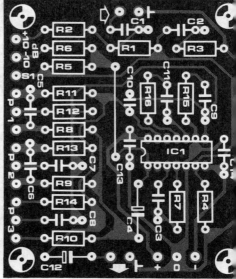

squarewave (upper trace) illustrates that the h.f. response of the preamp is fairly good. Indeed, the performance of the preamp is so good that, as well as its intended use, it may also be used in hi-fi systems.

97 Osculometer

1

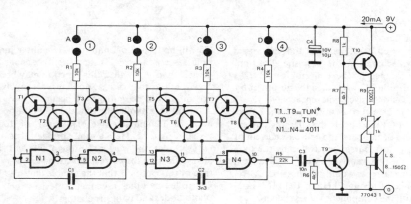

'Lie Detector' machines, which measure skin resistance, can provide great amusement at parties, especially if two participants each hold one electrode and indulge in some form of physical contact (e.g. kissing). The meter can then be calibrated in degrees of passion.

A variation on this theme is a circuit that produces an audible output rather than a meter indication, which is even more amusing. The circuit consists of two current controlled oscillators (described elsewhere in this book). The output of oscillator N1/N2 gates oscillator N3/N4 which produces some interesting effects. The output of N4 is used to drive an audio amplifier comprising T9 and T10.

The circuit has provision for eight electrodes for up to four pairs of participants. As the resistance between a pair of electrodes decreases then the frequency of the corresponding oscillator will rise, so the more ardent the embrace the higher the oscillator frequency. The gating effect between the two oscillators produces some unusual sounds.

For safety reasons the circuit should be battery powered by a 9 V transistor 'power pack', such as a PP3, PP6, PP9 etc.

98 CMOS CCO

Using two CMOS NAND gates (or inverters) and two transistors it is possible to construct a simple current-controlled oscillator (CCO). The circuit of figure 1 is based on a normal two-inverter astable multivibrator. When the output of N1 is high the output of N2 will be low and C1 will charge through T1 until the threshold voltage of N1 is exceeded, when the output of N1 will go low and the output of N2 high. T1 will now operate in a reverse direction, i.e. the collec-

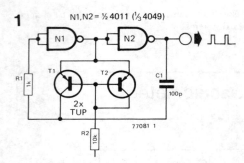

1 N1,N2 = ½ 4011 (⅓ 4049)

R1 1k T1 T2 2x TUP C1 100p R2 10k 77081 1

2 N1,N2 = ½ 4011 (⅓ 4049)

D1 D2 T1 2x TUP T2 R1 1k C1 100n D3 D4 D1...D4 = DUS 77081 2

tor will function as the emitter and vice versa, and C1 will charge in the opposite direction. When the voltage at the collector of T1 falls below the threshold of N1, then the output of N1 will go high and the cycle will repeat.

T1 and T2 form a current mirror, i.e. the collector current of T1 (which is the charging current of C1) tracks or 'mirrors' the collector current of T2, which is, of course, controlled by the base current. If the two transistors were identical then the collector currents would be the same. A frequency range of about 4 kHz to 100 kHz is obtainable with the component values shown.

When T1 is conducting in the reverse direction

T2 will be turned off and its base-emitter junction reverse-biassed. If the supply voltage is greater than + 5 V then this junction may break down, but as the voltages and currents involved are fairly small no damage will occur.

A circuit that avoids the unusual mode of operation of T1 and possible breakdown of T2 is given in figure 2. Here a diode bridge D1 to D4 ensures that the current through T1 and T2 always flows in the correct direction. The advantage of this circuit is that the astable may also be controlled by other asymmetric devices such as photodiodes and phototransistors.

99 LED tuner

This circuit can be used as a tuning indicator, instead of the more common pointer instrument. It gives a three-LED indication of correct tuning: 'off-to-one-side', 'correctly tuned', 'off-to-the-other-side'.

A voltage is derived from the AFC control voltage in the FM receiver and fed to two comparators (IC1 and IC2). The divider chain R2, R3, P1 and R4 produces two reference voltages. If the input voltage is higher than the greater of the two reference voltages T1 will be turned on and LED D1 will light. In the other extreme case, where the input voltage is lower than the lower reference voltage, T2 will be turned on and LED D2 will light. In the in-between range, where the receiver is correctly tuned and the input voltage is somewhere between the two reference voltages, T1 and T2 will both be turned off. In this case the output of N1 will go low, the trigger circuit N2/N3 will switch, the output of N4 will go high and T3 will be turned on − lighting LED D3.

Since the AFC voltage corresponding to 'correctly tuned' varies considerably from one receiver to the next, the values of R2, R3, R4 and P1 are not given in the circuit. It is a simple matter to calculate these values for any particular application. If the total resistance is to be 20... 30 k (a reasonable assumption), the voltage midway along R3 should correspond to the AFC voltage for correct tuning. To give two examples:

− assume that the 'correct' AFC voltage is 9.5 V. In this case the voltage across R2 + ½R3 should equal 2.5 V and the voltage across the selected as 4k7 and a 1 k preset is used for R3, the sum of P1 plus R4 should be approximately 20 k with P1 in the mid position. A good choice in this case would be R4 = 18 k and P1 = 4k7 (preset).

− assume that the correct AFC voltage is 5.6 V (as for the CA 3089!). In this case the voltage across the upper half of the divider chain should be approximately 6.5 V; reasonable values are

1

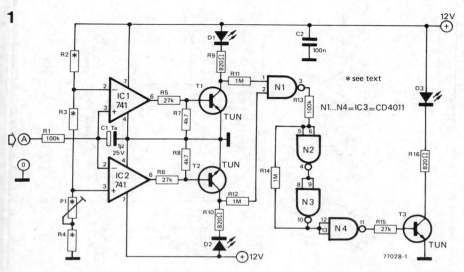

2

R2 = 12 k and R3 = 2k2. R4 + ½P1 should be approximately 10 k, so R4 can be 8k2 and P1 can be 4k7.

Note that R3 sets the sensitivity of the indicator, whereas P1 is used for correct calibration.

Some FM detectors, notably ratio discriminators, give a 0 V output when correctly tuned. In this case the circuit shown in figure 2 can be added, between the AFC output and the input to the circuit shown in figure 1.

W. Auffermann

100 Loudspeaker connections

Many hi-fi enthusiasts may not realise that significant distortion may be introduced into an audio signal by the connections between the amplifier output and the loudspeakers. In the first place, output current from the amplifier has to travel across several non-soldered metal-to-metal contacts, for example plug and socket connections at the amplifier outputs and the loudspeaker inputs, and loudspeaker switches within the amplifier (of which more later). For minimum distortion these contacts should not only have a very low resistance, but must also have a constant, linear resistance.

Oxidation of the metal surfaces of plugs, sockets

and switch contacts can produce a non-linear resistance which varies with the current flowing through it, thus distorting the signal fed to the loudspeakers. DIN loudspeaker plugs and sockets are particularly bad in this respect due to their very small contact area, and should be avoided. Where non-soldered connections must be made the use of screw terminals or robust 4 mm 'banana' plugs and sockets is to be preferred.

The second area which can cause degradation of the audio signal is the connecting cable itself. When a loudspeaker is being driven by an amplifier the loudspeaker cone should move exactly in

1

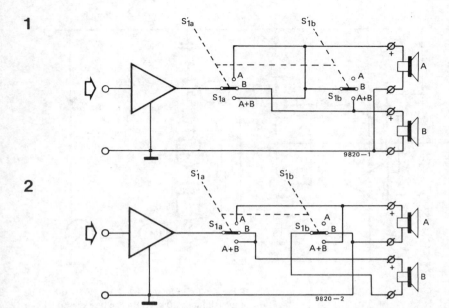

2

9820—2

sympathy with variations of the amplifier output voltage. Ideally, if a loudspeaker is fed with, say, a step input, the cone should move quickly to the appropriate position and stop. In practice, of course, this does not happen. A loudspeaker possesses inertia and compliance, so that the cone will tend to oscillate about its final position before settling down. Whilst this 'ringing' is in progress the loudspeaker acts as a generator and tries to pump current back into the amplifier output. If the amplifier output impedance is low (and it generally is) the loudspeaker sees a short-circuit and the cone movement is quickly damped by electromagnetic braking. The 'damping factor' of an amplifier is defined as the ratio of the load impedance to amplifier output impedance. As the output impedance of a modern transistor amplifier is generally a fraction of an ohm, damping factors are typically between 50 and 200 with an 8 ohm load. However, the resistance of the loudspeaker connecting cable appears in series with the amplifier output and must be considered as part of the amplifier output impedance. If the loudspeaker cable is thin its resistance will be high and the damping factor will be considerably reduced. In addition, some of the amplifier's output voltage will be dropped across the cable resistance rather than appearing across the loudspeaker.

Thus the second rule when connecting loudspeakers is to use heavy-duty cable.

Fuses, which are sometimes inserted in series with amplifier outputs for loudspeaker protection, should also be avoided since they can have a significant resistance.

Recent research, particularly by Japanese manufacturers, seems to indicate that the inductance of loudspeaker cables has a significant effect on transient response, and Hitachi, JVC, Pioneer and Sony are all introducing special loudspeaker cables which are claimed to give an improved sound. Whether or not these claims are true is still a matter for conjecture.

Returning to the subject of loudspeaker switching, figures 1 and 2 show two typical switching arrangements which allow two sets of speakers to be connected to an amplifier, either independently or simultaneously. One channel only is shown and the circuits are identical for the other channel. Although such switching arrangements offer convenience of use, they may not be such a good idea from a sound quality point of view due to the contact resistance of the switches. If loudspeaker switching is employed in an amplifier then the switches used should be rated at several amps to ensure minimum contact resistance. Both the switching arrangements shown in figures 1 and 2 have their advantages and disadvantages. In figure 1 both speakers appear in parallel across the amplifier output in the A + B position. Whilst this does mean that the damping factor is maintained the reduced load impedance can cause overloading.

In figure 2 the speakers are connected in series in the A + B position. Assuming that both speakers have the same impedance this connection, of course, doubles the load impedance, so there is no risk of overload. However the available output power is halved (since $P = U^2/R$) and the damping factor is reduced to less than unity, since each loudspeaker has the other in series with it as a source impedance.

In conclusion, anyone contemplating the building of an audio amplifier and/or loudspeakers

would be well advised to bear in mind all the points raised in this article. To summarise:

1. Connection to the loudspeakers should be made with the minimum number of non-soldered connections (plug and socket connections and switches) in series with the signal path.

2. The cable to the loudspeakers should have as low a resistance as possible. Fuses in series with the loudspeakers, although seemingly desirable from a circuit protection point of view, have a detrimental effect on sound quality and should be avoided.

101 Constant amplitude squarewave to sawtooth

Most electronic organs use squarewaves as the basic signal from which all the organ voices are obtained by filtering, simply because squarewaves are easy to generate and process. However, from a musical point of view, the sawtooth is a much more useful waveform, since it contains both odd and even harmonics of the fundamental frequency, whereas the squarewave contains only the odd harmonics. The main problems involved in generating sawtooth waveforms for organ circuits have been those of cost and reproducibility. However, the circuit described here, for which a patent is pending, suffers from none of these drawbacks and could, in principle, be integrated into a microcircuit.

Most electronic organs use octave dividers, which produce a symmetrical squarewave output.

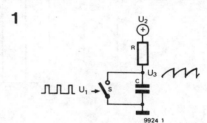

1

Figure 1. A sawtooth can be generated by charging a capacitor through a resistor and rapidly discharging it at regular intervals.

put. The harmonic content of this waveform is then altered by filtering to give the required organ voices. However, a symmetrical squarewave contains only the odd harmonics of the fundamental frequency, and those voices requiring even harmonics cannot be realistically imitated, since no amount of filtering can add harmonics which are absent. For this reason a sawtooth waveform, which contains both odd and even harmonics, is preferred as the 'raw material' for many organ voices.

A sawtooth waveform can be obtained from a squarewave as illustrated in figure 1. A capacitor is allowed to charge, either from a voltage source in series with a resistor or from a constant current source. The positive-going edge of the squarewave is used momentarily to close a (electronic) switch, which rapidly discharges the capacitor. This charging and instantaneous discharging of the capacitor produces the familiar sawtooth waveform.

Figure 2 illustrates the differences in the spectra

2a

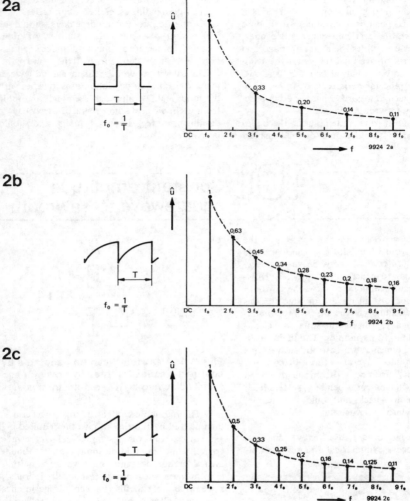

2b

2c

of the square and sawtooth waveforms. If the capacitor is charged from a voltage source then a sawtooth with an exponential curvature results, the spectrum of which is shown in figure 1b. If a constant current source is used then the sawtooth is linear, and has the spectrum shown in figure 1c.

For musical purposes an exponential sawtooth is preferred.

The disadvantage of this simple method is that the amplitude of the sawtooth waveform falls as the frequency on the input squarewave is increased, since the capacitor has less time to

Figure 2. Comparison of the spectra of square, exponential sawtooth and linear sawtooth waveforms.

Figure 3. Circuit for converting a square-wave to a constant amplitude exponential sawtooth.

Figure 4. By replacing R4 with a current mirror a linear sawtooth may be generated. This circuit also has an output buffer, T5.

112

3

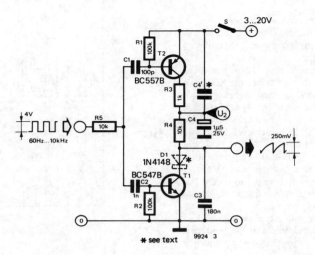

✷ see text   9924 3

4

✷ see text   9924 4

charge. This means that a different capacitor or charging resistor value would have to be used for each note of the organ to maintain equal amplitude over the entire compass of the instrument.

This problem can be overcome by arranging that the voltage of the source from which the capacitor is charged automatically increases as the frequency increases. This increases the charging current, which causes the capacitor to charge more rapidly and thus maintains a constant amplitude. A practical, constant amplitude, squarewave-to-sawtooth converter is shown in figure 3. Capacitor C3 is charged via R4 from

the voltage U_2, present on C4. The leading (positive-going) edge of the input squarewave is differentiated by C2 and R2, producing a short pulse which briefly turns on T1 to discharge C3.

The trailing edge of the squarewave is differentiated by C1 and R1, producing a short pulse which briefly turns on T2 and charges C4 via R3. Since T2 is turned on for a fixed time, as the input frequency increases T2 will be turned on for a greater proportion of the total time, so that C4 will charge to a higher voltage. This causes the charging current into C3 to increase, thus compensating for the fact that C3 charges for a

113

shorter time as the frequency increases.

The circuit given in figure 3 will produce a sawtooth of constant amplitude over the frequency range 60 Hz to 10 kHz.

A slight disadvantage of this circuit is that the shape of the sawtooth (and hence the harmonic content) alters as the frequency changes. This is no great drawback from a musical point of view. However, in some applications a linear sawtooth is preferred, and this can be achieved by replacing R4 with a current mirror (T3, T4) as shown in figure 4. This circuit is also equipped with a FET-source-follower, T5, which acts as buffer between C3 and the output and allows low impedance loads to be driven without degrading the sawtooth linearity.

The performance of this circuit is better than that of the simpler circuit in that it will produce a constant amplitude sawtooth over the frequency range 10 Hz to 20 kHz.

The sawtooth output may be switched on and off by a switch at the input or output of the circuit, or by a switch in the supply line. This latter method is particularly useful if several sawtooth converters are in use, since it allows them all to be controlled by a single switch. However, if switching of the supply line is employed then D1 must be included to prevent the squarewave signal from breaking through the base-collector junction of T1 when the supply is switched off.

C4′ can also be included to ensure that the sawtooth has a finite initial amplitude at switch-on. The amplitude depends on the value of C4′, which should be no more than 4.7   maximum. Figure 5 shows the effect of different values of C4′. If C4′ is omitted then the amplitude of the sawtooth builds up slowly after switch-on as C4 charges via T2 (figure 5a). After switch-off the sawtooth will decay gradually as C4 discharges.

The times taken for the sawtooth to build up to its steady-state value and to decay are dependent on the input frequency, being longest at low frequencies and shortest at high frequencies. This behaviour corresponds quite closely to that of conventional musical instruments.

If C4′ is included then the sawtooth signal will

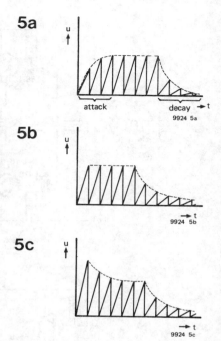

5a

5b

5c

Figure 5. Showing the effect of different values of C4′ on the attack and decay characteristics of the sawtooth.

assume a finite amplitude immediately after switch-on. In figure 5b this is shown as being equal to the steady-state amplitude. However, if the value of C4′ is made very large then the initial amplitude will exceed the steady-state amplitude, as shown in figure 5c. This effect will be more noticeable at low input frequencies.

In conclusion, it can be said that these circuits offer an economic solution to the problem of providing a sawtooth signal in squarewave divider instruments. By taking advantage of the high input resistances offered by MOS technology it should be possible to make the capacitor values sufficiently small to allow total integration of the circuit.

102 Ohmmeter

Using a CA 3140 FET op-amp it is easy to construct a simple, linear-scale ohmmeter. The

op-amp is connected in the non-inverting mode, with the non-inverting input fed from a 3.9 V zener. The op-amp output voltage is thus given by

$$\frac{(R_X + R_2)}{R_2} \times 3.9 \text{ V.}$$

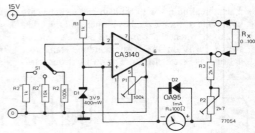

Since one end of the meter is returned to the zener the meter voltage is

$$\frac{R_X}{R_2} \times 3.9 + \frac{R_2}{R_2} \times 3.9 - 3.9 \text{ i.e. } \frac{R_X}{R_2} \times 3.9.$$

Since the zener voltage and R2 are fixed the voltage measured by the meter is proportional to R2. The full-scale deflection of the meter is about 3.9 V, but the exact value will depend on the tolerance of the zener.

Three ranges are provided by using different values of R2. With R2 = 1 k the full-scale reading of 3.9 V is obviously obtained when R_X = 1 k. With R2 equal to 10 k and 100 k full-scale readings are obtained at 10 k and 100 k. The voltmeter is simply a 1 mA meter with a nominal 3k9 series resistor, so the 0 to 1 mA scale can easily be converted to read 0 to 1 k, 0 to 10 k and 0 to 100 k. The germanium diode connected across the meter protects it in the event of an overload. To calibrate the meter it is first necessary to zero it by nulling the opamp offset voltage. To do this P2 is first set to minimum resistance to make the

meter most sensitive, and a wire link is connected across the R_X terminals. P1 is then adjusted to give a zero reading on the meter.

The meter may then be calibrated by connecting a close tolerance resistor of known value (e.g. 100 k 1%) across the R_X terminals and adjusting P2 until the meter reads correctly. To ensure good accuracy on all ranges R2, R2′ and R2′′ should be close tolerance types, 2% or better.

The maximum value which can be used for R2 and hence the maximum value of R_X that can be measured depends on the input resistance of the opamp, since any current flowing into the opamp input will cause errors. However, with the 1.5 T Ω input resistance of the 3140 it should be possible to use values up to 10 M, assuming 10 M close tolerance resistors can be obtained.

103 I see your point!

Whether a model railway is microprocessor-controlled or hand-operated, a visual display of the 'system status' is always worth while. If nothing else, it makes for an impressive control panel. For some functions, it is even essential to have a clear overview — unless, of course, your main aim is to realistically imitate crashes and derailments.

The points, in particular, are extremely important. As many model railway enthusiasts will have discovered, it is not at all easy to see what position the points are in from a distance. Even mechanical 'point position indicators' are not always particularly clear.

The indicator described here provides an unambiguous display on the main control panel. Different coloured LEDs can be used to provide a clear indication at a single glance.

The circuit could hardly be simpler. Electro-

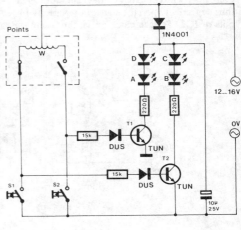

mechanical points with built-in end switches are used. One of these switches is open and the other is closed when the points are set. The closed switch turns on the corresponding transistor, lighting one set of LEDs. The pushbuttons, elec-

tronics and one LED out of each pair can be mounted in the control panel; the other LED in each pair can be mounted alongside the tracks near the corresponding set of points, to give an on-the-spot indication.

104 Musical doorbell

While on the subject of doorbells any kind of alternative gimmick is always worth considering. With the circuit described here, a pleasing effect is obtained. After even briefly pressing the bell-push, a short tune will be played. Holding the button down (or pressing it repeatedly in rapid succession) has two effects: a different melody is obtained, and it lasts longer. The circuit operates as follows.

By pressing pushbutton switch S1, the inputs of N1 and one of the inputs of N3 are taken low, with the result that pin 7 of IC2 (data input A) is taken high. IC2 is a four-bit static shift register, so that upon each successive clock pulse (provided by the clock generator, N4), this logic '1' is transferred to successive outputs. The clock frequency is approximately 5 Hz. The number of '1's clocked through the shift register will be directly proportional to the length of time that S1 is held down.

Each time that one of the outputs of IC2 goes high, a current is supplied via the corresponding resistor to the base of the current controlled oscillator, T1. The pitch of the resultant tone is thus dependent upon the state of the various outputs of IC2. At each clock pulse, the '1's in the

shift register move up one place, causing a change in pitch; if the pushbutton is depressed at that time, a new '1' will also be entered. One of the outputs (Q4B) is fed back via N2 and N3, so that the '1's in the register will keep going round the loop.

After the pushbutton is released, the circuit will keep running until C1 is discharged (through R1); if the button is pressed repeatedly, the ca-

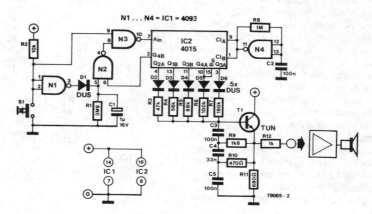

pacitor will remain charged and so the bell will 'run' continuously. The only difference between pressing repeatedly and holding the button down is therefore that a different succession of '1's will be entered, giving a different tune.

With this doorbell, it is necessary to add an out-put buffer amplifier.

The supply requirements are not critical (5...15 V, 10 mA).

Lucas Witkam

105 Battery saver

With many electronic games, such as heads-or-tails, roulette, or any of the versions of electronic dice, a considerable saving in battery life can be obtained by ensuring that the circuit, or at least the current-guzzling displays, are switched off after each throw or turn. Naturally enough, it would be somewhat tiresome to have to do this by hand, so the following circuit is intended to take care of this chore automatically. Basically the circuit is a simple timer. Push-button switch S1 is the start button for the die, roulette wheel, etc. When depressed, it causes capacitor C1 to charge up rapidly via D1. Transistor T1 is turned on, so that, via T2, the relay is pulled in, thereby providing the circuit of the game with supply voltage.

When the switch is released, initially nothing will happen. C1 discharges via R1, R2 and the base-emitter of T1, however it takes several secondes until it has discharged sufficiently to turn of T1. When it does so, however, the relay drops out, cutting out the power supply to the die, etc.

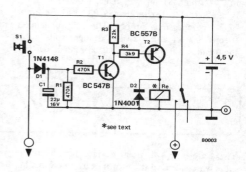

With the component values shown in the circuit diagram, a delay of roughly 3 seconds is provided in which to read off the display. If that interval is too short (or too long), it can be modified as desired by choosing different values for C1 and/or R1/R2.

W. Jitschin

106 Short-interval light switch

Even in today's well-equipped modern houses there are various 'corners' where additional lighting is required. For dark cupboards, meter boxes etc. temporary lighting is usually sufficient, so that making a connection to the mains is hardly worthwhile; a simpler and cheaper solution is to use a battery-powered circuit which will light a lamp for a short period of time. As is apparent from the accompanying circuit diagram, such a circuit is by no means complicated. Using only one CMOS IC, three resistors and one capacitor, the circuit will switch on a lamp for a presettable interval.

1

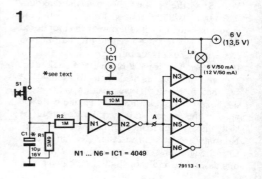

2

79113-2   < 500 mA

The operation of the circuit is perfectly straight-forward: when the button is pushed C1 charges up to the supply voltage. The outputs of the four parallel-connected inverters (N3...N6) are then low, so that the lamp will be lit. When the button is released, C1 discharges via R1 until the input of N1 reaches half supply. The Schmitt trigger formed by N1 and N2 then changes state, with the result that the lamp is extinguished. The

positive feedback resistor R3 ensures that the Schmitt trigger changes state very quickly.

With the resistor values shown in the circuit diagram, the lamp will remain lit for roughly 2.5 seconds per μF of C1. Thus a 10 μ capacitor would give an interval of roughly 25 seconds.

The circuit can be powered by four 1.5 V cells connected in series. If a larger lamp is required, three 4.5 V cells connected in series can be employed. Alternatively, for really 'heavy-duty' applications, the four parallel-connected inverters can be replaced by a transistor, as shown in figure 2. The supply voltage should be matched to the voltage rating of the lamp and may lie between 4.5 and 15 V. The current through the lamp should not exceed 500 mA in that case.

---

107 Car light reminder

There are many different designs for alarm circuits which remind the motorist to switch off his lights before leaving the car. The advantage of the circuit presented here is that no extra components have to be connected in series with the existing wiring, so that it will not effect the operation of the car electrical system. Furthermore the circuit is extremely simple, consisting solely of a DC buzzer, a double-pole double-throw switch, and a handful of diodes (depending upon the number of functions to be monitored).

The accompanying circuit diagram shows how the car headlamps, sidelights, fog lamps, and heated rear windscreen can be monitored. Note however that the circuit will not indicate if the above functions are actually working!

With S1 in the position shown in the diagram, the buzzer will be activated the moment the engine is switched off and one of the monitored functions is left on. Switching off the function concerned also cuts the buzzer.

If one wishes to leave a particular function on, e.g. the parking lights, then S1 should be switched to its alternative position, whereupon the buzzer is disabled until the engine is started again. The alarm can then be re-armed by switching S1 back to its original position.

Normally there is a resistance (R_L) in parallel with the ignition system (as a result of the various dashboard indicator lights, fuel guage etc.)

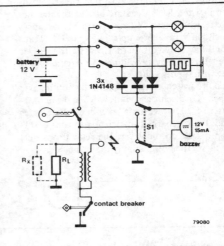

which is sufficiently small to ensure that the buzzer will be activated in the event of the contact breaker coming to rest in the open position when the car is stopped. If, however this resistance is too large, a 100...200 Ω resistor (2 W) can be connected in parallel with R_L. It may be preferable to use a small lamp – roughly 0.1 W/12 V – since due to its positive temperature coefficient, the more power it dissipates, the greater its resistance becomes.

M. Penrose

108 TAP switch

The advantage of this circuit for a touch activated switch is that it requires only one set of contacts and uses only two inverters, two resistors and a pair of capacitors. The circuit functions as follows: At switch on, the input of N1 is low, since C1 is discharged. Since the input of N1 is low, the input of N2 must be high and the output of N2 low, which of course holds the input of N1 low — thus the circuit is latched in a stable state.

In the meantime capacitor C2 charges up, via R2, to logic '1'. If the touch contacts are now bridged, the logic '1' on C2 is applied to the input of N1 (C2 > C1), taking the output low (and the output of N2 high). The state of the Q

1

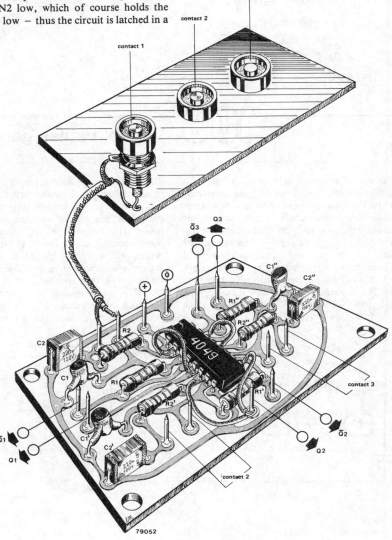

79052

2

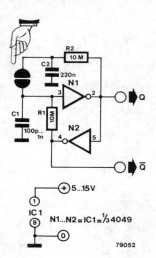

and $\overline{Q}$ outputs is thus inverted.

Bridging the contacts again causes C1 to discharge into C2 so that the outputs revert back to their original state. If the contacts are bridged for longer than the time constant R2 · C2, then the outputs will change state again. If the contacts are permanently bridged, the circuit will in fact oscillate at a frequency determined by the above time constant.

With the component values shown, the contacts should not be bridged for longer than approx. 1 second. This can be extended by increasing the value of C2.

U. Sussbauer

109 Variable pulse generator

Many digital applications require the use of a pulse generator of which not only the frequency, but also the duty-cycle can be varied. A problem with certain simple variable pulse generators is that altering the duty-cycle also affects the frequency of the output signal. The circuit described here, however, which uses only a handful of components, is free from this drawback; both frequency and duty-cycle are independently variable. The frequency range extends from approx. 1 kHz to 20 kHz, whilst the duty-cycle can be varied from almost 0 to 100%.

The complete circuit diagram of the variable pulse generator is shown in figure 1. As can be seen. the circuit is extremely simple indeed. The pulses are generated by an astable multivibrator round N1. This provides a symmetrical squarewave (duty-cycle = 50%), the frequency of which can be varied by means of P1a. The squarewave is cleaned up by N2 and is available via an extra external output.

To allow the duty-cycle to be varied without affecting the frequency of the squarewave, the circuit employs an integrating network

1

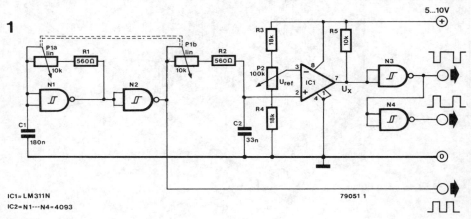

IC1= LM311N
IC2= N1---N4= 4093

79051 1

(P1b/R2/C2) and a comparator (IC1). The RC-constant of the integrating network (C2 = 1/6 · C1) is chosen such that the voltage across C2 may vary between approx. 20 and 80% of the supply voltage, U_b. Whenever this voltage exceeds the reference voltage on the inverting input of the comparator, the output of the latter changes state. The result is therefore a square-wave signal (U_x) whose duty-cycle is determined by the reference voltage (U_{ref}) of the comparator. This process is clearly illustrated in the timing diagram of figure 2. By varying the voltage at the inverting input of the comparator it is therefore possible to adjust the duty-cycle of the squarewave as desired without affecting the frequency.

There now remains the question of what happens to the duty-cycle if the frequency of the squarewave is varied. Normally the duty-cycle would be influenced by the frequency change, however due to the use of a twin-ganged potentiometer (P1a/P1b), in the circuit shown here, the RC-constant of the integrating network will vary in sympathy with that of the multivibrator. If the frequency, f, of the multivibrator is increased to x·f, the period of the resulting squarewave will be reduced by a factor x. However since the RC-constant of the integrating network is likewise reduced by a factor x, the duty-cycle of the squarewave at the output of the comparator will remain unchanged. It is not difficult to see that altering the RC-constant of the integrating network will not affect the shape of the charge curve of C2, so that the pulse diagram of figure 2 is also valid for any frequency x·f. The ratio T1/T2 and thus the duty-cycle (= T1/T2 x 100%) is therefore constant.

The values of R3, R4 and P2 are chosen such that the reference voltage at the inverting input of IC1 may vary between 13 and 87% of the supply voltage. As already mentioned, the voltage

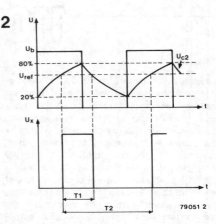

across C2 can vary between 20 and 80% of supply. Thus it is possible to vary the duty-cycle of the output signal between virtually 0 (i.e. no output signal) and 100% (DC voltage).

The two remaining Schmitt-trigger gates of IC2 are used at the output, N3 to further square up the output signal and N4 to provide an inverted version. Thus if a squarewave with a duty-cycle of 30% is present at the output of N3, the output of N4 will provide a squarewave of identical frequency but with a duty-cycle of 70%.

With the component values as shown in figure 1, the frequency range of the circuit extends from approx. 1 kHz to 20 kHz.

The frequency range can be altered if desired; the essential parameters of the circuit are given by the following equations:

$$C1 = 6 \times C2$$
$$P1a = P1b \text{ and } R1 = R2$$
$$f = \frac{1}{(P1a + R1) \cdot C1 \cdot 0.4}$$

It is also possible to control the amplitude of the output signal by connecting a 22 k potentiometer between the output of N3 or N4 and ground. The output signal can then be taken from the wiper of the potentiometer.

The supply voltage for the ciruit need not necessarily be stabilised, however if any sort of demands are to be placed upon the stability of the frequency, amplitude or duty-cycle, it is best to employ a voltage regulator. Since the entire circuit consumes no more than roughly 20 mA, a regulator from the 78L-series is the obvious choice. Depending upon the supply voltage, the 78L05, 78L06, 78L08, 78L09 and 78L010 should prove suitable.

Figure 1. The circuit of the variable pulse generator employs only two ICs, yet both the frequency and duty-cycle are independently variable.

Figure 2. This timing diagram illustrates how the duty-cycle of the output signal is determined by the reference voltage of the comparator (U_{ref}). Furthermore, by varying the RC-constant of the integrating network in sympathy with that of the multivibrator it is possible to make the duty-cycle independent of the frequency.

K. Kraft

121

110 DC polarity protection

Electronic equipment which is fed from an external DC voltage can easily be damaged if the terminals of the supply are inadvertently transposed. In circuits which have only a small current consumption this danger can be averted by connecting a diode in series with the supply line. The diode will then only conduct if the supply voltage is of the correct polarity. If the diode is replaced by a bridge rectifier, then it no longer matters which way round the terminals are connected. However, particularly in circuits with larger current consumptions, this approach is somewhat unsatisfactory, since it leads to noticeable power losses.

A more elegant solution, which results in no voltage loss and virtually no power loss, and hence is suitable for circuits carrying relatively large currents, is shown in the accompanying diagram. The component values were chosen for a DC supply of 12 V.

The circuit should be mounted inside the equipment it is meant to protect and the external supply voltage connected to terminals 1 and 2. Assuming the polarity of the supply is correct, once the on/off switch, S1, is closed, the relay, Re, will pull in, causing two things to happen. The normally closed contact, re1, will open, reducing the relay current through R1. Since the drop-out current is less than the pull-in current, assuming R1 is the correct value, relay Re will remain energised. This little trick reduces the dissipation in the protection circuit.

Secondly, the normally open contact, re2, will close, thereby applying power to the rest of the

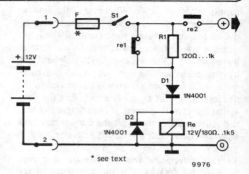

* see text

9976

equipment.

However, if the terminals of the supply are transposed, diode D1 will be reverse-biased, preventing the relay from being pulled in. Diode D2 suppresses any inductive voltages produced when the relay coil is de-energised.

If there is a fuse in the supply line of the equipment, then it is recommended that this be inserted between the supply and the protection circuit, so that it will blow should a fault occur in the latter. The current consumption of the protection circuit is so small compared with that of the equipment it guards that there is no need to alter the rating of the fuse.

The values of the components in the circuit can of course be modified to suit other supply voltages. One should bear in mind that the pull-in voltage of the relay, Re, should be the same as the supply voltage.

The value of R1 will depend to a certain extent on the type of relay used, and is best determined experimentally.

111 Disco lights

Flashing lights are very much an integral part of the disco scene nowadays. Usually the lights are controlled or modulated in some way by the music, i.e. the lights turn on and off or become dimmer or brighter in accordance with the volume or pitch of the audio signal. The circuit described here can be used either as a dimmer, 'running light' controller, or form the basis of a light organ.

The circuit, as shown in figure 1, is divided into a number of separate blocks, each of which has a distinct function. The supply stage is of course an essential, although if the circuit is used exclusively as a dimmer, IC2 and C6 can be omitted. The remainder of the dimmer circuit is contained in block (a).

1

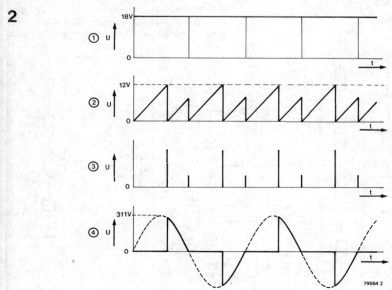

79554 1

Together with T3, components P1, R5, R6 and C1 form a sawtooth generator which, via the pulse transformer Tr1, is used to trigger the triac. To ensure good synchronisation with the mains waveform the triac is turned off every 10 ms. This is achieved by transistors T4 and T5 momentarily removing the supply to the oscillator (see figure 2). The position of P1 determines the brightness of the lamp, which is con-tinuously variable from zero to full on. With the aid of block (b), the brightness of the lamp can be varied by an external control voltage (4...8 V) which can be derived from a variety of add-on circuits. An example of one such control circuit is shown in block (d). By connecting each A-output of the 4017 to a circuit consisting of blocks (a) and (b), a running light effect is ob-tained. The 'speed' of the running light will of

2

79554 2

course be determined by the frequency of the clock signal applied to IC3.

If the brightness of the lamp is to be modulated by the music signal, block (c) is used. The audio signal (from a preamplifier) is first amplified by T6 and then rectified by diodes D6 and D7. A DC voltage proportional to the input signal thus appears across C10. This voltage is then fed via T7 and T8 to the base of T1. Particular attention has been paid to suppression of triac interference, since any mains transients etc. generated by the triac switching on and off will be rendered audible as pops and crackles in the loudspeaker. L1 is a conventional r.f. choke; the gauge of wire used for this coil, and indeed the rating of the triac itself, will depend upon the

size of lamp(s) to be switched. C2 and C3 also form part of the suppression circuit, and should be rated at 400 V.

The satisfactory operation of the circuit is largely dependent upon the quality of Tr1. This should be a transformer with a turns ratio of 1:1 and can be home-made by winding 2 x 150 turns of 0.3 mm enamelled copper wire on a partitioned coil former, into which a 6 mm ferrite core is screwed.

In view of the high voltages involved, it goes without saying that due care should be taken in the construction of the circuit.

G. Ghijselbrecht

112 3-state CMOS logic indicator

The following circuit will provide an audible indication of CMOS logic states. Logic '0' is represented by a low frequency tone (roughly 200 Hz), logic '1' by a high frequency tone (approximately 2 kHz), whilst an undefined level produces no output signal.

The circuit functions as follows: two comparators are connected such that at voltage levels between roughly 21 and 79% of the supply voltage the two oscillators formed by N2, R7, C1 and N3, R8, C2 are both inhibited. With input voltages greater than 79% of supply, the output of A1 swings low, thereby, (via inverter N1) starting the 'high frequency' oscillator. On the other hand, input voltages below 21% of supply take the output of A2 high, starting the 'low frequency' oscillator. The oscillator output signals

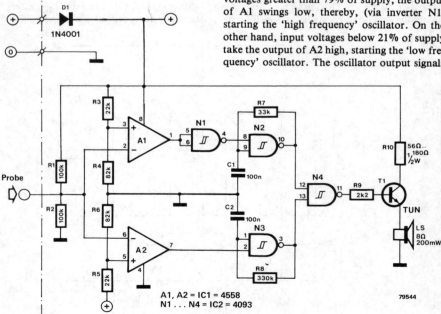

A1, A2 = IC1 = 4558
N1 ... N4 = IC2 = 4093

79544

are fed to a simple buffer stage and then to a suitable loudspeaker.

The power supply should be drawn from the circuit under test, and must lie between roughly 5 and 15 V.

D. Hackspiel

113 Model railway block section controller

This simple circuit offers model railway enthusiasts a cheap alternative to the fairly expensive block section controllers which are available commercially. The circuit suffers from one disadvantage, namely that it can be used to control traffic in just one direction. However, cost may dictate that this is acceptable.

The circuit and how it is connected to the rails, is shown in the accompanying diagram, where the direction of the trains is assumed to be from right to left. As can be seen, the 'earth' rail is broken at three places (using insulating track sections which are available in model shops). The lengths of rail sections A and B will influence at what point the train stops, and should be chosen to suit individual circumstances (the length of the train(s) for example). The red and green lamps (L1 and L2) are built into a set of signals.

The circuit works as follows: As long as there is no train in the vicinity, the green lamp (L2) will be lit and section A of the track is connected to earth via the circuit. Transistor T1 is turned off, so that transistor T2 is turned on via L1 and R2.

Should a train then approach, nothing will happen as long as it remains on block A of the track. When the train advances to block B, however, diode D1 is forward biased via the motor of the train, which will slow down slightly since the diode drops 0.7 V of the supply voltage. The voltage dropped across the diode also turns on T1, causing the red lamp (L1) to light up. At the same time T2 turns off, extinguishing the green

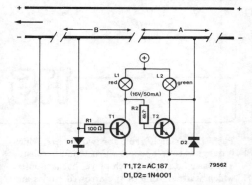

T1,T2 = AC 187
D1,D2 = 1N4001   79562

lamp and breaking the connection between block A of the track and earth. A subsequent train entering block A of the track is therefore forced to a stop.

As soon as the first train leaves block B, the initial situation is restored, i.e. T2 conducts, the green lamp is turned on and the connection between block A of the track and earth is restored. The train waiting in block A can therefore continue on its way.

The circuit can also be used to control a crossing. The 'A' sections of track are laid before the crossing and the B section forms the crossing itself. The signals are of course positioned on the approach to the crossing.

A. van Kollenburg

114 Burglar's battery saver

Elektor attempt to cater for everyone and included here is a circuit for gentlemen in the nocturnal profession. Put an end to stumbling in the shrubbery with the torch light controller described here. Incidentally it is also an excellent battery saver. Varying the brightness of a torch appears simple enough but using a series resistor or potentiometer is out of the question since power is dissipated in the form of heat. One solution is not to use a DC supply voltage but

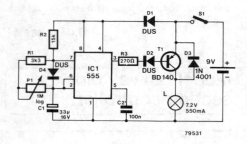

rather a squarewave with a variable duty cycle. The brightness of the lamp then depends upon the length of the duty cycle.

In the circuit shown, a 555 timer is connected as an astable multivibrator and used to supply the squarewave. The duty cycle of the squarewave can be varied by potentiometer P1. Diodes D1... D3 protect the circuit if the polarity of the battery is reversed in which case the circuit will not operate and the torch will be 'full on'. Gentlemen, do not change your batteries in the dark!

C. Hentschel

115 Pachisi

Pachisi is a simple game for two players, which is designed to test people's 'frustation quotient'. The basic idea is that each player has a counter, which starts on one of the arrowed circles and then attempts to move round the board to the white rectangle in the centre of the 'M'. The players move alternately and the first person's counter to reach 'home' is the winner. Four different types of move are possible: forwards, backwards, onto the next white circle, and onto

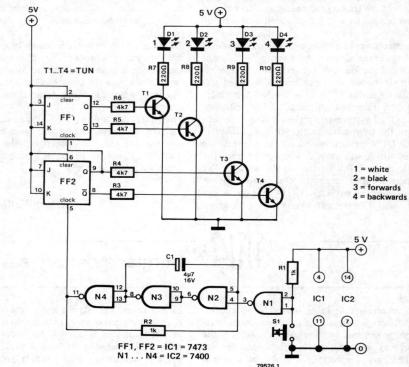

1 = white
2 = black
3 = forwards
4 = backwards

FF1, FF2 = IC1 = 7473
N1 . . . N4 = IC2 = 7400

79526 1

the next black circle. Thus it is effectively possible to move either one or two steps forwards or backwards each turn. If one player lands on the circle currently occupied by his opponent, the former is declared the winner, whilst if a player retreats backwards off the edge of the board, he is deemed to have lost.

The player's moves are determined by two pairs of LEDs. One pair decides whether the move is forwards or backwards, and the other pair whether it is to a white or black circle. Each time the pushbutton switch S1 (see circuit diagram) is pressed, a new random combination occurs. Thus it could happen that one player is on the point of winning when he is forced to take 'two steps backwards'!

The actual circuit is straightforward. Two flip-flops form a two-bit binary counter, which is clocked by an oscillator built round NANDs N1...N4. The oscillator is only enabled when S1 is closed. The output state of the counter is displayed via transistors on the four LEDs.

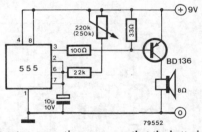

79526 2

H.J. Walter

---

116 Metronome

Although not exactly revolutionary, the circuit shown here is both very cheap and reliable. The well-known 555 timer IC is connected as an astable multivibrator, and delivers a regular train of pulses which are rendered audible via the transistor and loudspeaker. The frequency of the metronome can be varied with potentiometer P1. A 9 V supply voltage means that the circuit can easily be powered by batteries.

If a loudspeaker with an impedance of less than 8 Ω is used, it should be preceded by a series resistor (1 W) which will compensate for the difference in impedance (and — due to the lower

current consumption — ensure that the batteries last longer).

79552

W. Kluifhout

---

117 Improved DNL

Dynamic Noise Limiting (DNL) is a noise reduction system patented by Philips, which is particularly useful for the reproduction of (cassette) tape recordings. As the name suggests, the system is dynamic, i.e. the noise is only suppressed at the moments when it is most intrusive which, in the case of a music signal, is during passages. The system also exploits an

1

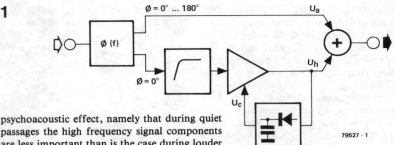

79527 - 1

psychoacoustic effect, namely that during quiet passages the high frequency signal components are less important than is the case during louder sections of the music. A DNL circuit utilises this fact by attenuating the high frequency components, and hence the noise, during low amplitude portions of the input signal.

The circuit described here is an updated and improved version of older DNL circuits. The most significant point in its favour is that the point at which noise reduction starts is continuously variable.

The operation of the circuit is illustrated by the block diagram of figure 1. The input signal is fed to a phase shifter, which provides two output signals. One of these signals, u_a, is equal to the input signal, but is subjected to a frequency-dependent phase shift varying from 0° for low frequency signals to 180° for high frequency signals. The second output signal is identical to the input signal in all respects, including phase, and is fed to a highpass filter and then to an ampli-

fier. The gain of the amplifier is determined by the feedback signal, u_c, which is obtained by peak rectifying the amplifier output. The result is dynamic compression/limiting of the high frequency signal components, i.e. the latter are amplified to a constant level, regardless of input signal level. The amplifier output, u_h, is summed with the phase-shifted version of the input signal. Since the phase shift was frequency-dependent, the high frequencies present in the two signals will tend to cancel. However due to the limiting effect of the amplifier stage, the

2

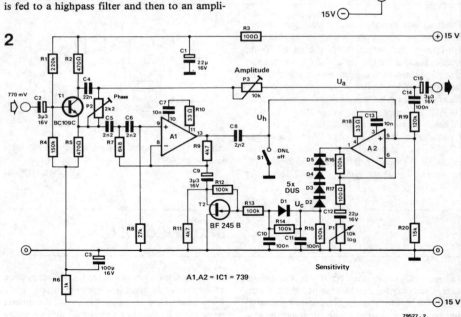

79527 - 2

greater the amplitude of the input signal, the less the cancellation, and the smaller the attenuation of the higher frequencies. The noise reduction is therefore severest at low input signal levels, i.e. during the quieter passages of music.

The complete circuit diagram of the DNL circuit is shown in figure 2. The phase shifter is formed by T1, the frequency dependence of the shift being obtained by combining the collector ($\Phi = 180°$) and emitter ($\Phi = 0°$) signals via P2 and C4. The highpass filter is realised by the circuit round op-amp A1. This filter has a third-order Butterworth response with a turnover frequency of 5.5 kHz. The filter output is amplified/limited by A2. The gain of A2, and with it the sensitivity of the circuit, can be varied by means of potentiometer P1.

The peak detector consists of 4 series-connected diodes, which ensures that the control signal, u_c, is only present when the input signal rises above a certain level. A FET, T2, is used to form the voltage controlled attenuator in the feedback loop of A2. The two signals u_a and u_h are summed via preset potentiometer P3 and the series connection of R19 and C14.

The DNL function of the circuit can be rendered inoperative by means of switch S1, which simply shorts the signal u_h to earth.

During construction care should be taken to ensure that the output signal of op-amp A2 is kept at least several centimetres from the signal-carrying leads, so as to prevent the possibility of crosstalk.

The circuit can be set up by driving it with a pure noise signal, such as that from an off station FM tuner, and varying P2 and P3 for maximum attenuation.

The circuit as shown is optimised for standard level audio signal levels, i.e. 0 dB = 770 mV RMS, but can also be used for other signal levels.

R.E.M. van den Brink

118 Resistance bridge

Generally speaking, resistors with a 5% tolerance are more than adequate for most circuits. From time to time there may be occasions when 1% resistors are required, or when the value of two resistors must be matched to within 1%. This is the case with for example digital meters, where it is worth the extra expense of using very accurate attenuator resistors in order to fully exploit the accuracy offered by a digital display. The circuit described here allows two resistors, R_x and R_y, of the same nominal value to be compared with one another, and the difference to be expressed directly in per cent. The accuracy and stability of the circuit are better than 0.1%, and resistors from 10 Ω to 10 M Ω can be measured, providing the maximum permissible dissipation is not exceeded, i.e. ¼ W types for example should be greater than 27 Ω .

The operation of the circuit is based upon the
The operation of the circuit is based upon the

resistance bridge formed by R_x, R_y and the voltage divider R1, P1 and R2. If R1 and R2 are exactly the same value, the bridge current will be proportional to the extent to which R_x and R_y deviate from the mean value of these two resistors. For small differences between R_x and R_y the current is, to all intents and purposes, proportional to the difference between the two resistors. The percentage difference between the two 'unknown' resistances is expressed directly on the scale regardless of which resistor is the greater. However with the aid of the simple comparator formed by T1 and T2, which of the two resistors is the greater can be displayed on LEDs D1 and D2.

The circuit can be adapted to suit a variety of different meters. If a centre-zero reading meter or a DVM (with a floating input) are available these would be ideal in which case components D1...D7, R4...R6, T1, T2 and the two LEDs can

Table:	scale	meter M	R1 = R2	P1	R3	DVM
	0- 3%	0- 60 μ A	1k2	100 Ω	5 k	− 0.3... + 0.3 V
	0-10%	0-200 μ A	1k2	100 Ω	5 k	− 1 ... + 1 V
	0-10%	0-500 μ A	475 Ω	50 Ω	2 k	− 1 ... + 1 V
	0-10%	0-200 μ A	1k2	100 Ω	500 Ω	− 0.1... + 0.1 V
	0- 1%	0- 50 μ A	475 Ω	50 Ω	2 k	− 0.1... + 0.1 V

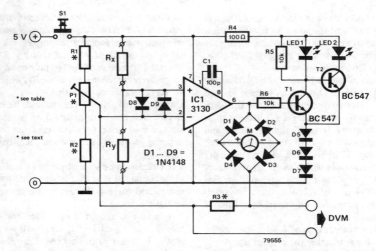

79555

be omitted. A universal meter with a 0-10 or 0-30 scale would also be suitable.

The table lists other examples of possible meters and indicates the component changes required as well as the range scale obtained.

High stability metal oxide or 1% precision wire-wound resistors should be used for R1, R2 and R3.

Calibrating the circuit is quite straightforward. P1, which should preferably be a multi-turn type, is provisionally set to the mid-position and two resistors of the same nominal value are connected in circuit. The meter reading is noted, and then the resistors changed over. If the new reading is the same as the first, no further adjustment is required. If that is not the case, P1 is adjusted until the average of the two readings is obtained. If desired the procedure can be repeated once more for an extra check.

J. Borgman

119 Octave shifter for electric guitars

Effects units for electric guitars are extremely popular. One of the popular weapons in the arsenal of the well-equipped rock guitarist is an octave shifter, a unit which doubles the frequency of the guitar signal.

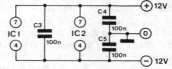

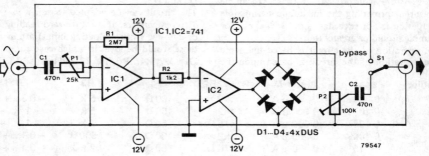

79547

One of the ways of achieving frequency doubling – and the approach adopted here – is full-wave rectification, as commonly carried out in power supply circuits. As can be seen from the accompanying circuit diagram, the rectification is performed by a diode bridge. By including the diode bridge in the feedback loop of IC2, the non-linear voltage characteristic of the diodes has no effect upon the signal.

Pre-amplification of the guitar pickup signal is provided by IC1. The gain of this stage is set (by P1) such that the signal is just on the point of clipping. Preset potentiometer P2 can be ad-justed so that the output signal level is the same as that of the input signal. A bypass switch, S1, is included allowing the unit to be switched in and out.

The signal is not only doubled in frequency, but is also distorted. The sound becomes considerably harsher, as well as being shifted up an octave. This feature would probably be considered an asset to the contemporary rock musician.

H. Schmidt

120 Liquid level sensor

An annoying drawback of many liquid level sensors is the effect of electrolytic reaction between the liquid and the sensors. Metal electrodes are prone to corrosion and consequent loss of effectiveness (reduced conductivity), with the result that they have to be replaced at frequent intervals.

One solution to this problem is to ensure that there is an AC, rather than DC potential between the sensor electrodes. The constant reversal of electrode polarity drastically inhibits the electrolytic process, so that corrosion is considerably reduced.

The actual circuit of the level sensor is extremely simple. The circuit around N1 forms an oscillator. If the two sensors are immersed in a conducting solution, C4 will be charged up via the AC coupling capacitors (C2 and C3) and the diodes, so that after a short time, the output of N2 is taken low and the relay is pulled in. The

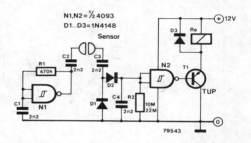

relay can be used to start a pump, for example, which in turn controls the level of the liquid. When a conductive path between the two sensors no longer exists, C4 discharges via R2, with the result that the output of N2 goes high and the relay drops out.

E. Scholz

121 Frequency ratio meter

There are certain situations, e.g. when checking frequency multiplier or divider circuits, PLL circuits, certain music circuits etc., where it is more important to measure the frequency ratio of two signals, rather than simple measurement of frequency itself. With the aid of the circuit shown here, the ratio between the frequency of two signals, f_1 and f_2, can be measured and displayed directly on three seven-segment displays. The circuit will measure ratios up to 99.9 with an accuracy of 0.1, providing f_1 is larger than f_2.

The heart of the circuit is the counter/display driver IC, MK 50398N, from Mostek.

The higher frequency, f_1, is fed via the input stage around T1 to the clock input (pin 25) of the counter. Pulses will be counted at this input pro-

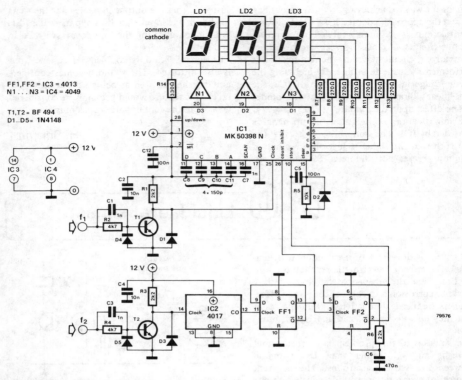

FF1,FF2 = IC3 = 4013
N1 ... N3 = IC4 = 4049

T1,T2 = BF 494
D1...D5 = 1N4148

vided pin 26 (count inhibit) is held low. Decade divider IC2 and flip-flop FF1 ensure that this pin is in fact held low for exactly ten cycles of the lower frequency signal, f_2. Thus a number appears on the displays which is ten times the ratio between f_1 and f_2. By arranging for the decimal point to light between the second and third digits, the resulting figure is thus exactly equal to the ratio f_1/f_2. Flip-flop FF2 is connected as a monostable, and is used to provide the counter IC with the correct 'store' and 'clear' pulses on pins 10 and 15 respectively.

W. Dick

122 LED lamps

When it comes to mains indicator lamps, there are basically three main options: neon lamps, incandescent lamps, and LEDs. Neon lamps have the advantage that they can be connected direct to the mains supply, and also that they consume very little power. Incandescent lamps, on the other hand, must be connected to a much lower voltage (e.g. to the secondary side of the transformer), and therefore provide only indirect indication of whether the mains supply is present, whilst as a rule dissipating a relatively large amount of power.

LEDs would represent an ideal alternative to both the above approaches, since they have a longer operating life than either neon or incandescent lamps, and dissipate no more than 20 to 30 mW. Unfortunately it is necessary to protect the LED from excessive currents by employing a series resistor, which, with a mains voltage of 240 V, will itself dissipate something over 3.5 W. The circuit shown here offers a better solution. The current through the LED is limited to a safe value not by a dropper resistor, but by the reactance of a capacitor. The advantage of this method is that no power is dissipated in the capacitor, since the current through the latter is 90° out of phase with the voltage dropped across it. The formula for calculating power dissipation for DC voltages is only valid for AC voltages provided the current and voltage are in phase i.e.

$$P_c = u_c \cdot i \cdot \cos \varphi$$

With a phase shift of 90°, which is the case with capacitors, P_c is therefore 0 W (cos 90° = 0). What little power is consumed by the circuit is entirely converted into light and heat by the LED.

The value of capacitor C, can be calculated for any given voltage, frequency and current with the aid of the following equation:

$$C \approx \frac{i}{6.28 \cdot u \cdot f} \quad \text{where:}$$

C is the capacitance in Farads

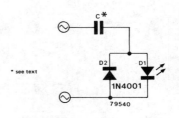

u is the RMS value of the mains voltage
f is the mains frequency in Hz
i is the current through the LED in Amps
With a mains voltage of 240 V, a frequency of 50 Hz and a current of 20 mA, the nearest suitable value of capacitor is therefore 330 nF. The working voltage of the capacitor should be at least twice the mains voltage.

Diode D2 is included to protect the LED from excessive reverse voltages.

U. Hartig

123 Linear thermometer

The circuit described here employs a forward-biased diode as temperature sensor. The forward voltage drop of a diode falls by approximately 2 mV for an increase in temperature of 1° C. Since this negative temperature coefficient remains the same regardless of actual ambient temperature, the scale of the thermometer will be linear.

The temperature coefficient of a diode is not of an NTC (negative temperature coefficient) resistor. However it is not possible to obtain a linear scale over a wide range of temperatures using an NTC resistor. Thus the use of a diode is justified by the wide measurement range obtained and by the ease of calibration.

The sensor diode – D1 in the circuit diagram – is a common-or-garden 1N4148, which can easily be mounted apart from the rest of the circuit.

The diode forms part of a resistance bridge, comprising P1, P2, R5, R6 and R7. A reference voltage is provided by a 723. Thus the voltage on the non-inverting input of IC2 is held to a (variable) reference value via R5 and P1. Assuming the circuit is initially nulled by adjusting P1 and P2, variations in the forward voltage drop of the diode as a result of temperature fluctuations will cause the output of IC2 to swing either high or low depending upon whether the temperature rises above or falls below zero.

By using a diode bridge, D2...D5, the meter will show a positive deflection regardless of the polarity of the temperature. To provide an indication of whether the temperature is in fact above or below 0°, the output of IC2 and the reference voltage are effectively connected to the non-inverting and inverting inputs respectively

Table 1	scale	meter M	temperature	R8	DVM
	0 - 30	0 - 300 µ A	− 30... + 30° C	1 k	− 0.3... + 0.3 V
	0 - 30	0 - 100 µ A	− 30... + 30° C	3 k	− 0.3... + 0.3 V
	0 - 50	0 - 300 µ A	− 50... + 50° C	1.67 k*	− 0.5... + 0.5 V
	0 - 50	0 - 500 µ A	− 50... + 50° C	1 k	− 0.5... + 0.5 V
	0 - 100	0 - 1 mA	− 100... + 100° C	1 k	− 1... + 1 V

* 2 x 3k3 parallel

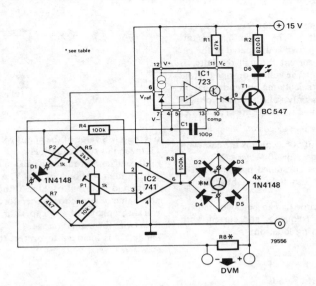

of the 723, which thus functions as a comparator. Assuming the circuit is calibrated for zero deflection at 0° C, as the temperature falls, the voltage drop across the diode increases, therefore the voltage on the inverting input of IC2 falls, the output of IC2 goes high, taking the non-inverting input of IC1 high and with it the output of IC1. Transistor T1 therefore turns on, lighting the LED. When the temperature rises above 0° C, the reverse process occurs, resulting in the LED being extinguished.

Resistor R8 is included to allow the use of a DVM (with floating input) as a means of display. The accompanying table lists a number of alternative values for R8 along with the measurement ranges obtained for various (moving coil) meter scales. Of course, if a DVM is used, then

the moving coil meter as well as D2...D5, R1... R4, T1 and the LED can be omitted.

The circuit can be calibrated by suspending the sensor diode (together with a suitable length of connecting wire!) in crushed ice which is beginning to melt. With P2 provisionally set to the mid-position, P1 is then adjusted so that zero deflection on the meter (or zero voltage across R8) is obtained. The diode is then dipped into boiling water, whereupon P2 is adjusted until a voltage of 1 V over R8 is obtained. The above procedure can then be repeated. It is best to use distilled or demineralised water for both steps of the calibration procedure.

J. Borgman

124 Ten channel TAP

TAP (read: touch) switches come in all shapes and sizes, mainly as momentary action or simple on/off (latched) switches. Using only a handful of components, it is possible to construct a 'ten-channel' TAP, i.e. a ten-pole touch switch. When one of the ten sets of contacts is touched, the corresponding output will be taken high.

The heart of the circuit is formed by a CMOS decade counter/decoder, 4017, which is clocked by a simple CMOS oscillator. However when the

contacts are open, the counter is inhibited, since the clock enable input is held high. The same is true if the contacts are bridged, but the corresponding output is already high, since in that case the additional skin resistance will have no effect. However, if the corresponding output is low when a set of contacts is touched, the skin resistance (which is negligibly small compared to the other resistances) forms part of a voltage divider, thereby pulling the clock enable input low.

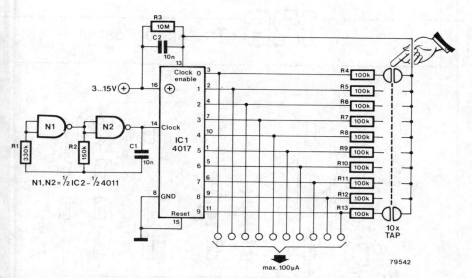

The counter is started and increments until the output in question is taken high, whereupon the clock enable input is once more taken high and the count is stopped.

Capacitor C2 is included to suppress mains transients etc., whilst R4...R14 prevent the possibility of a shock in the event of a short between the contacts.

It must be emphasised that when the counter is

started, each output in turn will go high (for a very short period) until the selected channel is reached. This should not prove to be a problem with most applications, however provision must be made for this when used with flip-flops and other edge triggered devices.

C. Horevoorts

125 Floating input for DVM

Digital voltmeters are now in widespread use and growing ever more popular. Many of the cheaper types of DVM however suffer from a slight drawback in that they have an earthed input (i.e. one of the input terminals is connected to earth or to a fixed voltage level). In many cases this is not particularly important, however there are situations (if the DVM is used in conjunction with an add-on unit such as an AC millivoltmeter, for example) where it can be something of a nuisance. With the aid of the following circuit, formed around a differential amplifier, any DVM can be provided with a floating input.

It is recommended that 1% (metal film) types are used for the 1 M resistors (R1...R4). The output voltage of the circuit is adjusted to 0 V by means of P1 (with the input short-circuited). The sup-

ply voltages $+U_b$ and $-U_b$ can be anywhere between 3 and 20 V (provided they are symmetrical).

J. Borgman

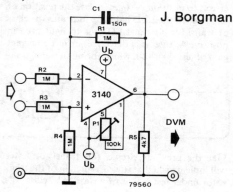

135

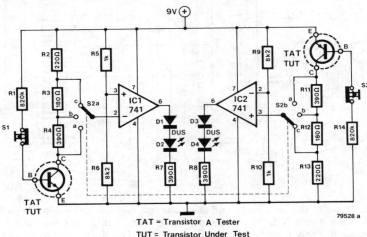

TAT = Transistor A Tester
TUT = Transistor Under Test

79528 a

Although not a precision instrument, this transistor tester should nonetheless prove a useful aid for checking the quality of 'job lots' of transistors. The circuit will determine whether or not a transitor is defective, and whether the current gain of the transistor puts it in the class of 'A'-type transistors (current gain 140...270), 'B'-type transistors (270...500), or 'C'-type transistors (greater than 500).

To test for example an NPN transistor, the device is inserted in the appropriate socket (TUT = transistor under test) and S2 switched to position C. If LED D2 lights up, the transistor is type C, if the LED remains out then S2 should be set to position B, or, if this fails to have any effect, to position A. In each case the position of S2 in which the LED lights up indicates the class of transistor. If the LED fails to light even in position A, then it is defective, or has a current gain of less than 140, which for small signal tran-

sistors means that they are basically unusable. The base current to the transistor under test can be interrupted by means of pushbutton switch S1. If the LED does not go out, it means a short exists between collector and emitter of the transistor.

The operation of the circuit is quite simple: The transistor under test receives a base current of 10 A via R1. Assuming the transistor is not defective, this results in a voltage drop across R2, R4, and depending upon the position of S2, portion of this voltage is compared with a fixed reference voltage by IC1. The operation of the right hand side of the circuit is virtually identical, except that it is arranged for PNP transistors.

The circuit can be powered by battery.

R. Stor

'De luxe' transistor tester

Like the previous circuit, this transistor tester will indicate whether the current gain of the transistor under test is that of a class 'A'-, class 'B'-

or class 'C' type. The circuit will also determine whether or not the transistor is defective. The advantage of this design, however, is that the

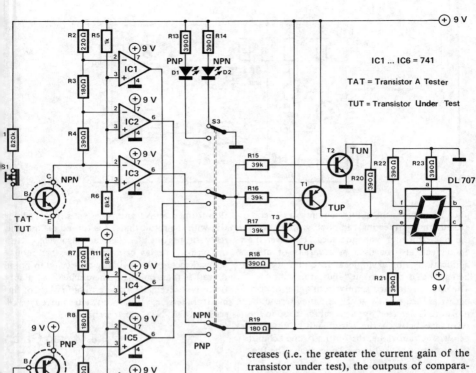

79528 - b

class of transistor is automatically determined and shown directly on a seven-segment display. The operation of the circuit is in many respects similar to its predecessor. Depending upon the current gain of the device under test, a certain DC voltage is dropped across resistors R2...R4 in the case of NPN transistors, or across R7...R9 in the case of PNP transistors. As this voltage in-

creases (i.e. the greater the current gain of the transistor under test), the outputs of comparators IC1...IC3 (IC4...IC6 for PNP transistors) will go low in turn. The output state of the three comparators is decoded by R15...R19, T1, T2 and T3, such that 'A', 'B', 'C' or 'F' appears on the seven-segment display. 'F' indicates a defective transistor, and is also obtained if no transistor is connected in circuit, or if the pushbutton switch in the base lead of the transistor is pressed (opened). If that is not the case, the transistor has an emitter-collector short.

S3 is used to switch between NPN and PNP types.

The display is a common-anode type.

R. Storn

128 Moisture sensor

When the circuit shown here detects the presence of moisture, it causes a reed relay to drop out. The relay can be used to disconnect a piece of equipment from its voltage supply, thereby eliminating the possibility of electrical shock.

The original application for the circuit was in an underwater camera which employed an electronic shutter. In the event of ingress of water

137

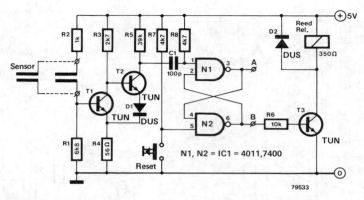

79533

into the camera, the shutter circuit was disconnected, thus protecting the photographer from the risk of a high voltage shock. However the circuit can also be used in a variety of other applications, for example a 'leak detector' for boats, or as a 'dry-washing' indicator, etc.

The sensor is formed simply from a pair of copper wires held slightly apart, and the presence of moisture is detected by the resultant drop in the resistance between the wires. When this falls below a certain value, the output of the Schmitt trigger formed by T1 and T2 goes high. The flip-flop formed by N1 and N2 is thus triggered via C1, with the result that T3 is turned off and the relay drops out. The circuit also allows the option of the relay being pulled in when moisture is detected. R6 is simply connected to point A, rather than point B. The circuit is of a sufficiently 'universal' character that in place of the moisture sensor, virtually any alternative type of sensor (LDR, NTC etc.) can be used.

J.M. van Galen

129 2 switches - 2 lamps - 1 wire

When housewiring, the addition of an extra switch and light to an existing circuit using the same power supply point would not normally cause any problems. However, the situation can arise where it is not possible to 'run' an extra cable between the additional switch and light thereby making it impractical to fit them.

The circuit described here is a simple but effective method of solving this problem by replacing the missing wire with a little ingenuity.

It will be seen from figure 1 that diodes D1 and D2 ensure that switch S1 controls lamp La1, whilst S2 controls lamp La2. The half-wave rectified mains voltage is partially smoothed by capacitors C1 and C2, so that an RMS voltage of approximately 240 V appears across the lamps, which therefore burn at normal intensity. The value of these capacitors is determined by the

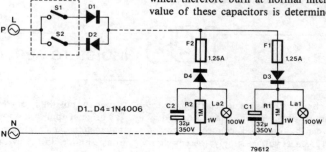

79612

power rating of the lamps used. The appropriate value can be calculated by using the following equation:

$$C_X = 32 \cdot \frac{P_X}{100}$$

where C_X is the new value of the capacitor (in μF) and P_X the power rating (in W) of the corresponding lamp.

W. Richter

130 Car anti-theft protection

The circuit described here is based on an unusual method of deterring a possible car thief. Shortly after it is started, an engine fault is simulated. Restarting gives the same result suggesting that the car may be more trouble than it is worth.

The actual circuit is extremely simple. A 555 timer provides a delay of roughly 5 seconds. The normally closed contact of the relay is connected in the lead from the ignition switch to the ignition coil. Switch S1, which is used to arm the circuit, should of course be hidden.

When power is supplied to the circuit (via the ignition switch), the relay contact is initially closed and the engine will start. After the delay period provided by the 555 has elapsed, the relay contact is opened and the ignition coil is switched

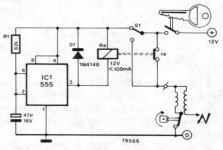

out of circuit. The delay period can be altered as desired by selecting different values for R1 or C1.

B.H.J. Bennink

131 Frequency multiplier

There may be occasions when it is required to measure low frequencies with a high degree of resolution. The circuit presented here is intended as a frequency multiplier for just this purpose which offers a resolution of 0.1 Hz with a fast measuring time.

A block diagram of the frequency multiplier is shown in figure 1. As can be seen, this configuration bears more than a passing resemblance to the (by now) fairly common PLL frequency synthesiser. However, in this instance it is the division ratio which is fixed and not the input (or reference) frequency. The VCO frequency is divided by 100 and then compared with the input frequency in a phase comparator. The resulting phase difference creates a DC signal which is used to correct the VCO frequency. This means that the VCO output frequency will be exactly 100 times that of the input.

In the circuit diagram of figure 2, the input fre-

1

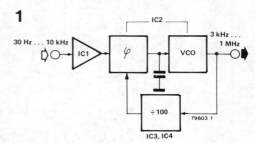

quency is first amplified by IC1 before being fed to the phase locked loop, IC2. The VCO output is divided by 100 by the two decade counters IC3 and IC4 whereupon its phase is compared with that of the input signal in the PLL itself. The VCO output frequency is fed to the meter via the inverter formed by N2. Switch S1 is included so that the overall frequency range of 30 Hz...

2

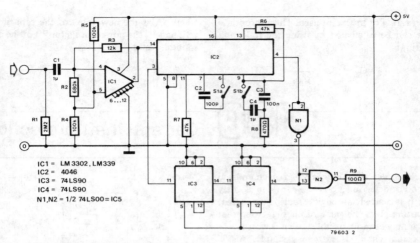

IC1 = LM 3302, LM 339
IC2 = 4046
IC3 = 74 LS 90
IC4 = 74 LS 90
N1, N2 = 1/2 74 LS00 = IC5

79603 2

10 kHz can be split into two separate ranges, namely 30 Hz...300 Hz and 200 Hz...10 kHz. The input sensitivity is quoted as being around 25 mV, and the output voltage is approximately 4.5 Vp-p. Power supply requirements are 7-18 V at around 30 mA.

H. Rol

132 Sinewave oscillator

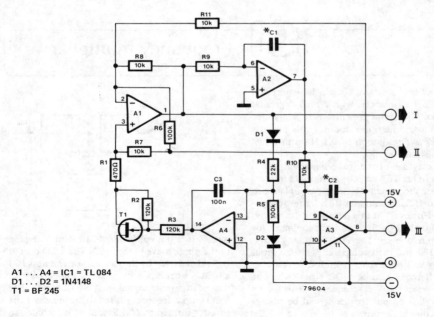

A1 ... A4 = IC1 = TL 084
D1 ... D2 = 1N4148
T1 = BF 245

* see text

140

Under certain conditions if the output of a selective filter is fed back to the input a sinewave oscillator is produced. In itself, the idea is not new, but the way in which it is realised in the circuit shown here is original.

The output of the state variable filter formed by A1...A3, R7...R11, C1 and C2 is fed back (from the output of A2) to the input (left hand side of R7). The amplitude of the output signal is stabilised by the action of FET T1, which in conjunction with R1 forms a voltage-controlled attenuator. The control voltage is derived from the output of A1 via a diode-resistor network and the integrator round A4.

The sinewave signal is available at the outputs of A1, A2 and A3. Since A2 and A3 are connected as integrators, i.e. as lowpass filters, the distortion at output III will be lower than that at output I.

The integrators have unity gain at the resonant frequency of the circuit.

The desired value of C1 and C2 can be calculated by:

$$C1 = C2 = \frac{16}{f}$$

where f is in kilohertz and C is in nanofarad.

G. Schmidt

---

133 Digital frequency synthesiser

A frequency range of 0.1 Hz to 999.9 kHz, a choice of CMOS or TTL output levels, and an accuracy/stability which is limited only by that of the crystal oscillator − these are the main features of the digital frequency synthesiser shown here.

As can be seen from the block diagram in figure 1, the heart of the circuit is formed by a phase locked loop (PLL). In principle such a PLL circuit can be likened to an op-amp connected with feedback, such that the output voltage of the op-amp varies to keep the voltage at both inputs the same; the PLL circuit varies the *frequency* of the output signal, so that the frequency of both input signals remain the same. If the output frequency is divided by a factor N, and then fed

back to one of the PLL inputs, the frequency of the PLL output signal will be exactly N times that of the *other* input signal. Thus all we have to do is ensure that the latter is a stable reference signal, and we have an output whose frequency is equally stable but is N times the reference frequency.

The next step is to provide for the division factor, N, to be made variable, with the result that the frequency of the output signal can also be varied. By including a divide-by-1000 counter, which can be switched in or out of circuit, the frequency range of the output signal can be extended down to as low as 0.1 kHz. Finally, output buffers which amplify the output to both TTL and CMOS levels give the circuit a more

1

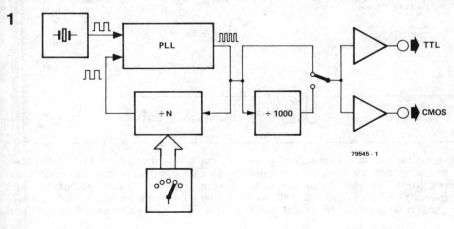

79545 · 1

'universal' character.

The complete circuit diagram of the digital frequency synthesiser is shown in figure 2. The reference signal is provided by a 3.2768 MHz crystal which is divided by a factor of 2^{15} (= 32768) by IC5 and IC6, so that a signal whose frequency is exactly 100 Hz is fed to one input of the PLL IC (IC7). The frequency divider for the PLL output is formed by IC8...IC11. The desired division ratio (N), and hence the output frequency, is set up on the decade switches, S3...S6. The output of AND gate N10 provides the other input signal to the PLL, and due to the action of the PLL, the frequency of this signal remains constant at 100 Hz.

The operation of the phase locked loop is dependent upon the value of the capacitor connected between pins 6 and 7 of the IC. Since the output frequency of the PLL can be varied over a fairly wide range, it is necessary to ensure that the capacitor value can also be varied with frequency. This is done via electronic switches ES2 and ES3, which connect either one or two extra capacitors

in parallel with C4. Control signals for these switches are derived, via suitable logic gating, from the decade switches, S3...S6.

The divide-by-1000 counter is formed by decade counters IC12...IC14. Depending upon the position of the range switch S1, the figure set up on S3...S6 will be in either Hz or kHz.

The output buffers are formed by means of inverters and a pair of balanced emitter followers. The outputs are short-circuit-proof. An additional electronic switch, ES1, is included to ensure that there is no output signal when the decade switches are set to 000.0. LED D1 lights up when the PLL is locked on, and thus provides a visual indication that the output frequency is correct.

The circuit requires two supply voltages: 15 V unstabilised, and 5 V stabilised. The unstabilised supply can safely be increased slightly. For example, two nine volt batteries connected in series will prove quite suitable.

R. Dürr and D. Hackspiel

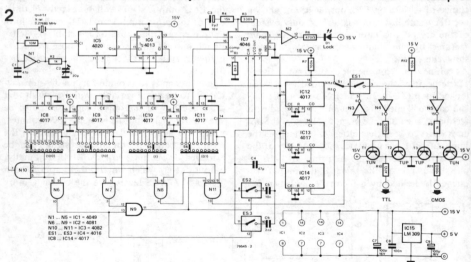

2

134 Dwell meter

Checking and adjusting the dwell angle of a contact breaker is really no problem − provided you have a good dwell meter. By 'good' we mean that it must be accurate and linear, and work over a large range of ambient temperatures. The

circuit described here meets these specifications. It is intended for use in combination with a multimeter (500 μA f.s.d.), although any other 500 μA instrument can also be used, of course. The dwell angle is measured in % (0...100%). If

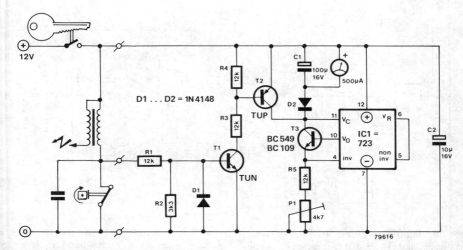

a reading in degrees is required, the actual reading must be multiplied by 3.6 and divided by the number of cylinders in the engine.

The circuit could hardly be simpler. The most important section is a constant-current source, consisting of T3 and a voltage-regulator IC (IC1). The extremely stable (and temperature-independent) reference voltage provided by the IC at pin 6 is connected to the non-inverting input of a differential amplifier inside the chip; the inverting input is connected to the emitter of T3. The IC will now adjust its output voltage (V_O) so that the emitter of T3 is maintained equal to the reference voltage. The result will be obvious: a constant voltage, independent of temperature, across a fixed resistance (R5 + P1) must produce an equally constant current. Since the base current of T3 is negligible, the collector current is equal to the (highly constant) emitter current. So far, so good.

The rest of the circuit either allows this constant current to pass through the meter, or else it

doesn't... When the contact breaker is open T1 and T2 will conduct, shorting out the meter circuit. As soon as the points close, T1 and T2 will turn off. The constant current determined by T3 now flows through the meter, charging C1 at the same time. As the points open and close at rapid intervals, an average voltage is developed across C1 and the meter. This voltage is proportional to the 'duty-cycle' of the breaker points: the longer the points remain closed (the larger the dwell angle, in other words), the larger the voltage across C1 will be — giving a correspondingly higher reading on the meter.

The calibration procedure is like the circuit: simplicity itself. After connecting the supply and shorting the input (R1 to supply common), P1 is adjusted for full scale deflection of the meter (100%). After all, a shorted input corresponds to a dwell angle of 100%.

J. Becela

135 Automatic voltage prescaler

If one wants to measure a voltage which is greater than the range (full-scale deflection) of a meter, there are two things which can be done. On the one hand, the input voltage can be reduced to an acceptable value by employing a voltage divider. This is tantamount to 'compressing' the entire range of voltages to be

measured. Alternatively we can arrange for the meter scale to cover only a certain portion of the total range of input voltages, depending upon the amplitude of the input signal. For example, with a voltage of 26 V, a 10 V meter will 'look at' the 20 V - 30 V range, and a reading of 6 V will be obtained. The circuit described here performs

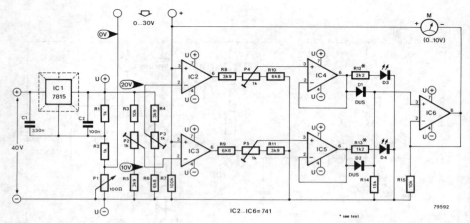

the function of 'prescaling' a 10 V meter automatically, and can be used to measure input voltages between 0 and 30 V.

With the aid of IC2 and IC3, the input voltage is compared with a reference voltage of 10 and 20 V respectively. Depending upon which comparator outputs go high, further reference voltages are fed via buffers IC4 and IC5 to diodes D1 and D2. The result is that a voltage which is equal to the greater of the two reference voltages minus the forward voltage drop of the diode, appears on the non-inverting input of IC6. The other diode remains reverse-biased. Since IC6 is connected as a voltage follower, the meter will thus show the difference between the original input voltage and the offset (reference) voltage of either 0, 10 or 20 V. LEDs D3 and D4 provide a visual indication of which scale (0...10 V, 10...20 V or 20...30 V) the meter is switched to. The brightness of the LEDs can be varied as desired by altering the values of R12 and R13.

Any type of meter with a 10 V fullscale deflec-

tion (e.g. a moving coil type provided with a suitable series resistor) can be used. However one should bear in mind that the current flowing through the meter forms a load to the remainder of the circuit. Thus the higher the impedance of the meter the better.

P1 is included to compensate for the fact that the op-amps cannot swing fully negative. This potentiometer is best adjusted by shorting the input of the circuit and adjusting the meter for zero deflection. To adjust the remaining potentiometers a 10 and 20 V reference voltage is required. The procedure is as follows: with an input voltage of 10 V, P2 is adjusted such that D4 is just on the point of lighting up. P5 is adjusted such that a zero deflection reading is obtained on the meter when D4 lights up. With a 20 V input, P3 and P4 are then adjusted in a similar fashion.

P. Sieben and J.P. Stevens

136 Bio-control

The growing awareness of the contributory role which stress plays in causing illness has led to increased interest in various forms of 'autogenic' training as a means of promoting relaxation. In particular, different types of 'bio-feedback' circuits have become popular, the idea being that certain physiological functions (heartbeat, body temperature, brain activity) can be monitored and brought under the conscious control of the

subject.

The circuit described here operates on the principle of monitoring skin resistance as a measure of how tense the subject is. The same approach is used in so-called lie detectors, however in that case it is the skilled interpretation of the subject's responses to a variety of both innocuous and pointed questions which is important.

The description of the circuit is as follows: vari-

1

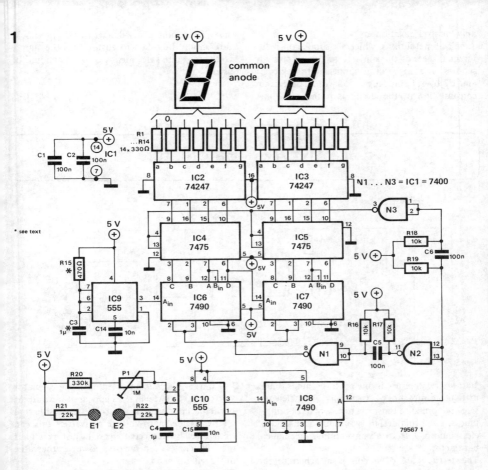

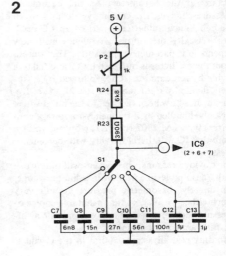

ations in skin resistance (between electrodes E1 and E2) vary the frequency of the oscillator built round a 555 timer (IC10). The output of the oscillator is fed to a 7490 divider (IC8), which in turn controls the reset inputs of the counter formed by IC6 and IC7. The result is that the period between successive pulses from IC10 determines the number of clock pulses fed to this counter from a second oscillator (IC9). The outputs of the counter are decoded and displayed on a pair of 7-segment displays, thereby providing a numerical indication of the subject's relative tenseness.

The frequency of the second oscillator, which is also formed by a 555 timer, is determined by C3 and R15. By incorporating the circuit shown in figure 2, several different clock rates can be chosen, thereby allowing the sensitivity of the circuit to be varied to suit different circumstances. Initially P1 should be adjusted to a suitably 'neutral' position.

A pair of metal rings, which are slipped onto different fingers of the subject, will prove suitable sensors. The rings can be connected to points E1 and E2 by suitable lengths of wire. The current consumption of the circuit is roughly 400 mA max. To eliminate any danger of electric shock, care should be taken to ensure that the supply voltage is quite safe, ideally a battery should be used.

J. Mulke

137 Barometer

L: a) 100 turns
   b) 25 turns
   ⌀ 0,3mm Cu Em

79598

Barometric pressure is one of those things that is difficult to measure electronically. A sufficiently sensitive pressure sensor is not easy to obtain — unless, as in this design, you add some kind of electronic pickup to a conventional mechanical barometer.

The ferrite core of a coil is attached to the 'drum' in the barometer. As the barometric pressure changes, the core moves to and fro in the coil. Since the latter is part of an LC oscillator circuit, the output frequency will now depend on barometric pressure. The output from the oscillator is buffered by T2 and fed to a divide-by-ten counter (IC1), followed by a further divide-by-eight counter (IC2). The frequency has now been reduced to the point where it can be handled by a frequency-to-voltage converter, type LM 2907 (IC3). The output voltage from this IC will therefore vary with barometric pressure.

For obvious reasons, this system will only work with reasonable linearity over a limited range. Fortunately, barometric pressure doesn't vary much either ($\pm 5\%$), so that a suitable choice of pressure sensor, core and coil will provide a sufficiently accurate 'barometer'.

The only real adjustment point in the circuit is P1. Initially, this is adjusted until the oscillator starts — a voltage will then appear at the output. If the oscillator frequency range is outside that of the frequency-to-voltage converter, this can sometimes be corrected by re-adjusting P1. If the frequency is too far off, however, the value of C2 will have to be changed.

The preset at the output (P2) is used to adjust the output level as required. A digital or analogue millivoltmeter can be connected at this point.

Y. Nijssen

Editorial note:
At first sight, there doesn't seem to be much point in stripping an existing barometer in order to connect an electrical pointer instrument instead of the mechanical pointer. However, having an electrical voltage available that is proportional to barometric pressure opens a whole range of possibilities. Just to name one: What about designing a home weather-forecasting computer?

146

138 Electronic weathercock

The disadvantage of most wind direction meters is the need for complicated mechanical drive systems which are necessarily prone to wear. The unit described here is intended to offer a solution to this problem. A disc which contains a number of slots is attached to the spindle of the weather vane. A light source is mounted above the disc, and a row of 3 light dependent resistors (LDRs) is situated below the disc — as shown in figure 1. Which LDRs are illuminated will depend upon the position of the disc, and therefore upon the direction of the wind. If the slots in the disc are correctly positioned (see figure 2), the information from the LDRs can be coded into BCD format, such that each of the eight main compass points will correspond to a particular BCD code. By means of a BCD-decimal converter, the resultant information, and hence the direction of the wind, can then be displayed on a circle of LEDs. The 'electronics' of the unit are shown in the circuit diagram of figure 3. If no light falls upon an LDR, the associated transistor is turned off and the input of IC1 is pulled down to 0 V via the 470 Ω resistor. As soon as sufficient

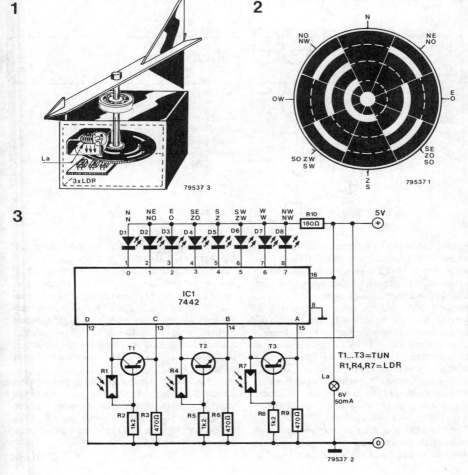

147

Table 1.

A	B	C	D	wind direction	LED
0	0	0	0	north	D1
1	0	0	0	north-east	D2
0	1	0	0	east	D3
1	1	0	0	south-east	D4
0	0	1	0	south	D5
1	0	1	0	south-west	D6
0	1	1	0	west	D7
1	1	1	0	north-west	D8

light falls on an LDR to turn the transistor on, however, the corresponding input of IC1 is taken high. Thus the state of the three LDRs is translated into a BCD code applied to the inputs of the 7442. Depending upon the combination of logic '0' s and '1' s at the four inputs, the 7442 takes one of its outputs low, with the result that the corresponding LED lights. The BCD code for each of the eight compass points is listed in table 1.

D. Maurer

Editorial note:
If the disc should come to rest exactly between two compass points, e.g. between south and south-east, then the effect of stray light may cause the wrong code to be presented to IC1, and the NW LED will light up. Therefore, it would be better to use the 'Gray code', i.e. 000 = N; 100 = NE; 110 = E; 010 = SE; 011 = S; 111 = SW; 101 = W; 001 = NW.

139 Slave flash

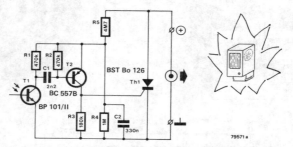

79571 a

With the aid of this simple circuit a normal flash unit can be converted into a 'slave' flash. In this way it is possible to take photographs using a number of separate flash units, without getting tangled up in a confusion of cables.

The slave flash does not require a separate supply voltage, but rather draws its current from the contact used to trigger the master flash. There is normally some 150 to 200 V on this contact, and this is divided down by R4 and R5 to provide a suitable low supply voltage. C2 is an AC-decoupling/reservoir capacitor. Since the current consumption of the circuit is not much more than several μ A, the extra drain on the power supply battery will be negligible.

When the light generated by another flash unit falls upon the photo-transistor, a voltage pulse is generated across R1. This is fed via C1 to T2, where it is amplified to a level suitable to trigger the thyristor, and with it, the flash.

The component values have been calculated to ensure that the flash will not be spuriously triggered by, e.g. incandescent lamps, but will react only to other flash units. The circuit is sufficiently sensitive that the master flash need not be focused on the phototransistor; it will react to the reflected light. It may be necessary, however, to shield the phototransistor from other sources of intense light.

Any 8 A/400 V thyristor should prove suitable, although it may prove necessary to increase the value of C2 slightly (since this capacitor supplies the greatest portion of the gate current). The socket for the flash unit cable can best be made using a flash extension cable.

F. Schäffler

140 Photo-flash delay

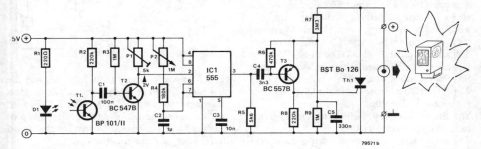

79571 b

One of the more specialised areas of photography is the use of ultra-short exposure times to capture events occuring at high speed. Everyone will have seen the results of this technique at one time or another: a light bulb in the process of disintegrating under the impact of a hammer, or, as in the picture shown here, a splash of water. Photographs of this type can be taken fairly simply by employing an 'open-lens' approach, i.e. the photo is taken in a darkened room and the lens of the camera is opened before the subject is illuminated. The lighting is provided by a high-speed (electronic) flash unit capable of providing extremely short exposure times.

One problem with this method is determining the exact moment at which the flash gun should be triggered. Because of the extremely short time intervals involved, this can really only be done electronically. In the case of the picture shown here, the drop of water was sensed by a photoelectric cell, which, with the aid of the following circuit, provided a predetermined delay before triggering the flash.

An LED (D1) and phototransistor T1 are used to form the light gate. When the light from the LED is interrupted, there is a sharp rise in voltage across R2. This is fed via T2 to the trigger input of the 555 timer (IC1). When the delay period provided by the timer has elapsed, a negative-going pulse appears at the output of this IC (i.e. pin 3), with the result that T3 and the thyristor are turned on, and the flash is triggered.

Any 0.8 A/400 V thyristor will prove suitable, however it may be necessary to increase the value of C5 slightly. The DC bias voltage on the collector of T2 should be adjusted to 2 V by means of P1.

With the aid of P2, the delay provided by the circuit can be varied between approximately 0.25 and 1.3 s. By altering several component values the range of possible delays can also be varied. The delay time is given by 1.1 x R x C2, where R is the series connection of P2 and R4. The minimum permissible value for R2 is 1 k. As one might expect, the light gate is the section of the circuit which will present the most difficulty when it comes to construction. Whatever arrangement is chosen will depend largely on individual circumstances, however the sensitivity of the circuit is greatest when the LED and phototransistor are mounted as close together as possible. Care should be taken to ensure that light from the LED cannot reach the lens of the camera.

F. Schäffler

141 Current dumping amplifier

The circuit exploits the fact that, due to the effect of the four passive components, R2, R3, L and C shown in figure 1, the non-linear characteristic of the output stage becomes unimportant. Thus it is possible to use a Class-B output stage (i.e. the output transistors are biased to

149

their cut-off points so that there is no quiescent output current) with all the advantages and none of the disadvantages (crossover distortion) of that configuration.

The circuit shown in figure 2 functions on the above described current dumping principle. According to the designer it is capable of delivering 100 W into 4 Ω with a claimed harmonic distortion of 0.006% at 1 kHz and 60 W. If one possesses the equipment to make accurate distortion measurements, C3 can be replaced by a 22 pF variable capacitor, and the latter adjusted for minimum distortion.

The circuit also has a useful extra facility in the form of a dummy load (R9).

The output stage is driven (via driver transistors T2 and T5) by transistors T1 and T4, which are connected in series with the positive and negative

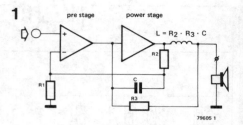

supply lines respectively of IC1. In this way the slew rate of the 741 is improved. If, however, a faster op-amp is desired (e.g. the LF 357), then the value of R4 and R7 should be altered to provide the correct quiescent current for the IC, so that the output stage draws no current.

G. Schmidt

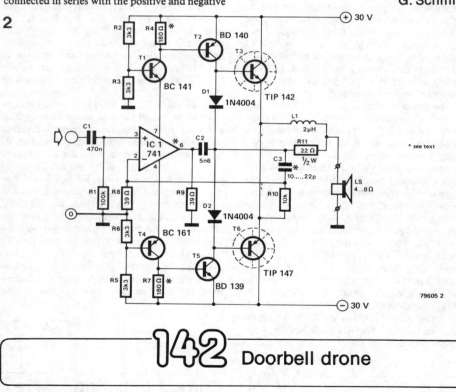

142 Doorbell drone

There seems to be no end to the variety of different sounding doorbells which people are prepared to design. Everything from the Hallelujah Chorus to the chimes of Big Ben have been simulated for the entertainment of visiting door-to-door salesmen.

The circuit presented here produces a sound which is somewhat akin so that of bagpipes, and while not exactly signalling the death knell of original bagpipes, should prove popular north of the border.

The circuit is also intended to foil ill-mannered

1

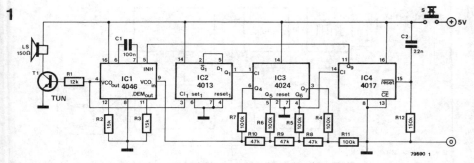

79590 1

2

79590 2

visitors who insist on pressing the doorbell for an annoying long time, since the bell automatically cuts out after approximately two seconds.

As can be seen from the circuit diagram in figure 1, very little in the way of components is required to build this 'exclusive' doorbell. A 4046 phase locked loop IC (IC1) is used as a voltage controlled oscillator with a nominal frequency of around 800 Hz determined by the values of R3 and C1. The actual frequency of the oscillator is controlled by feeding the output signal to one half of a dual flip-flop (IC2) which is connected as a divide-by-two counter, and then to a binary ripple counter. The ladder network of resistors R4...R11 provides a staircase voltage, which is fed back to the control voltage input (pin 9) of IC1, thereby producing the 'bagpipe' effect. At the end of the count cycle IC4 takes the inhibit input of IC1 high, thus ensuring that

the 'bagpipes' do not continue to sound if the bellpush is held down. R12 and C2 automatically reset IC4 the next time the bellpush is depressed.

S. Halom

Editorial Note:
Although the original circuit as shown in figure 1 will prove an effective remedy against over enthusiastic bell-pushers, unfortunately it does not take into account what will happen if the push-button switch (S) is only depressed for a brief moment. Since releasing the switch interrupts the supply voltage to the circuit, the bagpipes will be cut off in their prime! To forestall a flood of letters from incensed Scotsmen we include the following possible modifications. As CMOS ICs draw very little current they can be provided with a continuous supply voltage. By using the other flip-flop in IC2, the circuit can be modified to ensure that the entire 'melody' will be heard even if the bellpush is only depressed momentarily.

The circuit of figure 1 should be altered as follows:
– switch S is replaced by a link
– C2 and R12 are omitted
– the connection between pin 11 of IC4 and pin 5 of IC1 is broken
The circuit should then be connected as shown in figure 2.

---

143   Digital contrast meter

When enlarging photographs, two factors are of prime importance, the required exposure time, which is determined by the density of the negative, and the contrast of the negative. The latter determines which grade of paper should be used

in order to obtain a print with good overall tonal contrast. The contrast of the negative is basically the difference between the lightest and darkest portions of the exposed film. If we take the second log of this difference, we obtain the contrast

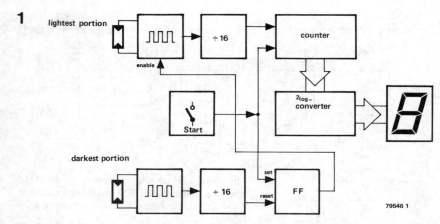

1

ratio of the negative. Thus, for example, if the lightest part of the negative lets through 8 times as much light as the darkest part, the contrast ratio of the negative will be 3 ($2^3 = 8$). The circuit employs two light dependent resistors as sensors, and displays the contrast of the negative directly on a seven-segment display. The operation of the circuit is illustrated in the block diagram of figure 1. The amount of light falling

upon the LDRs determines the frequency of the squarewave generators to which they are connected. The output of both oscillators are fed to a divide-by-sixteen counter. The pulses for the topmost counter (for the lightest portion of the negative) are counted for a period which is determined by the frequency of the signal from the lower counter. The result is that the value stored in the subsequent binary counter represents the

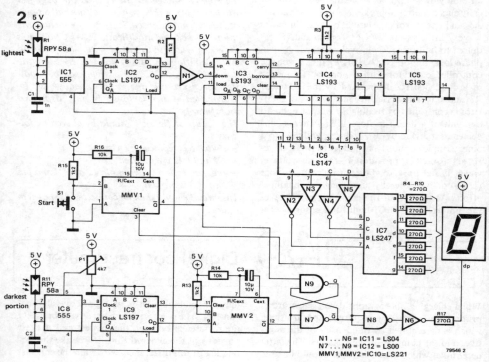

2

152

ratio of the two clock generator frequencies, and hence the ratio of the lightest and darkest portions of the negative. The contents of the 'ratio' counter, are then fed to the $\log_2$ converter, the output of which is decoded and displayed. A measurement cycle is initiated by closing the start switch, which sets the flip-flop and resets the counter.

The complete circuit diagram of the contrast meter is shown in figure 2. With the exception of the two clock oscillators, in which 555 timers are used, the circuit is low power Schottky TTL. IC2 and IC9 are the divide-by-16 counters, whilst the binary 'ratio' counter consists of IC3, IC4 and IC5. This counter uses negative logic, i.e. it begins with all outputs high, and then counts down. Thus at the start of each measurement cycle, a 'load' pulse, and not as one might expect, a 'reset' pulse, is applied to the counter. The paralleled data inputs of the counter are all held high, and the pulses to be counted are fed to the 'down' input. The reason for adopting this arrangement is the $\log_2$ converter, which also uses negative logic. This converter is formed by IC6, a decimal-BCD priority encoder. This IC recognises the highest order bit in the input signal which is active, i.e. logic 0, and outputs the BCD equivalent of that bit's 'weight'. For example, assume the counter holds the binary code for the number 8 (base 10). All bits will be logic 1, with the exception of 13 (remember, we are working with negative logic). IC6 recognises that the highest order bit which is logic 0, is the

third bit, therefore it outputs the BCD code for 3. As we have already established, 3 is $\log_2$ of 8, thus the conversion is complete.

The divide-by-sixteen counter, IC9, is followed by a monostable, which provides a reset pulse to the flip-flop formed by N6 and N7 at the end of each measurement cycle. The set pulse is provided by a second monostable, which is triggered by the start switch, S1. The decimal point on the seven-segment display is lit during each measurement cycle.

Since IC6 uses negative logic, its output signals must be inverted (by N2...N5) before they can be fed to the BCD-seven-segment decoder, IC7. The display is a common-anode type, e.g. HP 5082-7750, FND 557. Any type of LDR which is intended for measurement purposes, as opposed to switching applications, can be used. The type named in the circuit diagram is particularly suitable.

The circuit should be adjusted such that, as far as possible, the frequency of the two 555 oscillators is the same when identical amounts of light are falling on both LDRs.

The LDRs should therefore be laid upon a surface which is evenly illuminated. Coarse adjustment is performed by varying the values of C1 and C2, whilst fine adjustment − which in many cases will be all that is required − is carried out with the aid of P1.

J. van Dijk

144 Emergency flight controller

When flying radio controlled model aeroplanes there is always the chance that a fault will occur in either the transmitter or the receiver, and that the plane will no longer obey the control signals. If one is fortunate, the model will fall near the operator, however it may equally well happen that the plane will remain in flight for a considerable distance, and that the last the unfortunate owner will see of his model is it disappearing over the horizon! The circuit described here is designed to prevent the latter possibility, and also attempts to lessen the severity of the crash, by ensuring that the model will assume a glide trajectory.

The circuit reacts to a loss of output from the

receiver. When both transmitter and receiver are functioning normally, the position of the servos is determined by the transmitted control pulses. Depending upon the make of servo, a pulse width of 1.5 ms corresponds to the neutral position, whilst pulse widths of 1 and 2 ms correspond to the extreme positions of the servo. When the stream of control pulses is interrupted, the three multivibrators in the circuit set the servos to a predetermined position.

Input K4 is connected to the output of the receiver. Inputs K1, K2 and K3 are connected to the receiver servo control outputs for the elevator, rudder and engine throttle respectively, whilst outputs K1, K2 and K3 are connected to

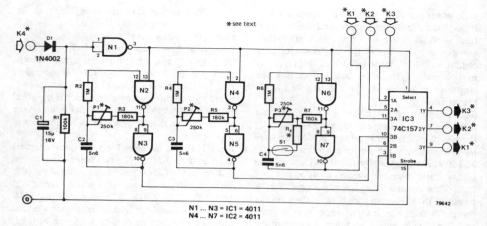

N1 ... N3 = IC1 = 4011
N4 ... N7 = IC2 = 4011

the corresponding servos. As long as control pulses are received via K4, the multiplexer, IC3, ensures that inputs K1, K2 and K3 are connected to the corresponding outputs (and servos). However when the control pulses are interrupted, the multiplexer switches to the outputs of the three oscillators. The position of P1, P2 and P3 then determine the position of the servo control

horns. A mercury switch is connected across P3 (elevator control). The switch should be mounted such that it will close when the angle of descent is greater than 10°, whereupon the position of the elevator servo will be determined by the value of R_X (10...200 k).

145 FM PLL using CA 3089

The following circuit should prove particularly interesting to those readers considering building their own FM tuner. The novel feature of the circuit is that the well-known CA 3089 IC is not used as a conventional IF amplifier/demodulator, but as part of a phase locked loop. The resulting circuit is slightly more expensive and complicated than the 'standard' amplifier/demodulator circuits, however the results obtained are a significant improvement on those of a 'classical' CA 3089 IF strip.

The circuit is intended as an IF amplifier/demodulator for a double conversion tuner operating at an intermediate frequency of 455 kHz. When using a PLL circuit for FM demodulation the S/N ratio of the demodulated signal is proportional to the ratio of frequency deviation/IF frequency, hence the PLL demodulator should operate at the lower IF of 455 kHz.

Briefly, the circuit functions as follows: The IF input signal is first fed to C1, which removes any high frequency signal components which might

affect the operation of the PLL. The exact value of C1 will depend upon the mixer circuit which converts the 10.7 MHz output of the front end to the desired IF frequency of 455 kHz. If the input signal is sufficiently 'clean' then lowpass filtering can be omitted. The CA 3089 amplifies and limits the IF signal to approximately 300 mV, whereupon it is fed to the on-chip quadrature detector. Output voltage U_1 can be used to drive a signal strength meter. The control voltage for the PLL VCO is taken from the AFC output (pin 7) of the IC. The voltage divider formed by R8/R9 is required to set the correct DC bias on pin 5 of IC2. Lowpass filtering of the control signal is provided by R10 and C8.

Largely for reasons of good linearity and high stability, a modern integrated circuit VCO, the NE566, was chosen. However the stability of the VCO is also significantly influenced by the associated frequency-determining components. P1 should preferably be a cermet trimmer, whilst a metal oxide resistor should be used for R11

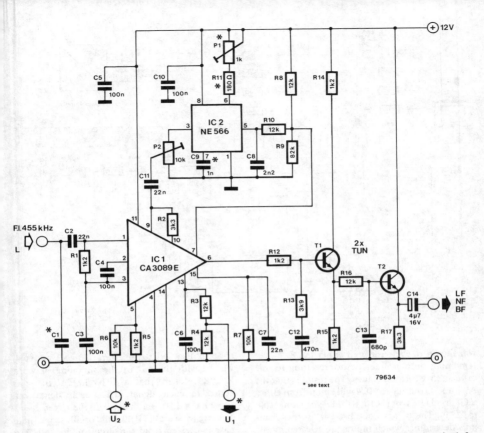

79634

* see text

and a ceramic disc capacitor with extremely low temperature coefficient should be used for C9. With the aid of a variable voltage divider (P2), the squarewave output voltage at pin 3 of IC2 (approximately 5.4 V) is reduced to roughly 0.3 V and then fed back via C11, to the input of the quadrature detector of IC1.

The demodulated output signal is available at pin 6 of the CA 3089. If a squelch (muting) facility is required, this can be realised by feeding a positive control voltage to pin 5 of IC1, thereby suppressing the audio output. Finally, the audio signal is lowpass filtered and this output can be used with virtually any stereo decoder.

J. Deboy

146 Logic analyser

Although the name 'logic analyser' is generally understood to denote a quite different type of circuit, there are good reasons for borrowing the title to describe the electronic switch presented here. The switch is intended to simultaneously display the logic state of a number of test points in a digital circuit on an oscilloscope screen.

The circuit functions as follows: The oscillator formed by N9/N10 generates a clock signal with a frequency of either 1 kHz or 100 kHz, depending upon the position of switch S2. This signal is fed to a counter, IC4, which, depending upon the position of switch S1, can be preset to either '1000' (8), '1010' (10) or '1100' (12). The counter

155

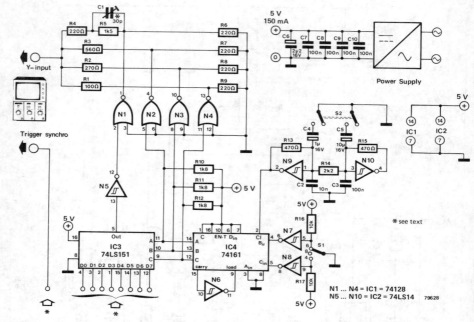

will therefore cycle through either the 8, 6 or 4 remaining output states before resetting to one of the above (preset) values. The result is that the A, B and C outputs of IC4 will count from either '000' to '111', from '010' to '111', or from '100' to '111'. The binary code present on these outputs determines which inputs are selected by the multiplexer, IC3. The multiplexer scans the inputs in turn, and transfers the input signal to the output. Depending upon the position of S1, therefore, 4, 6 or all 8 inputs will be scanned. To ensure that each input signal is displayed 'separately' on the screen, the corresponding binary code is also fed to inverters N2, N3 and N4, which, with the aid of the summing network R1...R4, ensure that a different DC offset is added to each signal. Thus each signal will appear at a different 'height' on the screen.

The trigger signal (TR) for the oscilloscope timebase is derived from the circuit under test. For slower scopes in particular, variable capacitor C1 can be adjusted to obtain optimal picture quality.

P.C. Demmer

147 Battery monitor

Only three LEDs are used to give an indication of the car (or boat) battery condition. The LEDs light as follows:

D3	< 12 V
D3 + D4	12...13 V
D4	13...14 V
D4 + D5	> 14 V

Preset P2 sets the voltage above which D3 goes out (13 V); P1 sets the point at which D4 lights

(12 V); finally, P1 sets the voltage above which D5 lights (14 V). The calibration procedure is rather critical, and will have to be repeated several times since the various adjustments affect each other.

The photo shows the author's prototype. All components are mounted in a small plastic tube, with the LEDs at one end and a 'cigarette lighter' plug at the other. The unit can then easily be plugged into the corresponding socket on the dashboard for a quick check of battery condition. If the suggested colours are used for the various LEDs, red will correspond to 'battery low'; yellow (with or without red) indicates 'battery normal'; and green will normally light when the battery is 'on charge'.

S. Jacobsson

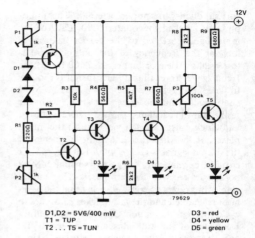

D1,D2 = 5V6/400 mW
T1 = TUP
T2 ... T5 = TUN

D3 = red
D4 = yellow
D5 = green

148 Analogue frequency meter

This circuit for a frequency meter offers six ranges: 100 Hz, 1 kHz, 10 kHz, 100 kHz, 1 MHz and 10 MHz. Switching between ranges is performed automatically, and the display is analogue.

The input signal is first amplified to TTL level by means of IC1, T2 and N1, whereupon it is fed to a series of a decade dividers (IC3...IC7). Thus

a signal with a frequency between 10 Hz and 100 Hz can be obtained either at the output of N1, or at the output of one of the decade counters. The analogue section of the circuit (MMV1, the moving coil meter and associated components) is designed to produce a full-scale meter deflection for an input signal of 100 Hz.

A multiplexer, IC8, is used to ensure that the

N1,N2 = IC2 = 7413
MMV1,MMV2 = IC9 = 74123

correct divider output is selected. The multiplexer is clocked by counter IC10. Each of the input signals are fed to the output in turn, as long as the frequency of the output signal is lower than 10 Hz or higher than 100 Hz. If the frequency is lower than 10 Hz, then it is too low to keep the retriggerable monostable MMV2 continuously in the triggered state, with the result that the oscillator formed by N2 is started and clock pulses are fed via IC10 to the multiplexer. If, on the other hand, the frequency of the output signal is greater than 100 Hz, MMV1 remains permanently triggered, so that MMV2 no longer receives trigger pulses. This monostable thus resets, thereby ensuring that the oscillator is enabled and the multiplexer continues to cycle through its inputs. Only when the output frequency of the multiplexer is between 10 Hz and 100 Hz is the oscillator stopped, since MMV1 is not triggered sufficiently often to keep MMV2 in the triggered state. The result of stopping the oscillator is that the multiplexer in turn stops at the input which provided the signal of the appropriate frequency. LEDs D5...D10 provide an indication of the range selected.

To calibrate the meter, P3 and P4 should initially be set to the midposition, whilst P1 and P2 are adjusted for maximum and minimum resistance respectively. A 100 Hz signal (with an amplitude of greater than 1 V) is fed to the input of the circuit and P3 adjusted such that the multiplexer begins to cycle through its inputs. This can be verified by checking that the LEDs light up in turn. P2 is now adjusted until the 100 Hz range LED (D5) lights up. P1 is then adjusted for full-scale deflection on the meter. Finally, the circuit can be adjusted for maximum input sensitivity (approximately 10 mV) by means of P4.

H. Bichler

149 D.J. killer

It is possible to distinguish speech from music by virtue of the fact that distinct pauses occur in speech, whereas music is more or less continuous. The DJ killer detects these pauses and mutes the signal whilst the DJ is speaking.

The left and right-channel signals are fed into the two inputs of the unit and are summed at the junction of R14, R15 and R16. For use with a mono radio only one input is required. The summed signal is amplified and limited by two high gain amplifiers IC1 and IC2, and is then fed to two cascaded Schmitt triggers, N1 and N2. The output of N2 is used to drive a retriggerable monostable IC4a, the Q output of which is fed to the input of a second retriggerable monostable IC4b.

So long as a continuous signal is present at the input IC4a will be continuously retriggered by the output signal from N2 and its Q output will remain high. The period of IC4a is adjusted, using P2, to be somewhat less than the average duration of a speech pause, so that during such pauses IC4a will reset. This will cause IC4b to be triggered, switching off the signal for a period which is adjustable by P3. LEDs D1 and D2 indicate the output states of IC4a and IC4b and are used to set up the circuit.

To adjust the circuit P2 is first set to minimum

1

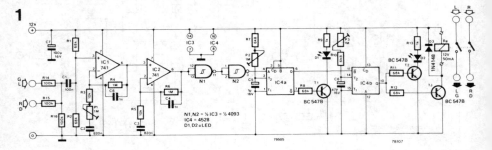

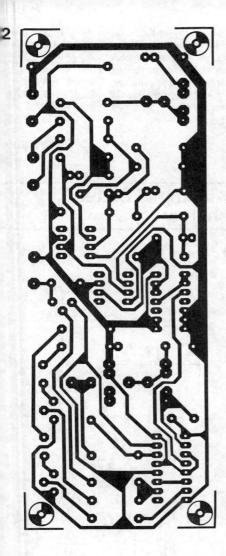

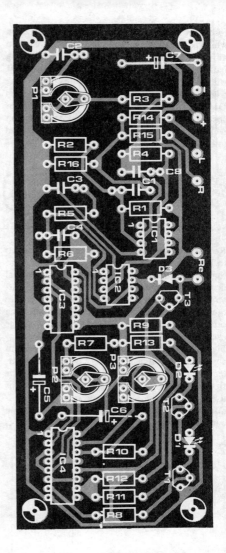

Parts list:

Resistors:
R1, R2, R8, R11, R12 = 68 k
R3, R5 = 10 k
R4, R6 = 1 M
R7, R10 = 6k8
R9, R13 = 1 k
R14, R15, R16 = 100 k
P1, P2, P3 = 1 M

Capacitors:
C1 = 100 n
C2, C3 = 820 n
C4, C8 = 1 n
C5 = 1 µ /16 V
C6 = 47 µ /16 V
C7 = 100 µ /16 V

Semiconductors:
D1, D2 = LED

D3 = 1N4148
IC1, IC2 = 741
IC3 = N1, N2... = 4093
IC4 = 4528
T1, T2, T3 = BC 547B

Miscellaneous:
relay 12 V/50 mA

159

resistance. The radio is then tuned to a station which is transmitting speech and P1 is used to adjust the sensitivity until D1 goes out during pauses. If the sensitivity is set too high then D1 will stay on continuously due to the circuit being triggered by noise, whereas if it is too low then D1 will extinguish during quiet passages of speech. The radio is then tuned to a station which is broadcasting music and P2 is adjusted until D1 stays on continuously.

Finally, the radio is tuned to a speech programme and P3 is adjusted until D2 remains permanently lit during speech.
It should of course be noted that the circuit will suppress only a pure speech signal. It will not, for example, suppress the voice of a DJ talking over the music.

R. Vanwersch

150 Automatic battery charger

Recharging lead-acid batteries is often assumed to be an extremely straightforward matter. And that is indeed the case, assuming that no special demands are being made on the life of the battery. On the other hand, if one wishes to ensure that the battery lasts as long as possible, then certain constraints are placed upon the charge cycle.
Figure 1 illustrates the ideal charge current characteristic for a normal 12 V lead-acid battery which is completely discharged. During the first phase (A – B), a limited charging current is used, until the battery voltage reaches approximately 10 V. This restriction on the charging current is necessary to ensure that the charger is

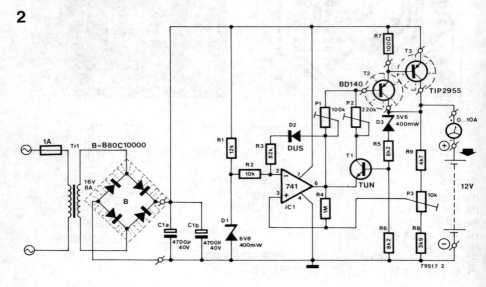

3

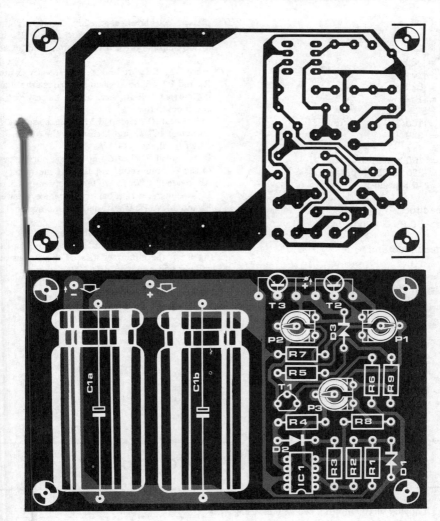

not overloaded (excessive dissipation). For the next phase (C – D), the battery is charged with the '5-hour charging current'. The size of this current is determined by dividing the nominal capacity of the battery in ampere-hours (Ah) by 5. At the end of this period the battery should be charged to 14.4 V, whereupon the final phase (E – F) starts. The battery is charged with a much smaller 'top-up' current, which gradually would decrease to zero if the battery voltage were to reach 16.5 V.

The circuit described here (see figure 2) is intended to provide a charge cycle which follows that described above. If the battery is completely discharged (voltage < 10 V), so little current

flows through D3 that T1 is turned off. The output of IC1 will be low, so that the base currents of T2 and T3, and hence the charging current, are determined solely by the position of P1.

If the battery voltage is between 10 and 14 V, D3 is forward biased and T1 is turned on. The output of IC1 still remains low, so that the charging current is now determined by both P1 and P2. If the wiper voltage of P3 exceeds the zener voltage of D1, then due to the positive feedback via R4, the output voltage of IC1 will swing up to a value determined by the zener voltage of D1 and the forward voltage drop of D2. As a result T1 is turned off and the charge current is once again determined by the position of P1. In contrast to

Parts list

Resistors:
R1 = 12 k
R2 = 10 k
R3 = 82 k
R4 = 1 M
R5, R6 = 8k2
R7 = 100Ω
R8 = 3k9
R9 = 4k7
P1 = 100 k preset
P2 = 220 k...250 k preset
P3 = 10 k preset

Capacitors:
C1a = C1b = 4700µ /40 V

Semiconductors:
T1 = TUN
T2 = BD138, BD140
T3 = TIP2955
D1 = 6V8, 400 mW zener diode
D2 = DUS
D3 = 5V6, 400 mW zener diode
IC1 = 741

Miscellaneous:
Tr = 16 V, 8 A mains transformer
B = B80C10000 bridge rectifier
fuse = 0.5 A slo-blo

phase A – B, however, the higher output voltage of IC1 means that current through P1, and hence the charging current, is reduced accordingly.

Since D2 is forward biased, the effect of resistors R2 and R3 will be to gradually reduce the charging current still further, as the battery voltage continues to rise.

To calibrate the circuit, P3 is adjusted so that the output of IC1 swings high when the output (i.e. battery) voltage is 14.4 V.

By means of P1 the 'top-up' charge current is set to the 20-hour value (capacity of the battery in Ah divided by 20) for voltages between 14.5 and 15 V. Finally, with a battery voltage of between 11 and 14 V, P2 is adjusted for the nominal (5-hour) charging current.

The initial charging current (phase A – B) is set by the value of the 'top-up' current, and depending upon the characteristics of the transistors, will be approximately 30 to 100% greater.

Siemens Components Report
Volume XIII, No. 1 March 1978.

151 Servo amplifier

A high quality servo amplifier can be built using only one IC and a handful of passive components. The SN28654 (Texas Instruments) contains a pulse-width modulator and an output stage that is capable of driving servomotors (see figure 1).

An input pulse at pin 3 is compared to a pulse that is generated by an internal monostable multivibrator (the 'monoflop'). The resultant pulse is stretched (using RC networks and Schmitt triggers) and passed to the output stage and from there to the motor.

The complete circuit is shown in figure 2. Apart from the RC networks (R5/C4 and R8/C5) and some decoupling capacitors, the only external components are the servo-motor and the associ-

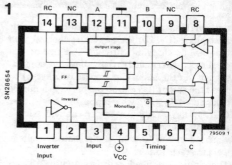

ated servo-potentiometer. This potentiometer controls the timing of the internal monoflop, so that the motor will run until the internal pulse

2

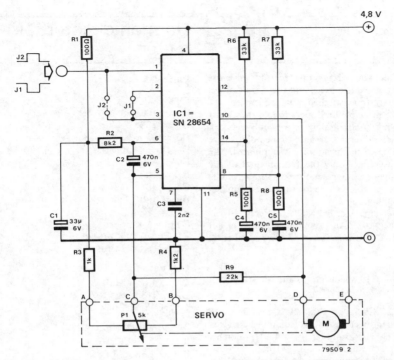

3

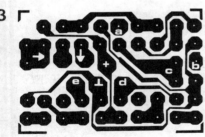
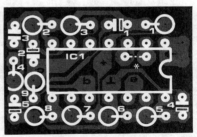

Parts list.

Resistors:
R1, R5, R8 = 100 Ω
R2 = 8k2
R3 = 1 k
R4 = 1k2
R6, R7 = 33 k
R9 = 22 k

Capacitors:
C1 = 33 μ /6 V
C2, C4, C5 = 0.47μ /6 V
C3 = 2n2

Semiconductors:
IC1 = SN 28654

length corresponds to the input pulse – provided the motor is connected the right way round, of course!

The printed circuit board (figure 3) offers the option of including the inverter (between pins 1 and 2) in the circuit if required. This means that either negative or positive input control pulses can be used.

The advantages of this servo amplifier are:
- high output current: 400 mA without external transistors;
- motor control in both directions with a single supply voltage;
- adjustable 'dead zone' (determined by C3);
- power consumption less than 800 mW.

163

Harmonic distortion meter

In the following circuit, in place of transistors J-FET op-amps are used, and the circuit offers the choice of four switched spot frequencies.

The basic principle and operation of the circuit is: applying bootstrapping to a twin-T network the Q of the filter is increased to the point where attenuation of the harmonics is eliminated. The filter thus rejects only the fundamental of the input (sinewave) signal, allowing the harmonic distortion products to be measured or examined on an oscilloscope.

The input signal is fed via C1 directly to the twin-T network. An input buffer stage is not required. Capacitors C6...C13 have a value C, where

$$C = \frac{4.82}{f} \text{ (C is in nanofarads and f in kilohertz),}$$

whilst C2...C5 have a value 2C. Odd values can be obtained by choosing two suitable capacitors in parallel. For example, for a 1 kHz 'notch', 4n82 can be formed by 4n7 + 120 p.

The filter is coarse tuned by P1/P3, and fine tuned by P2/P4. Inexpensive multi-turn trimmer potentiometers of the type used for station pre-set controls in radios and TV's can be employed. When tuning for zero fundamental, the two branches of the network (P1/P2 and P3/P4) should be adjusted alternately.

The distortion signal is available at two outputs,

Parts list

Resistors:

R1 = 100 k
R2 = 33 k
R3 = 27 k
R4, R5 = 1 k
R6 = 10 k
R7 = 2k2
R8 = 18 k
R9 = 1k8
R10 = 12 k
R11 = 1 k
P1, P3 = 10 k preset
P2, P4 = 4k7 preset

Capacitors:

C1 = 1 μ (MKM)
C2a...C13b: see text
C14, C15 = 2μ2/16 V

Semiconductors:

IC1, IC2 = LF356
IC3 = LF356, LF357

Miscellaneous:

S1 = three-pole, multi-way switch

D1 and D2. The signal at D2 is amplified by IC3 so that it is ten times greater than that at D1. Once the filter has been optimally tuned and no further reduction in the fundamental can be

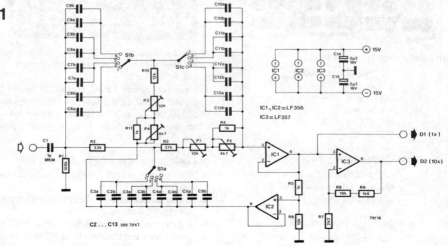

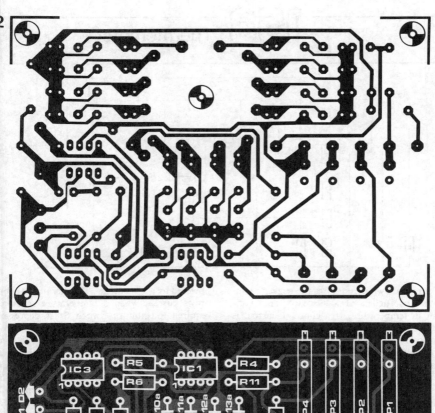

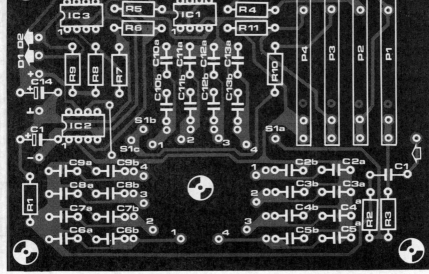

obtained, the peak-peak value of the distortion signal (D_{pp}) and the peak-peak value of the input signal U_{ipp} should be measured. The percentage distortion can then be calculated as follows:

$$\%d_{pp} = \frac{U_{Dpp} \cdot 100}{U_{ipp}} \text{ for D1, and}$$

$$\%d_{pp} = \frac{U_{Dpp} \cdot 10}{U_{ipp}} \text{ for D2.}$$

153 Thermometer

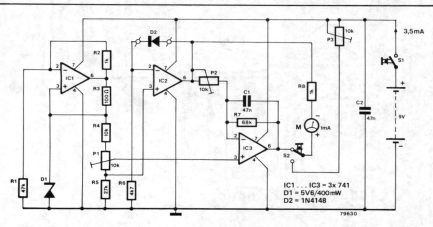

The circuit shown here utilises the negative temperature coefficient of a diode to sense variations in temperature. If a constant current is flowing through a forward-biased diode, the voltage dropped across the diode is inversely proportional to temperature.

In order to obtain a stable reference voltage, a 'super zener' configuration is used. IC1 ensures that a constant current flows through the zener diode, so that the zener voltage is unaffected by variations in the supply voltage. A 5.6 V zener was chosen for its low temperature coefficient. When the temperature of the sensor diode changes, the output voltage of IC2 varies by roughly 2 mV per °C. This voltage is amplified by IC3 and fed to the meter. The meter is calibrated for zero reading at the lower end of the desired temperature scale (e.g. 0°C) by means of P1, and for full-scale deflection at the top end of the scale by means of P2.

The circuit consumes relatively little current (roughly 3.5 mA), which means that it can be powered by a 9 V battery. The thermometer only draws current when a temperature reading is required (pushbutton switch S1 is depressed). Switch S2 allows the state of the battery to be monitored, and P3 should be adjusted to give a suitable deflection. However since the meter reading will also be influenced by the temperature of the sensor diode, the measurement thus obtained should only be taken as a rough indication of the battery state. With the component values shown in the diagram, the circuit has a measurement range of roughly 50°C (depending upon the setting of P2). The range can be varied by altering the value of R7 (e.g. R7 = 33 k gives a range of 100°C). A further possibility is to reverse the meter connections, i.e. if the scale was previously 0 to 50°C, reversing the connections to the meter would give a scale of −50 to 0°C.

S. Jacobsson

154 Digisplay

The idea itself isn't new, but, the simplicity of the circuit described here lends it a special charm... Only three ICs and a handful of other components are required to recognise the logic levels of sixteen different signals and display them on an oscilloscope screen. The display consists of two rows of noughts and ones. This is achieved as follows. If a sine-wave is applied to the Y-

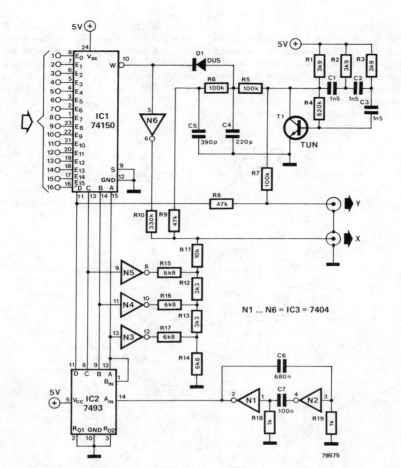

79575

input of an oscilloscope, the display depends on the signal applied to the X-input. If a sawtooth is applied, the sinewave is traced on the screen; if there is no signal on the X-input, a vertical line will be displayed; and, finally, if a sinewave of the same frequency as the first but with different phase is applied, a circle or ellipse can be obtained. The vertical line or circle can be positioned at any point on the screen by adding a suitable DC offset to the X- and/or Y-input signals. In the circuit described here, two rows of eight lines or circles are displayed.

The circuit is shown in figure 1. Up to sixteen input signals are fed to the inputs of IC1. IC2 is a four-bit binary counter, and it applies binary numbers from 0 to 15 to the A, B, C and D inputs of IC1. When the number '0000' is applied, the signal at input 1 (E0, pin 8) of IC1 is passed (in inverted form) to its output, W. As the count

at the A...D inputs proceeds, the rest of the inputs 2...16 are also scanned in sequence and passed to the output. When a '1' is present at the selected input, the output signal from IC1 is at logic zero. The voltage at the R5/R6 junction is clamped to supply common via D1 and the output of N6 is 'high', so the X-output signal is determined by the output of IC2 and the resistor network R11...R17. This signal is the 'DC component' that is required to step the display along the eight positions in one horizontal row.

The Y-output signal consists of two components. A 'DC shift' signal is taken from the D-output of IC2, to switch the display from the upper to the lower row and back, as required. Superimposed on this signal is the output from a simple RC oscillator (T1). If all 16 inputs to IC1 are at logic one (so that the W output is always '0'), the display will therefore consist of two

167

rows of eight short vertical lines.

When the W output goes to '1', however, the voltage at the R5/R6 junction is no longer clamped to supply common by D1. R5, R6, C4 and C5 are a phase-shifting network, so the sine-wave output from the oscillator is applied to the X-output (via R9) with a phase-shift with respect to the Y-output. The result: a circle on the screen.

If the 16 inputs of IC1 are connected to the pins of a TTL IC (using a DIL test clip, for instance), the logic levels at the pins of the IC will be displayed on the screen. The upper row corresponds to inputs 0...7, the lower row to inputs 8...15. Unconnected pins are shown as 'ones'.

A. Kraut

155 Nerves of steel

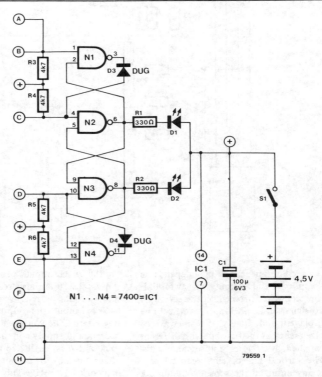

Behind the above title lies a wellknown type of dexterity game, in which two players each attempt to pass a ring along a length of wire without touching it. The first player to reach the end of the wire is the winner. If however a player's ring should happen to brush the wire, an LED lights, indicating that he must go back to the start and begin again. The circuit incorporates an additional refinement in that, whilst one player's 'go-back-to-start' LED is lit, the other

player can touch his own wire without incurring a penalty (i.e. without his own LED lighting up), thereby enabling him to speed up. However the second player must be careful, since the moment the first player reaches the start again, his LED will go out, simultaneously enabling the LED of the second player.

The actual circuit is straightforward, being based on the operation of two flip-flops formed by N1...N4. At the start of the game, once both player's rings have touched the start electrodes (C and D), the outputs of N2 and N3 are high (and LEDs D1 and D2 are extinguished), whilst the outputs of N1 and N4 are low. The free inputs of N2 and N3 are also low, i.e. at a potential just above the forward voltage drop of a germanium diode (roughly 0.2 V). Assume now that player 1 touches his wire (B). The input of N1 is momentarily taken low, which takes the output of N1 high and the output of N2 low. The 'go-back-to-start' LED of player 1 thus lights up, whilst the outputs of N3 and N4 remain unchanged.

What happens now if player 2 touches the wire (with D1 still lit)? The input of N4 (E) is momentarily taken low, thus taking the free input of N3 high. Since the other input of N3 is low, the output of N3 will remain high, so that LED D2 cannot light up. This situation will only change when the first player once more touches the start electrode, taking the output of N2 high again. Figure 2 shows a sketch of a possible layout for the game. Ordinary fairly stiff copper wire can be used, and obviously the 'difficulty factor' can be varied depending upon the shape into which

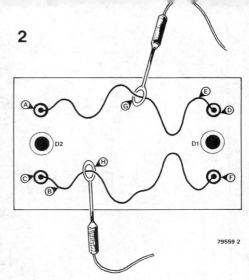

2

79559 2

the wire is bent and upon the diameter of the rings.

R.J. Horst

156 Bicycle speedometer

Circuits for bicycle speedometers have been fairly common, the difference in this particular design being the digital readout. The speed sensing is carried out by a number of magnets attached to the spokes or rim of the wheel which operate a pair of reed switches. The principle is illustrated in the drawing in figure 1, where the reed switches are shown fitted on the bicycle front forks. The main advantage that a digital display has over a moving coil meter is that of robustness in a situation where the younger generation can create a very harsh environment. Current consumption is kept to a minimum by arranging for the power supply to be switched on only when a readout is required. This switch (S2) should ideally be mounted on the handlebars (i.e. using an electric bicycle horn button or similar).

The circuit diagram for the digital speedometer is shown in figure 2. The principle behind the circuit is uncomplicated: The pulses from the reed switches are fed to a counter (IC1, IC2) for a predetermined length of time. The counter is

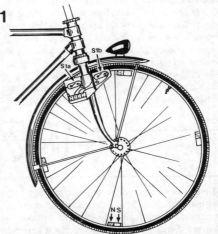

1

then inhibited and the count decoded and displayed. Decoding and display drive is performed by the counter itself. N3 and N4 serve to eliminate contact bounce from the reed switches, S1a and S1b, whilst the count pulses are fed to IC1

169

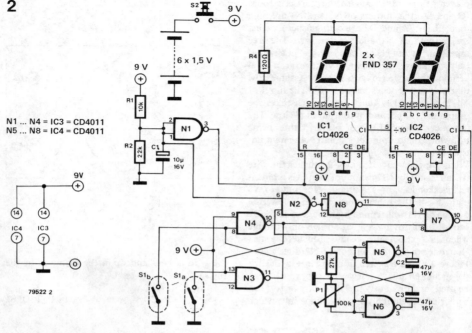

79522 2

N1 ... N4 = IC3 = CD4011
N5 ... N8 = IC4 = CD4011

via N7. The measurement period is determined by the circuit round N5, N6, and can be varied by adjusting P1. The meter can therefore be calibrated with the aid of this preset. The charge time of capacitor C1 will ensure that the counters are reset by N1 before a new count cycle starts. Gate N2 prevents a count cycle starting before the reset is cleared. In view of the high current consumption of LED displays, a continuous readout is not feasible. A 'push-button'-type display was therefore chosen, i.e. each time S2 is depressed the speed of the bicycle at that particular moment is displayed. This approach

also means that the components which would have been required to ensure that the counter is automatically reset after each count can be dispensed with.

In principle any number of magnets can be employed, however in order to avoid excessively long count periods, a minimum of three is recommended. The circuit should be calibrated (i.e. P1 adjusted for the desired count period) with the aid of an existing speedometer.

P. de Jong

157 Noise level meter

There are many potential applications nowadays to justify the use of a noise level meter — for instance, monitoring the sound output at dances, discos etc. The unit described here was designed primarily to establish the noise level produced by model engines. It has five switched ranges from 70 dB to 120 dB in 10 dB steps and is readable to ½ dB. The prototype was found to be accurate to ± 1 dB.

The circuit for the noise level meter is shown in figure 1. The sound signal is picked up by the microphone M1 and filtered by the network C1, C2, R1 and R2. These components, together with the capacitance of the microphone and the input impedance of the amplifier, ensure that the frequency response of the system is corrected to suit the internationally standardised 'A' weighting curve shown in figure 2. This 'weighted' sig-

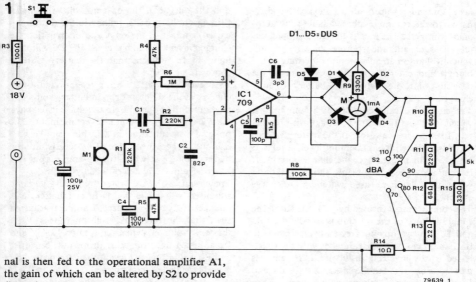

1

79639 1

nal is then fed to the operational amplifier A1, the gain of which can be altered by S2 to provide five noise ranges.

The AC output of the op-amp is then rectified by diodes D1...D4 and fed to the meter via resistor R9. As this rectifier is included in the feedback loop the meter reading remains linear over the entire scale. Diode D5 is included to limit the current through the meter to a safe value, thereby reducing the risk of damage if a 'loud' noise is measured on a 'quiet' range. Components C5, C6 and R7 are included to provide frequency compensation and to prevent insta-

bility.

Under normal operation the circuit will only draw about 2 mA, so it can be powered by two PP3 (or similar) batteries. The push-button switch S1 ensures that the circuit is not inadvertently left on. The meter should be calibrated in dBs and should have a full scale deflection of + 10 (normal log scale).

P. Barnes

2

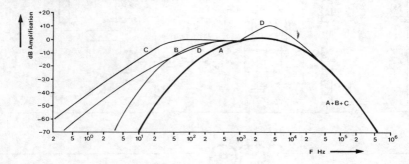

158 Automatic battery charger

Automatic battery chargers are not particularly cheap, however the protection they afford

against overcharging and possible battery damage is highly desirable. The circuit shown here is intended to provide an inexpensive alternative to the commercially available fully automatic chargers. The idea is to take a simple battery charger and incorporate an add-on unit which will automatically monitor the state of the battery and cut off the charge current at the desired point, i.e. when the battery is fully charged.

The circuit basically consists of a comparator, which monitors the battery voltage with respect to a fixed reference value. If the battery voltage exceeds a presettable maximum level, a relay is actuated which interrupts the charge current. If the battery voltage falls below a lower threshold value, the relay is released switching the charge current back in.

The comparator is formed by a 741 op-amp. The supply voltage of the op-amp is stabilised by R3 and D1, and is thus unaffected by variations in the battery voltage. The reference voltage, which is fed to the inverting input of the op-amp, is derived from this stabilised supply via R4 and D2. The reference voltage is compared with a portion of the battery voltage, which is taken from the voltage divider, R1/P1/R2. As the battery voltage rises, at a certain point (determined by the setting of P1) the voltage on the non-inverting input of the op-amp will eventually exceed that on the inverting input, with the result

that the output of the op-amp will swing high, turning on T1 and T2, pulling in the (normally-closed) contact of the relay and interrupting the charge current to the battery. LED D3 will then light up to indicate that the battery is fully charged.

To prevent the battery being reconnected to the charger at the slightest drop in battery voltage, a portion of the op-amp output voltage is fed back via P2 and R5 to the non-inverting input. The op-amp thus functions in a fashion similar to a Schmitt trigger, the degree of hysteresis, i.e. the battery voltage at which the op-amp output will go low again, being determined by P2.

The circuit is best calibrated by using a variable stabilised voltage as an 'artificial battery'. A voltage of 14.5 V is selected and P1 adjusted such that the relay just pulls in (opens). The 'battery' voltage is then reduced to 12.4 V and P2 adjusted until the relay drops out. Since P1 and P2 will influence one another, the procedure is best repeated several times.

A final tip: if the charge current is too large to be switched by the relay, the circuit can still be used by connecting the relay in the primary of the battery charger transformer.

H. Heere

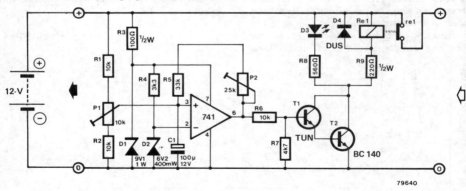

159 5-minute chess clock

In games of speed chess, where each player has only 5 or 10 minutes to complete all his moves, mechanical chess clocks leave something to be desired in terms of accuracy, especially when both players have only 30 or 40 seconds left. The

author of the circuit described here offers a solution to this problem by employing LEDs to provide an unequivocal display which counts off the time remaining in multiples of 10 seconds. The clock uses two counters, one for player A

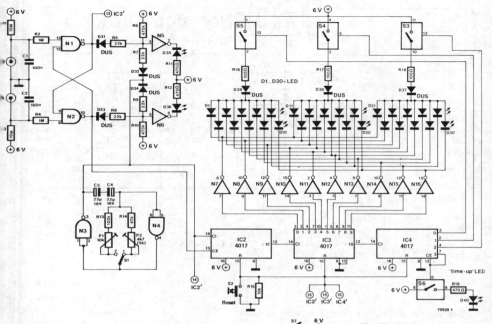

N1 . . . N4 = IC1 = 4011
IC2 . . . IC4 = 4017
S3 . . . S6 = IC5 = 4066
N5 . . . N10 = IC6 = 4049
N11 . . . N16 = IC7 = 4049

IC2' . . . IC4' = 4017
S3' . . . S6' = IC5' = 4066
N7' . . . N10' = IC6' = 2/3 4049
N11' . . . N16' = IC7' = 4049

and one for player B. By bridging a set of touch contacts each player can stop his own counter and start his opponent's. The state of each counter is displayed on a circle of 30 LEDs (see figure 2). In a 5-minute game S1 is set to position 1, whereupon each LED lights up in turn for (300 seconds/30 =) 10 seconds. With S1 in position 2, the time limit is increased to 10 minutes per player, i.e. each LED lights up for 20 seconds.

If a player exceeds his time limit, then LED D40 (A) or D40' (B) lights up. The counters can be reset for the start of a new game by pressing S2. LEDs D35 and D36 provide a visual indication of who is to move.

Assuming player B has just made a move on the board, he presses TAP switch B, which takes the output of N1 (which together with N2 forms a set/reset flip-flop) high. The output of N2 goes low, causing counter A (IC2, IC3, IC4) to start counting the clock pulses provided by N3 and N4; counter B is inhibited until TAP switch A is touched. Since D31 is now reverse biased, D35 will be turned on and off via D32 at a rate equal to the clock frequency. D33 is forward biased, pulling the input of N6 low, so that D36 will be extinguished.

The circuit can be powered by four 1.5 V batteries or by ni-cads. The current consumption is approximately 45 mA. P1 and P2 can be calibrated using a known accurate timebase; each LED should light up for 10 seconds with S1 in position 1 and twenty seconds with S1 in position 2.

S. Woydig

2

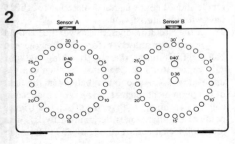

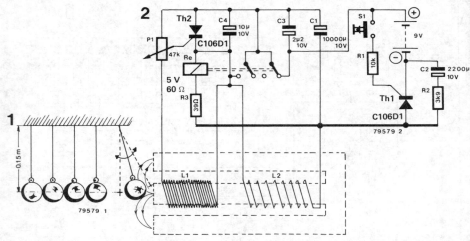

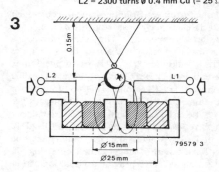

Most people will have seen the desktop ornament/toy known as a 'Newton's cradle' (see figure 1), which consists of usually five steel balls suspended in a row from a pair of threads. When one of the end balls is lifted and then released so that it falls back and strikes the next ball, the energy of the impact is transmitted through the other balls, with the result that the ball on the opposite end of the row swings up. It then in turn falls back, energy is again transmitted through the row, and the first ball swings up, and so on. The energy losses of the system are fairly high, and after a number of oscillations the balls are returned to rest. The idea behind the circuit described here, is to compensate for the natural energy losses of the system, so that it continues to oscillate indefinitely (i.e. until the circuit is disconnected or the batteries run out!).

If, for the moment we ignore the energy losses, the frequency at which the system oscillates will be:

$$f = \frac{1}{2\pi \cdot \sqrt{\dfrac{l}{g}}}$$

where l is the length of the thread and g is the force of gravity (9.81 m/s²). Thus with a length of 0.15 m, the fundamental frequency of the system will be approximately 1.3 Hz. In order to compensate for natural energy losses, the magnetic field system shown in figure 2 has been de-

L1 = 10.000 turns Ø 0,1 mm Cu (= 1kΩ)
L2 = 2300 turns Ø 0.4 mm Cu (= 25 Ω)

3

signed. Together with the accompanying circuit, the idea is that a magnetic force is applied to one of the end balls in the cradle. If the circuit is powered by 6 1.5 V cells (manganese-alkali), the cradle should continue to oscillate for roughly 5 days without interruption.

To set the circuit in operation, switch S1 should be pressed immediately before or after the end ball is set in motion, thereby triggering thyristor Th1 via resistor R1. Capacitor C1 then charges up, as does C4. As soon as a ball enters the field of the permanent magnet, a voltage is induced in coil L1, turning on thyristor Th2; the trigger point of the thyristor is determined by P1. The relay connected in the cathode of Th2 pulls in, so that current flows through coil L2, and an additional magnetic field is created which repels the ball. As soon as the ball leaves the magnetic field, the voltage induced in L1 collapses and Th2 is turned off. The process then repeats itself at the natural frequency of the system.

If the ball is stopped, no charge current will flow to C1, with the result that C2 will discharge. If the discharge current is smaller than the holding current of Th1, the latter turns off and circuit switches off. Figure 3 shows a cross-section of the coil and magnet system. L1 (10,000 turns of enamelled copper wire, 0.01 mm diameter, 1 k) and L2 (2300 turns enamelled copper wire, 0.4 mm diameter, 25 Ω) are wound on a permanent magnet core, and enclosed in transformer laminations. Any readily available alternative type of thyristor can be used.

K. Bartkowiak

161 Varispeed windscreen wiper delay circuit

In most windscreen wiper delay circuits the wiper speed is independent of the speed of the car. However the faster the car travels, the more rain falls on the windscreen, therefore, ideally, the shorter the delay should be. A variable delay circuit could be controlled by a sensor mounted in the speedometer cable. However this approach would be fairly complicated. The simpler solution adopted here, is to derive the control signals from the contact breaker, so that the wiper speed is varied in accordance with the engine speed.

The input of the circuit is connected to the contact breaker; when the contacts open, the full battery voltage appears across the input, with the result that T1 provides a short output pulse. The resultant pulse stream is used to trigger the monostable multivibrator formed by N1 and N2. The frequency of the multivibrator is then divided by ten by the counter, IC2. The output of the counter is fed to a second monostable, N3/N4, which provides an output pulse duration of approximately 0.5 s. Depending upon the speed of the engine, the time between successive pulses will be between roughly 10 and 40 seconds. Thus transistor T2 is regularly turned on for a short period, causing the wiper relay to pull in and the wipers to perform a single sweep. By arranging for a capacitor of roughly 2.2 μ F to be switched in parallel with C4, the wipers can be made to perform a double sweep every cycle.

The zener diode D1 is included to protect the circuit from excessively large surge voltages appearing across the contact breakers, whilst diode D2 protects T2 against the back EMF induced by the relay. Preferably, the holding current of the relay should not exceed 100 mA; if that is the case, however, a transistor with a higher output current capability should be used.

D. Laues

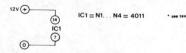

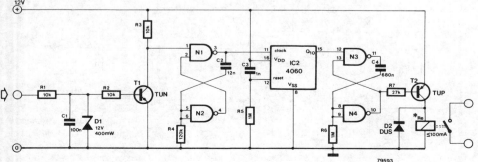

79593

The following circuit is intended as an infra-red lock for house doors, garage doors, etc. Since the 'key' is almost impossible to copy, it should provide an effective obstacle to unwanted visitors.

Figure 1 shows the infra red transmitter. An astable multivibrator, formed by NAND gates N1...N3, drives an output transistor, T1, which turns the infra-red emitter diode on and off at a frequency which can be varied by means of P1.

The receiver circuit is shown in figure 2. Light pulses received by the phototransistor T1 are amplified by IC1 and fed to an LC circuit tuned to roughly 23 kHz. The filtered output signal is rectified by D1 and fed to op-amp IC2, which is connected as a Schmitt trigger. The trigger threshold is set by zener diode D4 to 2.4 V. The unfiltered output of IC1 is also fed to a second Schmitt trigger, (IC3). The output of this op-amp (point 1) will remain high as long as the voltage level at its input is 2.4 volts or greater regardless of the frequency of the received signal.

Assuming point 1 is high, a positive going edge at the output of IC2 (point 2) will 'turn the lock' as follows: when point 2 goes high, the output of N1 also goes high, and with it the input of monostable multivibrator MMV1. However, since this monostable is triggered by a negative going edge, the output state of the monostable remains unchanged, i.e. the Q output remains low. The

1

positive going edge at point 2 is also transferred to the trigger input of MMV2, which since it is triggered by positive going pulses, turns on the Darlington pair T3/T4 and pulls in the relay. Thus for the pulse duration of MMV2 the lock is 'opened'.

If the modulation frequency of the transmitter signal deviates from 23 kHz, only point 1 will be high; point 2 will go low, with the result that, via N1, the negative going edge will trigger MMV1. Thus for the pulse duration of MMV1 – which is several minutes – MMV2 cannot be triggered. Even if the modulation frequency is subsequently corrected, since one input of N5 is held low, the lock cannot be opened during this period. If a flip-flop is used in place of a relay, the circuit could, for example, be used to switch a car alarm system on and off.

H.J. Urban

2

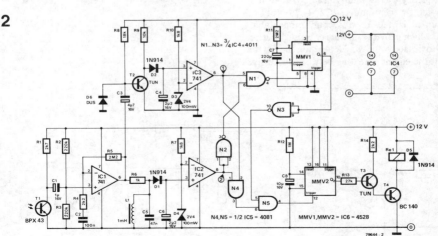

1

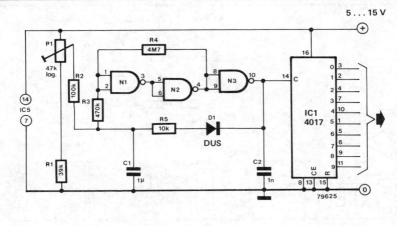

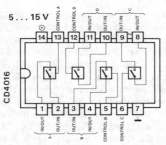

2

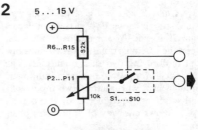

N1 ... N3 = 3/4 IC5 = 4011
S1 ... S10 = IC2,IC3,IC4 = 4016

The following design for a sequencer, which will generate a 10 note analogue waveform, is distinguished by its relative simplicity. To control a synthesiser two types of signal are required: a gate pulse to trigger the envelope shaper (ADSR), and a control voltage for the voltage controlled oscillators (VCOs).

The VCO voltages are generated as follows. An oscillator, formed by N1, N2 and N3, clocks a decade counter (IC1). Each output of the counter is connected to an analogue switch (as shown in figure 2), the input voltage of which can be varied by means of a potentiometer. The outputs of all the switches are joined together, so that an analogue waveform, composed of 10 discrete voltage levels, is generated at this point. The frequency of the resultant signal can be varied by means of P1.

The gate signal for the ADSR is derived from the clock signal, however since each synthesiser places different demands on the type of gate pulse required, no circuit is given.

Readers may wish to experiment with extending the circuit. One possibility is to include a monostable multivibrator (at the clock input of IC1), which allows one to cycle through the analogue waveform step by step. Each of the preset voltage levels on the inputs of S1...S10 are then compared with a reference voltage. If a shorter cycle (i.e. less than 10 steps) is required, the appropriate output of IC1 should be connected to the reset input (pin 15).

J.C.J. Smeets

164 Four quadrant multiplier

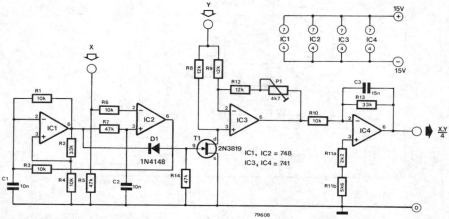

Multiply X and Y and you get XY – all very simple and straightforward – at least on paper. But what if X and Y are analogue voltages, which may be of either polarity? How does one go about multiplying two such quantities? The following circuit for a 'four quadrant multiplier' – a circuit which will multiply two input voltages and ensure the product is of the correct polarity – shows one way of approaching this problem.

Basically the circuit generates a squarewave signal, whose duty-cycle is proportional to one of the input signals and whose amplitude is proportional to the other. The average value of the squarewave, and hence the value of the product voltage, is obtained by lowpass filtering.

The squarewave generator is formed by IC1, R1, R2, R4 and C1. The output of IC1 is lowpass filtered by R7 and C2, then compared with the input voltage, X. The duty cycle of the squarewave is modulated via the output of IC2, R3 and C1, whilst the amplitude of the output signal of IC1 is held constant. The output of IC1 is also used to control the FET switch, T1. When this switch is 'closed' i.e. T1 is turned on, a voltage

equal to −Y is present at the output of IC3; assuming P1 is correctly adjusted, this op-amp then functions as an inverting amplifier. If T1 is turned off, i.e. the switch is 'open', IC3 is connected as a non-inverting amplifier. Thus at the output of IC3 will be a squarewave voltage with an amplitude which is proportional to Y, a duty-cycle proportional to X, and whose average value is proportional to XY. The latter is obtained by the lowpass filter formed by IC4, R10, R13 and C3. The turnover frequency of this filter is approximately 330 Hz. The circuit will quite happily multiply analogue signals with frequencies which are an order of magnitude lower than the turnover point of the two lowpass filters. The author has used the circuit for correlation measurements on very low frequency EEG signals.

The adjustment of P1 is necessary since, when conducting, T1 has a significant resistance. With an input voltage X = 0 (input grounded) and Y = +6 or −6 V, P1 should be adjusted for minimum output voltage of IC4 (roughly ± 40 mV).

P. Creighton

165 Ribbon cable tester

For microcomputer enthusiasts and anyone working with large scale digital circuits, a ribbon

cable tester can prove a useful aid.
The circuit described here will simultaneously

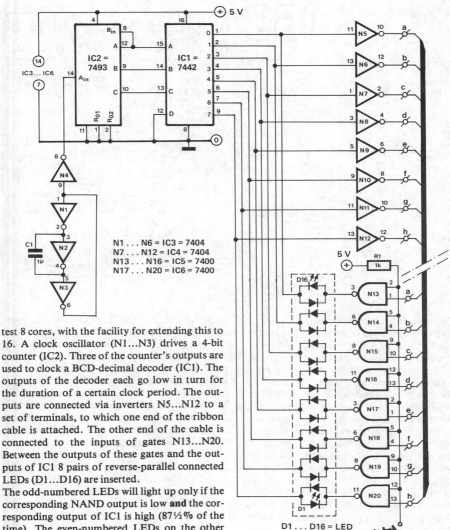

N1 ... N6 = IC3 = 7404
N7 ... N12 = IC4 = 7404
N13 ... N16 = IC5 = 7400
N17 ... N20 = IC6 = 7400

D1 ... D16 = LED

79594

test 8 cores, with the facility for extending this to 16. A clock oscillator (N1...N3) drives a 4-bit counter (IC2). Three of the counter's outputs are used to clock a BCD-decimal decoder (IC1). The outputs of the decoder each go low in turn for the duration of a certain clock period. The outputs are connected via inverters N5...N12 to a set of terminals, to which one end of the ribbon cable is attached. The other end of the cable is connected to the inputs of gates N13...N20. Between the outputs of these gates and the outputs of IC1 8 pairs of reverse-parallel connected LEDs (D1...D16) are inserted.

The odd-numbered LEDs will light up only if the corresponding NAND output is low and the corresponding output of IC1 is high (87½% of the time). The even-numbered LEDs on the other hand, will light up only if the NAND outputs are high and the outputs of IC1 are low (12½% of the time).

If there is a break in one of the cores, the corresponding NAND output will be low and the associated LED will light up. If the core is intact, then the LED will be extinguished, since the logic levels on either side of the LED change state simultaneously.

The circuit will also check for shorts between cores, since in that case the anode of an even-numbered LED will be high, whilst the cathode will be low, causing the LED to light up. Note that series resistors for the LEDs are not necessary. If no cable is connected, the odd-numbered LEDs will light up. Switch S2 functions as a lamp test for the even-numbered LEDs.

For a 16-core version of the circuit a 74154 should be used in place of IC1 (the D-input is of course used), whilst the number of inverters, NAND gates and LEDs is doubled.

J.J. van der Weele

179

1

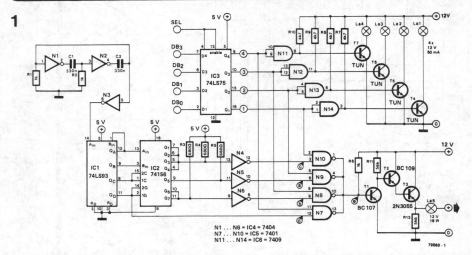

In the world of model railways, electronics is playing an increasingly important role, and it is only a matter of time before the microprocessor becomes a standard component in any large lay-out. The design described here brings this prospect nearer to becoming a reality. With the aid of the following circuit a µ P can be used to automatically control the speed of a train. The speed of the train is controlled by varying the pulse width of the squarewave supply voltage of the motor. The squarewave signal is generated by the oscillator N1/N2, and fed to a 4-bit binary counter. The counter outputs are in turn fed to a 1-of-8 decoder. The decoder outputs are connected together such that at points a...d there are four squarewave signals, whose pulse widths are in the ratio 1 : 2 : 4 : 8 respectively (see figure 2). By combining one or more of these wave-forms a choice of 16 different duty cycles (0, 1, 2, 1 + 2, 4, 1 + 4, etc.) can be obtained.

Which duty cycle is selected is determined by NAND gates N7...N10; the output state of these gates is in turn determined by the information present on the data bus (DB0...DB3) of the microprocessor system. Between the µ P data bus and the NAND gates is a 4-bit latch (IC3). Information is only transferred from the data bus to the gates when a select pulse is received.

The waveform selected by the µ P is amplified by T1/T2/T3. Lamp L5 protects the circuit from excessive current in the event of a short on the track, whilst lamps La1...La4 indicate the speed of the train in binary code.

If a µ P system is not available, the 'manually-operated' processor circuit shown in figure 3 can be used instead. The circuit performs the same basic function as a µ P, with the exception that the 'brainwork' is done by the hobbyist himself. By pressing either S1 or S2 the speed of the train can be increased or reduced in single steps. If the circuit of figure 3 is used, then IC3 in figure 1 can of course be omitted.

2   **W. Pussel**

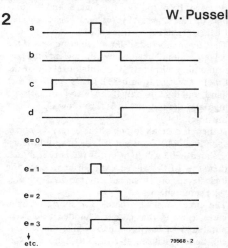

3

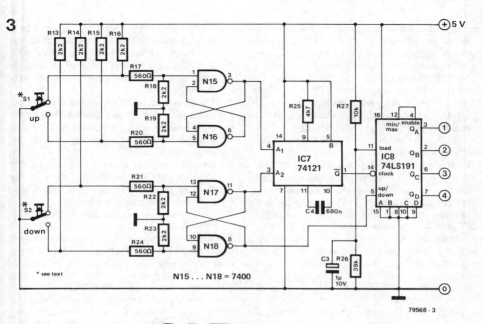

167 pH meter circuit for DVM

To accurately measure the concentration of hydrogen ions (pH value) in a solution, a 'glass electrode' is often used in chemistry laboratories. The electrode is constructed on the principle of a galvanic cell, and the output voltage of the electrode is proportional to the pH value of the solution to be measured. The temperature of the solution considerably affects the pH value, thus a pH meter is effectively a temperature compensated millivoltmeter.

The circuit shown employs an op-amp (A1) to amplify the output voltage of the electrode. The

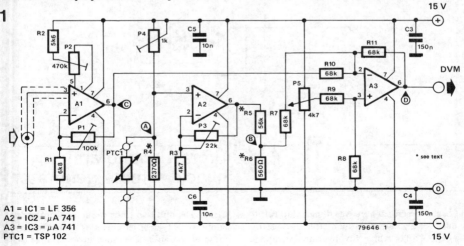

A1 = IC1 = LF 356
A2 = IC2 = μA 741
A3 = IC3 = μA 741
PTC1 = TSP 102

input impedance of the circuit is thus equal to that of the op-amp, which is $10^{12}\ \Omega$, so that there is negligible loading of the electrode. The positive temperature coefficient (PTC) resistor TSP 102 (Texas) compensates for the effect of variations in the temperature of the solution. Together with the shunt resistor of exactly 2370 Ω , which should be made up of several metal film resistors (e.g. 2k2 + 150 Ω + 10 Ω + 10 Ω), the resistance of the PTC varies linearly with temperature.

The voltage at point A is amplified by op-amp A2, the output of which is divided by R5/R6 such that it varies the total output voltage by just the right amount. Op-amp A3 is connected as a combined summing and differential amplifier and provides the output voltage for the DVM, which displays the pH value of the solution directly. Trimmer potentiometers P1 and P3 set the gain of the input stage while P2 ensures that A1 is correctly biased.

The calibration procedure for the circuit is as follows:

1. With the inputs short-circuited P2 is adjusted for zero volts at point C.
2. Again with the inputs shorted, potentiometer P5 (wirewound type) is adjusted such that 7 volts are present at point D.
3. Trimmer potentiometer P4 (spindle type) is adjusted such that, with the PTC at a temperature of 25° C, zero volts are present at point A.

4. A glass electrode, which is suspended in a solution with a pH of 7, is connected to the input of the circuit. P5 is then adjusted until a reading of 7 volts is obtained at point D (note that the temperature of the solution should be 25° C).
5. The glass electrode is suspended in a solution with a pH value of 4 and trimmer P4 (spindle type) is adjusted for a reading of 4 volts at point D. Once again the temperature of the solution must be 25° C.
6. Heat the solution to approximately 70° C, and with the PTC suspended in the solution check to see that a reading of 4 volts is still obtained. If necessary, readjust P3.
7. Repeat the above procedure from point 3 onwards.

The high input impedance of the circuit renders it sensitive to r.f. pick-up, hum etc. and it should therefore be well-screened, preferably by mounting it in a metal case. The connections to the PTC must be water, acid and alkali proof.

The accuracy of the circuit depends upon a stable supply voltage (± 15 V), and upon the accuracy of the reference solution used during calibration (not to mention the accuracy of the DVM).

Glass electrodes are available commercially, and are supplied with instructions on how they should be used.

Th. Rumbach

2

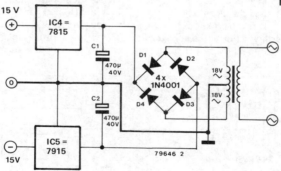

168 Aircraft sound and 'hijack' effects generator

The circuit described here was designed to fulfill the need for a jet airliner sound effects generator in a school play which involved an attempted

hijack. The unit had to be capable of producing a number of typical jet noises as heard from the inside of the aircraft — start-up, idle, take-off,

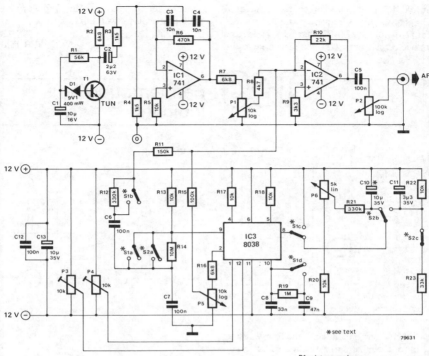

P1 = jet roar volume
P2 = overall volume
P5 = compressor whistle volume
P6 = throttle
S1 = gunfire
S2 = tyre squeal

*see text

79631

in-flight, approach, landing and reverse thrust conditions – together with tyre squeal on landing and machine-gun fire.

To simulate the sound of a jet engine both the roar from the 'hot end' of the engine and the whistle from the compressor (whose pitch varies with engine speed) are required. The engine roar is obtained by feeding white noise through a band pass filter which emphasises frequencies around 800 Hz. Transistor T1 and the zener diode D1 form the white noise generator whose output is fed to IC1, the band pass filter. The volume of the roar can be altered by potentiometer P1.

The whistle is derived from the sinewave output of the 8038 waveform generator IC3 whose frequency range is set by C8 and is typically between 10 Hz and 10 kHz. The actual frequency is determined by the throttle control P6 which is connected to the FM input of IC3 via switches S1c and S2b, while the whistle volume is controlled by potentiometer P5. Engine inertia (lag in response to throttle demands) is realistically imitated by the integrating network R21/C10. C10 should be a low-leakage type – if available, a 10 μ paper capacitor would be a good choice.

Both these signals, the engine roar and compressor whistle, are then summed by IC2 and passed to the external amplifier through the overall volume control P2. By varying the settings of these controls all of the above mentioned jet engine sounds can be realised. The purity of the sinewave signal can be adjusted by potentiometers P3 and P4.

The gunfire effect is obtained from the squarewave output of IC3 when switch S1 is closed. By closing this switch the squarewave is allowed to pass through to the summing amplifier and the FM input of IC3 is taken high to give minimum frequency whilst the frequency range itself is also decreased by the addition of C9 in parallel with C8. Resistor R19 is included so that C9 is always kept charged to the average voltage across C8 to prevent a 'chirp' when S1 is first closed.

The tyre sqeal effect is also obtained from the squarewave output of IC3. When switch S2 is closed the squarewave is enabled, and the FM input of IC3 is initially taken to a potential which gives a high frequency output via the potential divider R22/R23, but as R23 is now disconnected capacitor C11 will discharge to the positive supply rail and the frequency of the squarewave output will fall rapidly.

M.J. Walmsley

169 Fermentation rate indicator

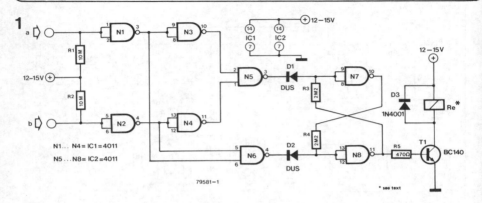

79581—1

When making one's own wine, the fermentation rate can for the most part be estimated by counting the number of times the level of the (sterilising) liquid in the air-lock rises and falls as a result of the CO_2 which is produced. Towards the end of the fermentation process however, the level tends to 'jitter' somewhat, so that accurate measurements are not possible. One solution to this problem is to employ two electrodes, one of which is mounted higher than the other — see figure 2. The difference in height between the two should be greater than that by which the level of liquid fluctuates (approximately 2 mm).

The circuit shown in figure 1 is designed to produce an output pulse only if both electrodes are suspended in the liquid, after previously having been clear of the liquid. Enamelled copper wire, 0.3 mm in diameter is used for the electrodes. Insulating sleeving is pushed over the wire, whilst an earth connection is also suspended in the liquid.

As is apparent from the circuit diagram, the input of inverters N1 and N2 are held high via pull-up resistors R1 and R2 when neither of the electrodes is in contact with the liquid. The output of the OR-gate formed by N3, N4 and N5 is therefore low, as is the output of the set-reset flip-flop N7/N8. The output of NAND gate N6 is high. If the level of the liquid in the fermen-

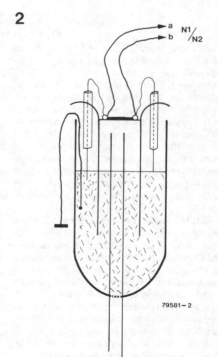

79581— 2

tation lock rises to cover the lower of the two electrodes, the output of the corresponding inverter will go high. This has no effect upon the output of the NAND gate, but the output of the OR-gate will be taken high also. Due to the effect of diode D1, however, the set-reset flip-flop remains in its original state. Should the liquid level fall, the only result will be that the output of the OR-gate is returned low once again. Only if the level rises still further to cover

the second electrode will the output of N6 go low and the flip-flop be triggered, turning on T1 and feeding a pulse to the counter (Re). Since the flip-flop can only be triggered by '0' logic levels via D1 and D2, both electrodes must clear the liquid before the flip-flop is reset and another pulse can be counted.

Any normal 12 V impulse counter can be used.

J. Ryan

170 Frequency to voltage converter for multimeter

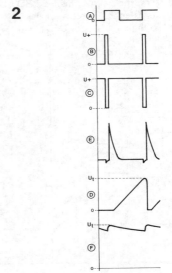

Most frequency measurements are carried out by means of a digital frequency meter or else on an oscilloscope. However both these instruments are relatively expensive, and thus not often 'standard equipment' for the hobbyist. One way to measure the frequency of a signal without investing in specialised equipment is to use a frequency-voltage converter, which can then be 'plugged in' to an ordinary multimeter. That is the function of the circuit described here. A meter with a 5 V range should be used; the conversion ratio is linear, assuming the scale is calibrated in ms (1 V = 5 ms). The circuit is built round a quad analogue switch IC, type 4066. The squarewave signal at point A is switched via S1 to the differentiating network, C2/R6. The resulting pulses are then fed via S2 on the one hand to the inverter formed by T1, and on the other hand to S4. The result is that S3 and S4 open and close alternately, i.e. S3 is open when S4 is closed, and vice versa. Assuming that S4 is closed, capacitor C4 will be charged linearly by the constant current source T2. The charge is transferred via S4 to storage capacitor C5. S4 and C5 thus function as a sample and hold circuit. If now S4 is opened, S3 will close; capacitor C4 will discharge via S3 to ground, and new measurement cycle will begin. Depending upon

185

the characteristics of the FET, T3, the sample and hold circuit will increase the voltage by approximately 2 V. Thus a maximum charge voltage of around 6.5 V is possible.

The circuit is calibrated as follows: With the input unconnected, the wiper of P2 is turned to the positive end stop (junction of P2 and R13). A DC voltage of 6.5 V is applied to the gate of T3, and P2 is adjusted for full-scale deflection on the meter. Potentiometer P4 is adjusted for zero reading on the meter with 0 V on the gate of T3. A known frequency is then fed to the input of the circuit (e.g. 50 Hz mains signal from a doorbell transformer), and P2 is then fine tuned for a reading of 20 ms.

The pulse diagram in figure 2 illustrates the signals obtained at points A...E in the circuit, and across C4 and C5. With the component values shown in the circuit diagram, the meter will display frequencies between 40 and 2000 Hz (0.1 V = 0.5 ms = 2000 Hz).

Different frequency ranges can be obtained by altering the value of components R11, R12 and C4 accordingly.

The appropriate values can be calculated by using the formula:

$$U_{C4} = \frac{I_{C4}}{C4 \cdot f_{in}}$$

where $I_{C4} = \frac{U_{R11} + U_{P1}}{R11 + P1}$

Finally one or two specifications:
supply voltage: 10...15 V
current consumption: 5 mA
input impedance: 1 MΩ
input sensitivity: minimum 1.5 V pp

F. Kasparec

171 Transistor tester

This simple tester circuit will determine whether a transistor is an NPN or PNP type and also measure the current gain of the unknown device. When the pushbutton switch, S, is depressed, one of the LEDs D13 or D14 will light to show the polarity of the transistor, whilst the h_{FE} can be read directly off the meter, M. If neither LED lights, the transistor is either defective or has a current gain of less than 50. If both LEDs light

up, there is a short between collector and emitter.

The circuit functions as follows: IC1a forms the basis of a squarewave oscillator, the frequency of which is roughly 1 kHz. The squarewave oscillates about half supply voltage and, with the aid of IC1b, is used to generate a base-emitter voltage which is alternately positive and negative. Thus whenever the polarity of the base bias

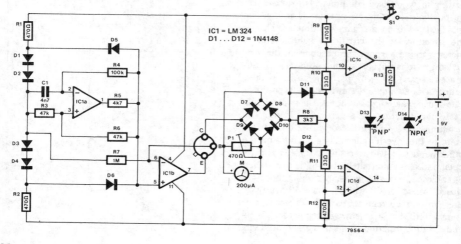

voltage is of correct polarity for the type of transistor under test, a base current will flow, causing a collector current to flow through R8. Depending upon the direction of the current through R8, either a positive or negative voltage is dropped across this resistor, with the result that, via IC1c or IC1d, the appropriate LED will light to signify the polarity of the transistor under test.

The collector current of the transistor also flows through the diode bridge and the meter, M.

Since the base current remains more or less constant, the size of the collector current can be taken as a measure of the current gain of the transistor. Full-scale deflection of the meter corresponds to an h_{FE} of 500.

The meter can be calibrated with the aid of P1, the simplest method being to use a transistor with a known current gain.

H.G. Brink

172 FSK modem

The most notable feature of this circuit for an FSK modulator/demodulator is its extreme simplicity:
– it requires only one supply voltage
– uses only 4 common ICs
– is simple to set up
The circuit conforms to Kansas City Standard (CUTS) format, i.e. logic Ø = 1200 Hz, logic 1 = 2400 Hz, and the transmission rate is 300 Baud.

The modulator circuit is quite straightforward. The clock signal is derived from the frequency of the UART, which is 16 times the baud rate (i.e. 4800 Hz). After the clock signal has been divided down by FF1 and FF2, 2400 Hz and 1200 Hz signals are available at the inputs of S1 and S2.

Depending upon the logic level of the data input signal, one of these two switches is closed and a signal of the appropriate frequency is present at the modulator output. At the input of the demodulator circuit, N2, N3 and N4 form an amplifier/limiter. The actual demodulation is performed by the two re-triggerable monostable multivibrators, MMV 1 and MMV 2. The pulse duration of MMV 1 is roughly 420 µ s, whilst that of MMV 2 is approximately 850 µs (depending upon the position of P1). With an input frequency of 2400 Hz, MMV 1 is continuously retriggered, so that its Q output is held high. No trigger pulses are fed to MMV 2, with the result that the $\overline{Q}$ (data) output remains high. However, with an input frequency of 1200 Hz, MMV 1 will

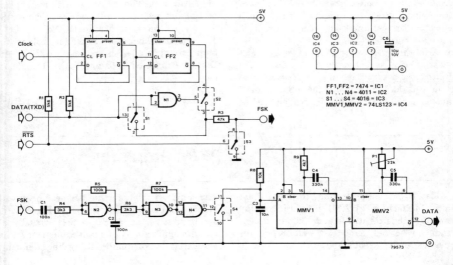

187

not be retriggered before the Q output goes low, so that MMV 2 is triggered and the data output also goes low. By adjusting P1 to keep the pulse duration of MMV 2 as short as possible, the delay between rising and falling edges of the data signal can also be kept short.

Users of the Elekterminal can take the clock signal for the modulator from either pin 17 or pin 40 of the UART. The Baud rate switch on the Elekterminal should be set to the 300 Baud position. The $\overline{RTS}$ input should only be used in conjunction with UARTs provided with such an output.

H. Stettmaier

173 Voltage trend meter

The advantages of a digital multimeter are sufficiently well known that they do not need to be repeated here. However there are situations where it is useful to determine whether the quantity being measured is increasing or decreasing, particularly if it is subject to sudden fluctuations. An opamp connected as an AC amplifier is particularly suited to this task.

Most simple DVMs contain an LSI chip with an input sensitivity of 200 mV and an extremely high input impedance. A suitable opamp is the LF 355 used as a voltage-current converter, which has an input impedance of $10^{12}\ \Omega$.

The circuit shown here is designed for an input voltage of 200 mV and a current through the moving coil meter of 100 µ A. For other input voltages and/or output currents the trimmer potentiometer P1 and resistor R1 should be altered accordingly.

The opamp requires two supply voltages (positive and negative) between 5 and 18 V. In view of the nominal current consumption of the circuit (several milliamps), these can easily be provided by two 9 V batteries.

The calibration procedure is quite straightforward. With the input short circuited, P2 is adjusted for a meter reading of zero volts. A 200 mV signal is then fed to the input, and P1 adjusted for the corresponding reading on the

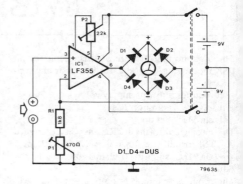

meter.

If the meter has a scale of e.g. 0...3/30, then by calibrating the moving coil meter to read '2' for a maximum reading (with e.g. 200 mV in) on the DVM, an 'overload' range up to 300 mV can be obtained. In the above case, with a constant current of 100 µ A through the analogue meter, the value of R1 should be increased to 2k7.

The circuit functions in a similar fashion for both current and resistance measurements. The DVM is connected in parallel with the analogue meter.

H. Ehrlich

174 PWM amplifier

In spite of some initial teething troubles, Pulse Width Modulation (PWM) is considered by many to be the next step in audio circuit design. Although it has only a modest 3 watt output, it is a practical and efficient amplifier.

The subject of digital audio has been dealt with before and certainly will be again. The benefits are impressive, so much so that virtually all major manufacturers of audio equipment are investigating its possibilities. Recording companies

1

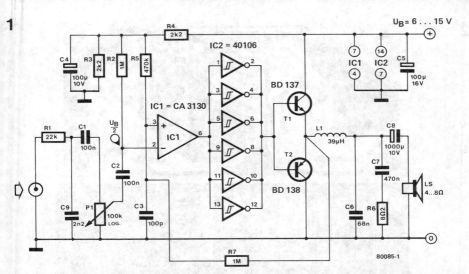

too are aware of the potential of a digital system (digitally recorded records are already available commercially).

Until quite recently, the performance of PWM amplifiers was disappointing due to the poor quality semiconductors used. With the introduction of modern high speed switching transistors, PWM is now coming of age.

The PWM amplifier

It might be a good idea to recap the principles briefly. A PWM amplifier contains a symmetrical squarewave generator. The duty cycle of this squarewave is then modulated by the audio signals. The output transistors do not operate linearly but function as switches, that is, they are

Figure 1. The self-oscillating PWM amplifier. With a 12 V supply, it will deliver 3 watts into 4 ohms.

either full on or off. Under quiescent conditions the duty cycle of the output waveform is 50% which means that each of the output transistors is fully saturated (conducting) for an equal amount of time. The average output voltage is therefore zero. It therefore follows that if one of the output switches is closed for a longer period than the other, the average output voltage will then be either negative or positive depending on the polarity of the input signal.

It can be seen then that it is the average output voltage that is proportional to the input signal. Since the output transistors function exclusively as switches, very little power loss occurs in the output stage.

A self oscillating PWM amplifier is one in which the squarewave generator, the pulse width modulator and the output stage formes a single

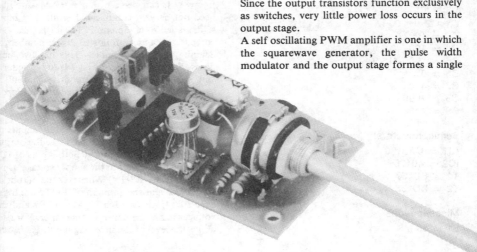

2

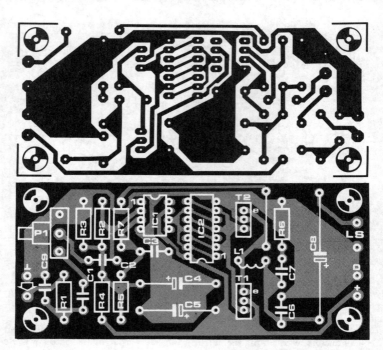

Figure 2. The printed circuit and parts layout of the PWM amplifier.

Parts list

Resistors:
R1 = 22 k
R2, R7 = 1 M
R3, R4 = 2k2
R5 = 470 k
R6 = 8 Ω 2
P1 = 100 k log. potentiometer

Capacitors:
C1, C2 = 100 n
C3 = 100 p
C4 = 100 µ /10 V
C5 = 100 µ /16 V
C6 = 68 n
C7 = 470 n
C8 = 1000 µ /10 V
C9 = 2n2

Semiconductors:
IC1 = CA3130
IC2 = 40106
T1 = BD137
T2 = BD138

Miscellaneous:
L1 = 39 µ H

unit. This produced an efficient amplifier with only a very small number of components. A version of this is described here.

The circuit diagram

The circuit of the complete amplifier is shown in figure 1. It can be seen that a PWM amplifier need not be very complicated at all. The input signal is fed to an opamp IC1. This is used as a comparator and is followed by a number of Schmitt triggers in parallel. This has two purposes. Firstly the waveform needs to be 'square' and secondly sufficient base drive current is needed for the output stage which uses two ordinary but fairly fast transistors (BD 137/138).

The entire amplifier oscillates and produces a squarewave. This is because one of the inputs of the comparator (IC1) is connected to the output by means of an RC network. Both inputs of IC1 are biased to one half of the supply voltage using voltage divider R3/R4. Whenever the output of IC1 is low and the emitters of T1/T2 are high, capacitor C3 is charged by way of R7 and the voltage rises at the non-inverting input. If it rises above the level of the inverting input, IC1's output changes low to high and the emitters of T1/T2 change from high to low. As a result, C3 is now discharged through R7, the voltage at the plus input drops below that of the minus input and the output of IC1 switches back to a low state. The result is a squarewave output; the frequency of which is determined by R7 and C3. The values given result in an oscillation at 700 kHz.

Provided Murphy doesn't get in the way, we should have an oscillator. Now we have to pulse width modulate it. The level at the inverting input of IC1, which is used as a reference, does not remain constant but is determined by the audio signal. The point at which the output of the comparator changes, is also determined by the amplitude. As a result the *width* of the squarewaves is constantly changed (modulated) by the audio signal.

At the output of the amplifier, filtering is required: it is not supposed to act as a 700 kHz transmitter! An LC/RC network is used, consisting of L1/C6 and C7/R6.

With a load of 8 ohms and a supply voltage of 12 volts, the amplifier produced 1.6 watts. At 4 ohms, 3 watts were measured. Cooling the output transistors was not necessary. The harmonic distortion proved to be surprisingly low for such a simple design. Less than 0.32% total harmonic distortion from 20 Hz-20 kHz was measured.

Figure 2 shows the printed circuit board and parts layout for the amplifier. Its construction requires little time and money, so it offers an excellent opportunity for anyone wanting to become better acquainted with PWM.

E. Postma

175 Mini drill speed control

Miniature electric drills have been available for some time. Most of them are battery powered. For precision work, it is useful to have a speed control; if constant speed can be maintained, independent of the load, so much the better. Both of these objectives can be achieved fairly simply, using an integrated voltage regulator.

Before going into the actual circuit, it is a good idea to take a brief look at how these little DC motors work. Why does the speed drop when the motor is loaded?

Normally, a fairly constant voltage is applied to the motor. Off load, the speed increases until the power consumption is exactly sufficient to cover the electrical and mechanical losses in the motor. When the motor is loaded, the speed drops. This reduces the back EMF, so the current through the motor increases; a new equilibrium is reached when the increased power consumption equals the reduced electrical and mechanical losses plus the power delivered to the load. In other words, the motor supplies the power required by the load — but at reduced speed. Obviously, there is a limit: if the motor is loaded too heavily, it will stop.

If the speed is to remain constant, the voltage across the motor will have to be increased when the motor is loaded. In this way, the current (and

the power output) can increase without affecting the speed.

In the circuit described here, the main active component is a voltage stabiliser IC, the 79G. This is a negative voltage regulator; it was chosen because its output voltage can be reduced to as low as −2.23 V. The minimum output voltage of its positive voltage counterpart, the 78G, is approximately 5 V. The extended control range at the low voltage end is important, since the motors in miniature drills are all fairly low voltage types — they are intended for battery use. This circuit can be used to power 2.5...12 V motors, with any current rating up to 1 A.

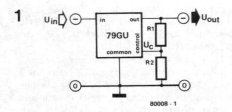

1

79GU

80008 - 1

As figure 1 illustrates, the basic regulator circuit using this IC is very simple. The output voltage is determined by the ratio between the two resistors, as follows:

$$U_{out} = \frac{R1 + R2}{R2} \times U_{control}$$

For the 79G, $U_{control}$ is -2.23 V.

As can be seen, the output voltage of this regulator is determined by the voltage on the control input – i.e. that at the R1/R2 junction in figure 1. To be more precise, it is the voltage between the control input and the 'common' connection that sets the output voltage. Knowing this, the actual circuit (figure 2) is not so difficult to understand.

When the motor is loaded, its speed will tend to drop. The current through the motor increases, producing a larger voltage drop across R2. The IC will now try to restore the original voltage difference between the 'control' and 'common' connections, by increasing its output voltage. This, in turn, means that more power is supplied to the motor – counteracting the tendency for the speed to drop.

Basically, this is a feedback system – and positive feedback, at that. For correct operation, the amount of feedback must obviously be set accurately. One solution would be to use a preset potentiometer for R2. This is not very practical, however: where do you find a 4.7 Ω pot that will happily tolerate a current of up to 1 A?

Adding P2 is an infinitely better solution. With its slider turned right up, the circuit becomes identical to that given in figure 1, as far as the regulator is concerned; the voltage across the motor is held constant. As the slider of P2 is turned down, more and more positive feedback is added. With P2 set correctly, the motor speed will remain almost constant, independent of load.

Construction

A suitable printed circuit board is given in figure 3. The only components not mounted on this board are the transformer, fuse, and potentiometer P1.

Having built the circuit, and before connecting the motor, an initial check is advisable. The slider of P2 is turned fully clockwise. Power is then applied, and P1 is set to maximum resist-

Figure 1. In the basic regulator circuit, the IC adjusts the output voltage to maintain a constant − 2.23 V between its control input and the 'common' connection. This means that the output voltage is determined by R1 and R2.

Figure 2. The complete circuit. P1 sets the motor speed; preset P2 is adjusted so that the speed remains constant under load. On some drills, a lower value for C2 and/or C3 may give better results. In fact, one of the drills we tried ran best when these capacitors were omitted!

Figure 3. Printed circuit board and component layout. Note that only two connections are provided to P1: the connection between the wiper and one end is made at the potentiometer.

2

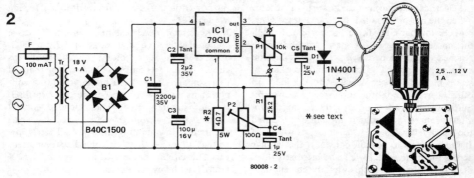

80008 - 2

3

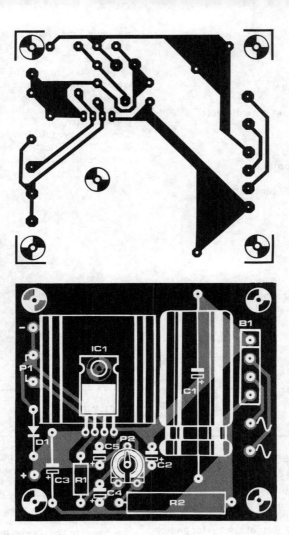

ance – corresponding to the maximum output voltage. This voltage (between the '+' and '–' output terminals) is measured. It should be safely below the maximum permissible motor voltage – say about 20% down. If it is too far off this value, the value of R1 will have to be modified: increasing R1 reduces the voltage, and reducing R1 brings the voltage up.

P1 is now turned back about halfway, and the drill is connected. Preset P2 is carefully adjusted so that the motor speed is on the verge of increasing. The idea is that too much feedback will cause the drill speed to run right up, out of control; too little feedback, on the other hand, will make the circuit less effective. It is possible that,

with a given motor, even the lowest setting of P2 is not low enough: the speed still drops when the motor is loaded. In that case, the value of R2 will have to be increased and the calibration procedure repeated.

Obviously, this circuit is no miracle worker. If the motor is loaded further when it is already running flat out, at maximum voltage, the speed will drop. Which is just as well – a higher voltage than the maximum permissible will burn out the motor. This is why it is so important to select the correct value for R1 – it determines the maximum voltage that can be applied to the motor. For that matter, it is a good idea to check this again once P2 has been adjusted: set P1 to

Parts list

Resistors:
R1* = 2k2
R2* = 4.7 Ω /5 W
P1 = 10 k lin.
P2 = 100 Ω preset potentiometer

Capacitors:
C1 = 2200 µ /35 V
C2 = 2µ2/35 V tantalum
C3 = 100 µ /16 V
C4, C5 = 1 µ /25 V tantalum

Semiconductors:
IC1 = 79GU
D1 = 1N4001
B1 = B40C1500

Sundries:
Tr = 18 V/1 A transformer
F = 100 mA fuse, sloblo
Heatsink for IC1

* see text

maximum, and measure the motor voltage as it is loaded more and more. It should not run up to more than 20% above the nominal motor voltage; if it does, the value of R1 will have to be increased further. Alternatively, a resistor can be included in parallel with P1 — reducing the maximum resistance value that can be set by this potentiometer.

There is no need to worry about damaging the IC — it is internally protected against output short-circuits and thermal overload.

---

176 Stop thief!

who wants to steal a car with engine trouble?

Protecting one's property is a popular hobby — particularly when that property is attractive to others. There are all sorts of systems for protecting cars, but the one described here is unusual: it is deception, rather than protection. It doesn't make it impossible to steal the car (for that matter, no system does), but it makes it very unattractive: who wants to steal a car with an engine that stalls every few yards?

Even the most effective of theft prevention systems normally suffer from the drawback that it is immediately apparent to a thief that some kind of protective device is built in. If he is sufficiently courageous, persistent and experienced, he can put the device out of action and make off with the car. If he's a professional thief, it's 'Goodbye, car!'; if he's joy-riding, you *may* just

be lucky... but normally the vehicle ends up severely crumpled or burned-out. An alarm system that sounds the car horn even seems to be attractive to certain types of 'joy-rider'. Amazing, but true.

All in all, no theft prevention system can be guaranteed to keep thieves out of your car. Once

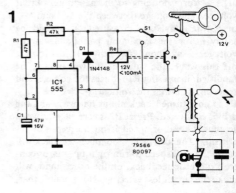

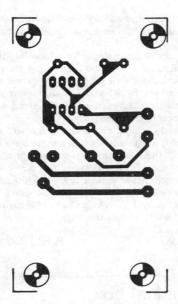

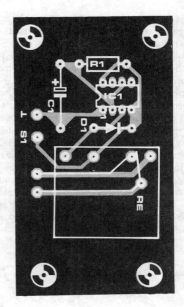

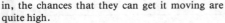

in, the chances that they can get it moving are quite high.

The system described here should give adequate protection against joy-riders. It should even discourage most 'professional' thieves – all except the type who is prepared to steal a furniture removal van first and then run your car into it! At the same time, this system has the advantage that it does the job on its own, without giving silent or raucous alarm signals to the owner or other passers-by. There's no need to chase after your property in the middle of the night, wearing only pyjamas and a dressing gown: you can rest assured that it will never end up far away. It is highly unlikely that the would-be thief will drive more than a few hundred yards. What is the basic principle behind such an effective system? Simple! The engine is about as reliable as that of a twenty-year old car with water in the petrol tank!

In practice

The wire from the positive side of the ignition

Figure 1. Only six components – cheap ones, at that! – are needed for a quite effective anti-theft device.

Figure 2. Printed circuit board and component layout. There is room for a miniature relay, but a larger type can be mounted off-board. 'Sound-proofing' is important!

Parts list:

Resistors:
R1 = 82 k

Capacitors:
C1 = 47 µ /16 V

Semiconductors:
IC1 = NE555 or equ.
D1 = 1N4148

Miscellaneous:
S1 = single-pole changeover switch
Re = 12 V/100 mA relay with heavy-duty break contact.

coil to the 12 V supply from the ignition switch is cut, and passed through the break contact of a relay. As long as the relay is not energised, power is supplied to the ignition coil and the engine runs smoothly. However, when the relay pulls in it breaks the connection. No power to the ignition coil – no spark – no go. One dead engine! It can be started again – no problem – and it will run as smoothly as before. Until the relay pulls in again, that is.

The circuit is given in figure 1. It is put into operation by operating switch S1. A 'secret' switch, of course. Bear in mind that the best place to hide a switch is very often the most obvious:

right in the middle of the dashboard, say. As long as you don't lable it 'theft protection'. Anyway, to get to the circuit: the timer IC (a 555) is used as a multivibrator. As soon as power is applied, via the ignition switch and S1, it starts to produce a squarewave output at about 0.2 Hz. A period time of 5 seconds, in other words. After bridging the ignition switch (that's how they do it), the thief can start the engine without any problems. However, after five seconds the relay pulls in. The ignition coil is cut off, and the engine stalls. After a few seonds of frustrated fiddling, the engine will fire again (the relay has dropped out!), but the feeling of achievement is doomed. Five seconds later, the engine will again stall. To sum it up: the engine *will* run, so apparently there is no theft prevention circuit in the car, but it conks out at short notice. Very frustrating for any thief. His best bet is to leave the car where it is and try someone else's. Always hoping *that* owner doesn't read this book as well.

The circuit can be modified, according to personal taste. The period time of the 555 (corresponding to the time that the engine will run) is determined by R1 and C1. Too short is suspicious, too long corresponds to a longer walk to your car next morning.

A printed circuit board and component layout for this unique anti-theft device are given in figure 2. There is room on the board for a miniature relay; a larger type can obviously be mounted 'off-board'. It is a good idea to look for a relatively 'silent' type, or else mount it in a sound-proof box. A loud Click as the engine cuts out would give the game away!

B.H.J. Bennink

177 Musical box

Readers who collect musical boxes will probably think that an 'electronic musical box' sounds as crazy as a gas telephone or a steam radio. After all, what made the musical box so enjoyable was winding it up and listening to its familiar tune. The circuit presented here shows that electronics can be used to replace the wear-prone internal workings of a musical box. In fact, an advantage over its old-fashioned counterpart is that this circuit is able to play no less than 27 tunes. Applications can also include toys, video games and doorbells.

As can be seen from figure 1, the actual melody generator is a single IC (IC4). It is the AY-3-1350 from General Instrument Microelectronics, a company with an excellent name for solid state musical devices. The circuitry around IC4 generates the clock signal, selects the melody required and amplifies the output level.

To select a particular tune, one of the connections marked A...E will have to be grounded and pin 15 of the melodic chip must be connected to one of the points marked 1...4. There are several ways in which the desired code can be presented to the IC. One method is to use wire links, another is to incorporate switches and a combination of the two is also possible. The printed circuit board has been designed to accomodate either of the two methods shown in figure 2.

If the circuit is constructed exactly as shown in figure 1 and wire links are placed between points K...N and R...V (see figure 2a), the following procedure will take place.

When one of the pushbuttons, $S_A...S_E$ is pressed, one of the points marked A...E will be connected to ground via one of the diodes D1... D5. Each pushbutton has a total of five melodies at its disposal. The choice can be cut down to one by means of a wire link. Thus, one of five predetermined melodies can be selected per switch and, in addition, two well-known chimes may be 'played' by depressing S_F or S_G. Table one shows the melodies which are available and the combination of connections required to select each one. The code numbers and letters correspond to those given in the circuit and in the component layout shown in figure 3.

The second method is to use a pair of multi-way

Figure 1. The complete circuit of the 'electronic musical box'.

Figure 2. Using wire links, as shown in figure 2a, five melodies can be pre-selected. If this is considered too much of a restriction, two five-way switches can be used, as shown in figure 2b.

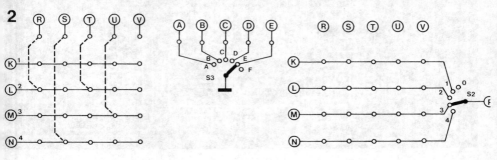

switches, in which case the area inside the dotted line in figure 1 may be omitted. This will enable any one of 25 melodies to be selected. As can be seen from figure 2b, points A...E can be grounded by means of a six position wafer switch, S3. Switch S2 connects one of the points K...N to point P. The melody will be initiated upon depressing S_F. Resistor R6 and the electronic switch ES5 are not necessary for this latter option. They are shown outside the dotted line

as ES5 is contained in a separate IC to ES1... ES4.

The oscillator is formed by C7, R8 and P1 together with part of IC4. The pitch of the melody being played can be adjusted by P1, the length of each note can be adjusted by P2, leav-

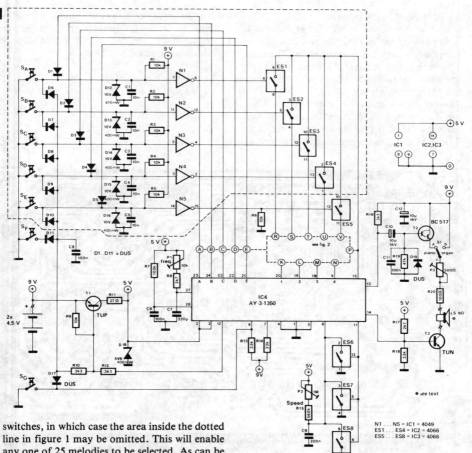

197

ing P3 to regulate the volume.

Two 4.5 V batteries are all that is required to power the circuit as the quiescent current consumption is only a few microamps. Transistor T1 and the zener diode D18 are included to drop the voltage down to 5 V for those parts of the circuit requiring a lower voltage.

The nominal loudspeaker impedance is 8 , but if one with a higher impedance is to be used, the value of R20 can be reduced accordingly. Switch S1 is still to be mentioned. Its function is

to select between a 'piano' sound with slow decay (position (a)) and a constant volume 'organ' sound (position (b)). It should keep the children amused for hours!

3

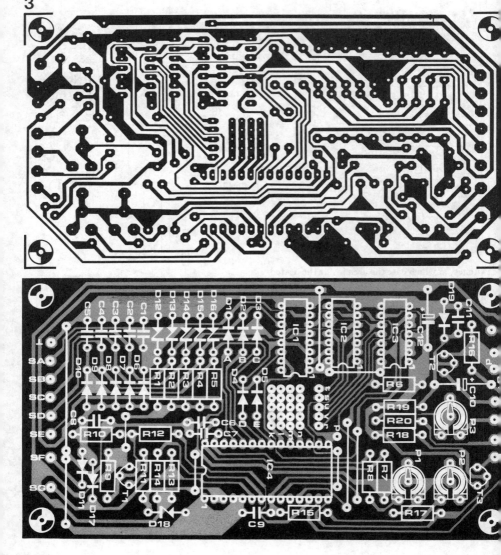

Parts list

Resistors:

R1...R6, R9 = 10 k
R7 = 100 k
R8, R17 = 2k7
R10, R12, R16 = 3k3
R11 = 27 Ω
R13, R14, R18 = 33 k
R15 = 560 k
R19 = 47 k
R20 = 100 Ω
P1 = 10 k preset
P2 = 1 M preset
P3 = 500 Ω preset

Capacitors:

C1...C5 = 10 n
C6, C8, C11 = 100 n
C7 = 220 p
C9 = 220 n
C10, C12 = 10 Ω /16 V

Semiconductors:

D1...D11, D17, D19 = DUS
D12...D16 = 10 V/400 mW zener
D18 = 5V6/400 mW zener
T1 = TUP
T2 = BC 517
T3 = TUN
IC1 = 4049
IC2, IC3 = 4066
IC4 = AY-3-1350

Miscellaneous:

SA...SG = pushbutton switch
S1 = S.P.D.T.
S2 = 5 position wafer switch
S3 = 6 position wafer switch
LS = 8 Ω /0.5 W loudspeaker (see text)

Table 1

figure 2a	figure 2b		melody
		S2	S3	
–	S_A	0	A	Toreador
–	S_B	0	B	William Tell
–	S_C	0	C	Hallelujah Chorus
–	S_D	0	D	Star Spangled Banner
–	S_E	0	E	Yankee Doodle
KR	S_A	1	A	John Brown's Body
KS	S_B	1	B	Clementine
KT	S_C	1	C	God Save The Queen
KU	S_D	1	D	Colonel Bogey
KV	S_E	1	E	Marseillaise
LR	S_A	2	A	America, America
LS	S_B	2	B	Deutschland Lied
LT	S_C	2	C	Wedding March
LU	S_D	2	D	Beethoven's 5th
LV	S_E	2	E	Augustine
MR	S_A	3	A	A Sole Mio
MS	S_B	3	B	Santa Lucia
MT	S_C	3	C	The End
MU	S_D	3	D	Blue Danube
MV	S_E	3	E	Brahm's Lullaby
NR	S_A	4	A	Hell's Bells (specially composed)
NS	S_B	4	B	Jingle Bells
NT	S_C	4	C	La Vie en Rose
NU	S_D	4	D	Star Wars
NV	S_E	4	E	Beethoven's 9th
	S_F			Descending Octave Chime
	S_G			Westminster Chime

178 Din can

The number of possible applications for noise emitting circuits is absolutely astounding — far too many to be listed in the available space. This is particularly true of the unit described here. Although not exactly original in concept, the can is capable of producing a din which will almost certainly leave your ears tingling for quite a while.

The circuit consists of very few components which together form a 'Kojak' type siren. The majority of the work is done by two (555) timer ICs. The first (IC1) generates an audible tone whose frequency can be adjusted by means of potentiometer P1. The output of this timer is fed directly to a loudspeaker. The loudspeaker however does not emit a constant tone, as IC1 is

199

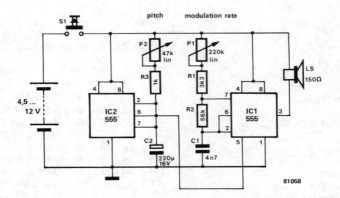

Figure 1. IC1 generates a tone which is modulated in frequency by IC2.

modulated by a low frequency sawtooth waveform generated by IC2. The frequency of the sawtooth can be regulated by means of potentiometer P2. As a result, the complete circuit generates a frequency modulated signal which sounds just like a siren. The pitch can be adjusted with P1 and the modulation rate with P2.

The circuit is compact enough to be mounted in a can together with the batteries and loudspeaker

and can be used quite successfully on children's cycles, skate boards etc. or as an 'anti-attack' alarm.

L. van Ginderen

179 Transistor curve tracer

I_C/U_{CE} characteristics directly onto the screen

There are never enough simple circuits which provide useful and low-cost additions to the 'home lab'. This particular design possesses all the advantages to make it a glorious example of its kind. It offers oscilloscope owners a neat,

additional measurement facility. It is easy to build, contains common parts and is inexpensive. Reason enough to design a printed circuit board for it.

The design

This is an economic curve tracer for transistors and diodes. No really professional test instru-

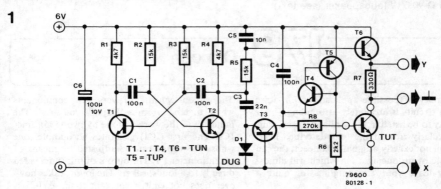

ment, of course, but an extremely useful aid to quickly carry out a general test either to compare transistors or select them. Naturally, hobbyists will have to have an oscilloscope (with separate x and y inputs), because the curves will be displayed on the oscilloscope screen.

Since it is impossible to tell which transistor characteristic is more important than another, there is no such thing as the 'most important curve'. Transistor handbooks speak of the most read curve. This involves the I_C/U_{CE} characteristics where the collector current is plotted as a function of the collector/emitter voltage at different drive currents. Figure 2 gives an example of such a characteristic. At the same time it (roughly) indicates the drive currents the curve tracer uses. The current amplification may be directly derived from the I_C/U_{CE} characteristics and, after a few calculations, so may the transistor's output impedance. The latter is affected by the curve's slope. Generally speaking, the more horizontal and straight it is, the higher the collector/emitter impedance.

Back to the schematic. The transistor under test is indicated as 'TUT' as usual. Between the points which are connected to the Y input and the ground connection of the oscilloscope 'hangs' resistor R7. This is the TUT's collector resistor and the voltage across it is naturally proportional to the collector current of the transistor tested. In this way, an 'I_C' will appear on the vertical axis of the oscilloscope. The TUT's emitter is connected to the X input so that the collector/emitter voltage (U_{CE}) can be read horizontally on the screen.

What causes the curves to appear on the screen? Two signals are fed to the TUT. A 5 step position staircase waveform is fed to the base and during each step a sawtooth is fed to the collector. This means the collector voltage changes continually at a certain base drive current. This occurs at quite a speed so that the oscilloscope screen simultaneously shows 5 characteristics for 5 different base drive currents. The staircase signal and the sawtooth waveform are controlled by means of an astable multivibrator. The AMV consists of T1 and T2 and generates a square wave with a frequency of approximately 1 kHz.

Figure 1. The circuit diagram of the curve tracer.

Figure 2. I_C/U_{CE} curves of a transistor. In our circuit five different base drives are measured.

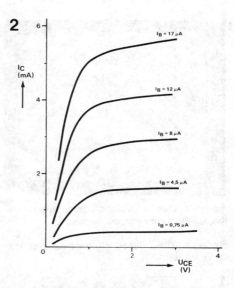

The sawtooth is obtained very easily by integrating the square wave via R5 and C5. Creating the staircase voltage is a little more complicated. During the positive half-cycle of the square wave produced by the AMV, C3 is charged to a maximum which is equal to the supply voltage. During the negative half-cycle, C3 will turn on transistor T3 and thus the voltage at T4's emitter (connected to the TUT's base via R8) will become a little lower. By loading C4 intermittently, each successive negative half-cycle will reduce the emitter voltage of T4 in steps until T4 starts to conduct turning on T5. C4 is soon discharged and a new cycle starts.

The number of stages which make up a single cycle is determined by the ratio of C3 to C4 and is 5 here. By adjusting the value of C4 the number of stages (and thus the number of curves indicated on the screen) can be changed as required.

In practice

The photo in figure 3 shows how the curves appear on the oscilloscope screen. The circuit's only flaw now comes to light — the characteristics are traced from right to left, instead of the other way around. Unfortunately, nothing can be done about this. In practice it does not present a problem. What is serious however, is that the tracer is only suitable for NPN transistors. NPN types cannot be tested with it. If this is considered to be a drawback, however, there is a cheap solution: two printed circuit boards may

3

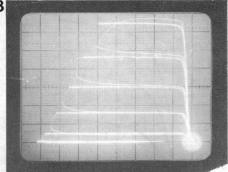

Figure 3. This is how the curves appear on the oscilloscope screen.

Figure 4. The printed circuit board of the curve tracer.

4

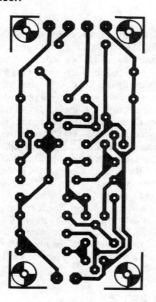

Parts list

Resistors:
R1, R4 = 4k7
R2, R3, R5 = 15 k
R6 = 2k2
R7 = 330 Ω
R8 = 270 k

Capacitors:
C1, C2, C4 = 100 n
C3 = 22 n
C5 = 10 n
C6 = 100 μ /10 V

Semiconductors:
T1...T4, T6 = TUN
T5 = TUP
D1 = DUG

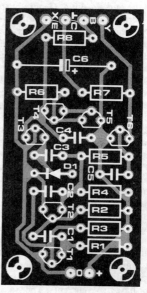

be built instead of one. The circuit requires few components, so why not? The second circuit will then be a PNP version. For T1...T4 and T6 use TUPs, T5 will be a TUN, C6, D1 and the supply leads will be switched around. Furthermore, such a PNP version will trace the curves from left to right, only now the Y axis will be negative so that they will appear upside down on the screen. A little strange perhaps, but you'll soon get used to it...

As mentioned above, diodes may also be tested. These are connected with the anode to R7 (⊥) and the cathode to the supply zero (X). The I/U characteristics of the diode in question will now appear on the screen. Figure 4 shows the printed circuit board. It is highly compact and can be built in less than no time.

Last word. Since the circuit only requires a few mA, the supply will not have to be very 'heavily' tested. However, the supply voltage must be well regulated for it to work properly.

B. Darnton

180 Infrared transmitter

This is a very simple circuit and is really intended for hobbyists who like experimenting with infrared or with VFETs, or even both, for that's what this is all about.

The circuit diagram shows an infrared transmitter in its simplest, most elementary form. Its simplicity is achieved with the aid of a VFET. Since FETs unlike other bipolar transistors, reveal a neat linear input to output voltage ratio, it is enough to feed a low frequency signal to the gate and to include an infrared LED in the drain lead. The intensity of the infrared light produced by the LED will then vary according to that of the LF voltage put across it and there you have it — a transmitter.

In order to increase the infrared LED's lifespan, a transistor has been added to achieve current limitation, thereby reducing the FET's maximum drain current to about 60 mA. If the current were to rise, the voltage across R2 would become so high that T2 starts to conduct and the gate of the FET is then short circuited to ground. The low frequency modulation signal which is supplied needs to have a value of around 250 mV$_{eff}$ if the transmitter is to achieve full output. Potentiometer P1 is preset with the input short circuited, so that a voltage of 0.3 volts (drain current 30 mA) is measured across R2.

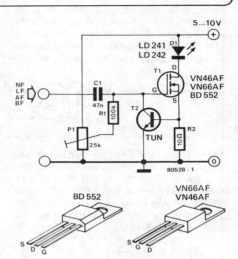

It doesn't matter what type of VFET or what type of infrared LED is used. This is why various types are given in the schematic. In the event of insufficient 'transmission power' several infrared LEDs may be connected in series, as required.

ITT applications

181 Infrared receiver

A transmitter needs a receiver. A receiver will be described here to act as a counterpart to the infrared transmitter. Again, simplicity itself with the aid of a VFET.

The infrared light which falls on the infrared photo diode (here a BPW34 type, but any other will also do) will cause the voltage across R1 to vary. This will of course affect the VFET's gate and the drain current, therefore, will fluctuate according to the modulation of the infrared light received. The modulation can be heard with a set of headphones.

Such simplicity of course has its disadvantages.

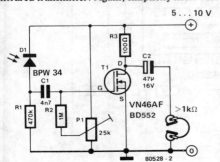

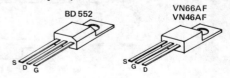

For instance, mains light bulbs which happen to be 'on' in the vicinity will be heard as a humming noise. In quiet surroundings, however, fair reception is possible within a range of a few metres, which can be extended by using lenses and other optical aids. With a few infrared LEDs and a photodiode this transmitter/receiver combination can be built very easily. It really works and is ideal for experiments.

One other thing... for it to function properly, P1 will have to be preset so that when the photodiode is completely shielded from light, exactly half the supply voltage will be measured on the FET's drain.

ITT applications

182 Frequency conversion using the XR 2240

Frequency conversion can be carried out very easily with the aid of this IC. For instance, when using American clock ICs there may be a requirement to convert a signal with a frequency of 50 Hz into a signal with a frequency of 60 Hz. The formula for determining the output frequency of the XR 2240 is:

$$f_o = \frac{m}{N + 1} \cdot f_{in}$$

where

f_o = the output frequency

m = the ratio of the input frequency to the time base frequency. This ratio is determined by the position of the potentiometer and is a whole number between 1 and 10.

N = a whole number between 1 and 255 which may be selected by connecting one or more of pins 1...8.

f_{in} = the input frequency

When $m = 6$ and $N = 4$ the output frequency will be 60 Hz for an input frequency of 50 Hz. Similarly, when $m = 5$ and $N = 5$ the output frequency will be 50 Hz for an input frequency of 60 Hz.

The XR 2240 contains a control flip-flop FF, a time base generator TB and an eight bit binary counter. The period T of the signal produced by the time base generator is determined by the RC product of the components connected to pin 13. Signals are then available at the outputs on pins 1...8 with periods of T, 2T, 4T, 8T, 16T, 32T, 64T and 128T respectively.

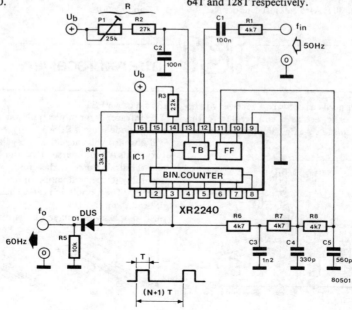

80501

204

If, for example, the outputs T and 4T (pins 1 and 3) are connected to the 3k3 pull up resistor (R4), the generated signal will have a period of T + 4T = 5T. This provides the 'N' factor given in the formula.

A positive going input signal at pin 12 will trigger the time base generator and reset the binary counter. The counter will then operate until the next positive going input pulse occurs.

In the circuit shown the required output frequency is 60 Hz for an input frequency of 50 Hz. Therefore, the frequency of the time base generator needs to be preset to the sixth harmonic of

50 Hz which is 300 Hz (m = 6). This is accomplished with the aid of the potentiometer. With the output from pin 3 (4T) connected, the result is N = 4.

The circuit will operate satisfactorily with a supply voltage of between 4 and 15 volts. With a supply voltage of 9 volts the current comsumption is approximately 8 mA. The synchronisation (input) signal needs to be a square wave with a minimum amplitude of 3 V. The maximum frequency of the time base generator is quoted as being 100 kHz (C2 = 6n8, R = P1 + R2 = 1 k).

183 Sensibell

Remember the old-fashioned copper bell-on-a-chain? In many ways it had considerable advantages over its modern electronic counterparts, advantages which were probably not appreciated at the time. It happened to provide a lot of useful information about the visitor. The way in which he rang — loud, soft, long, short, repeatedly, persistently, etc. said a great deal about him. All this of course is lost with the splendid electronic versions of today.

There are two ways of salvaging the old type of doorbell. First, you can hunt around until you find one in a second-hand shop. After all, they use very little electricity. Second, the electronic way, which is to build a 'Sensibell'.

The important component involved is a piezo

element, from an ultrasonic transducer. When a voltage is connected to it it becomes distorted, when distorted it produces a voltage. If we use the element as a bellpush, two voltage peaks are obtained — one when it is pressed and one when released. The height of the voltage peaks corresponds to the pressing force. The interval between both peaks depends on how long the button is pressed.

A simple solution is to construct a ding-dong-bell where the volume of, and duration between

A1 . . . A3 = IC1,IC2,IC3 = 741 DIP
N1 . . . N4 = IC4 = 4011

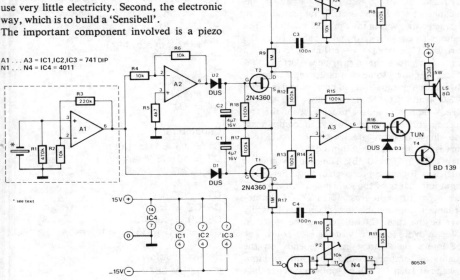

* see text

80535

'ding' and 'dong' is determined by the caller. The circuit diagram shows how this is done. The signal originating from the piezo crystal is amplified by A1. Because of the high impedance of piezo elements A1 is best mounted in the doorbell push button. The low impedance output of the amplifier as well as the supply voltage connections can then be connected to the rest of the circuit by a four-core cable. The output of A1 is inverted by A2 so that positive pulses are available both at the beginning and the end of the bell signal. Via T1 and T2 these signals are used to shape the envelopes which modulate the amplitude of two oscillators. The two oscillators produce the 'ding' and 'dong' and are constructed around a single 4011 IC. Their pitch can be preset with P1 and P2 respectively.

A simple output amplifier (T3/T4) completes the circuit.

One word of advice − it is best to power the LF amplifier separately − from the rectified bell transformer voltage, for example. The double 15 V supply then only has to provide a few mA. If after installing the device, the bell sounds like a 'dong-ding' instead of a 'ding-dong', this can be remedied by exchanging the piezo element connections. In any case, the piezo element needs to be removed from its original case with the greatest of care before the connecting wires can be soldered to it.

The element can be protected against outside influences with a coat of epoxy resin or double compound glue.

W. van Dreumel

184 Stereo dynamic preamplifier

The circuit diagram shows how simple it is to use it to build a high quality dynamic preamplifier using just one opamp, in this case the LM 387 from National.

The input impedance has the standard value of 47 k, and is almost exclusively determined by the value of R1. R1 (metal film) may be altered for cartridges requiring a different terminal impedance, to achieve a straight reproduction characteristic, within the range 22 k...100 k. The same is true of the terminal capacitance of the cartridge. The average was estimated to be 100 p for C5 whereas some cartridges (Ortofon included) require a somewhat larger capacitance.

By connecting capacitors in parallel and in series (C3/C4 and C6/C7 respectively), the official RIAA time constants are achieved in the frequency compensating network. If components with high tolerance are used, the ideal RIAA curve is approached to within 1 dB.

Gain is set at 100 (40 dB). The output voltage is sufficient for most pre/control amplifiers. The input impedance of the following control amplifier needs to be at least 100 k Ω. If the impedance is considerably lower, which will hardly ever be the case, C9 will have to be raised in value to avoid losing any of the bass notes. The maximum signal/noise ratio depends on the quality of components used, but with an input voltage of 10 mV it will be somewhat better than 80 dB.

If we double everything shown in the diagram with the exception of the decoupling com-

Parts list

(everything 2x, except for IC1, R7, C8 and C10)

Resistors:
R1 = 47 k (metal film)
R2, R6 = 100 k
R3 = 1 k
R4 = 10 k
R5 = 1 M
R7 = 1 Ω

Capacitors:
C1 = 1 μ /6 V tantalum
C2 = 10 μ /6 V tantalum
C3 = 2n7
C4 = 470 p
C5 = 100 p
C6, C7 = 1n5
C8, C9 = 100 n
C10 = 0,47 μ /35 V tantalum

Semiconductors:
IC1 = LM 387

1

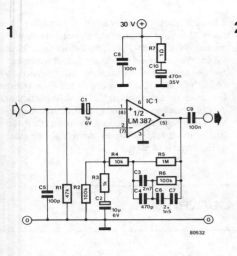

2

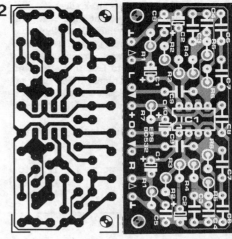

ponents (C8, C10, R7) a stereo dynamic pre-amplifier can be constructed. Because of the small size of the IC and the few components re-quired, a highly compact printed circuit board can be made, for which room can be found in the majority of pre/control amplifiers.

185

4.4 MHz crystal filter

When building a communication receiver one of the main problems encountered is how to obtain the high selectivity required. If an interchannel spacing of 9 to 10 kHz (used for AM broadcasting) is maintained, an excellent filter is needed. One advantage of this type of filter is that fairly cheap crystals can be used. These are called PAL crystals and, because they are used in every (PAL) colour TV set, they can often be bought at a very reasonable price. Their only possible disadvantage is that the receiver design includes a rather outlandish crystal frequency of 4.433 618 MHz, as far as the IF is concerned.

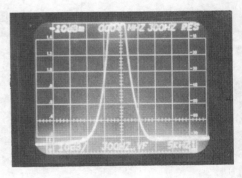

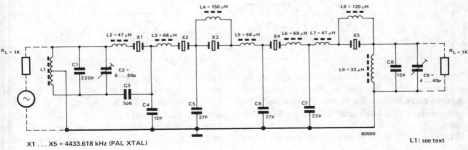

X1 . . . X5 = 4433.618 kHz (PAL XTAL)

L1: see text

Often, however, this forms an excellent IF.
The circuit diagram shows that it is a 'ladder filter' with a total of 5 crystals. Generally speaking, this configuration will produce a low-pass filter, in other words, with asymmetrical pass characteristics. The photo here shows that, on the contrary, the by-pass obtained is highly symmetrical due to a few design tricks. The 6 dB bandwidth is 5.2 kHz and the −60 dB points are at 12.4 kHz.
Out of all the coils included in the design, only

L1 needs to be wound by hand. It consists of 15 turns of 0.4 mm copper enamelled wire double wound on an AMIDON T50-2 ring core. Time saved by not having to make L2...L9 which can be bought ready-made, can be used to carefully build the filter. This is always worth while where HF circuits are concerned. In this particular case, for instance, it is highly important to separate the various filter sections by means of metal partitions. It is also wise to connect all the cases of the crystals to earth.

186 Converter

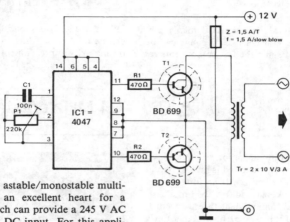

The 4047 low power astable/monostable multivibrator constitutes an excellent heart for a simple converter which can provide a 245 V AC output from a 12 V DC input. For this application, of course, the IC is connected in the astable mode. The symmetrical squarewave signals available at the Q and Q̄ outputs are amplified by a pair of darlington transistors (T1 and T2) and then fed to the secondary winding of a low voltage transformer (2 x 10 V 60 VA). The

245 V AC output is then available from the primary winding of the transformer. The frequency of the output voltage can be varied between 50 and 400 Hz by adjusting the preset potentiometer P1.

M. Cafaxe

187 Simple opamp tester

This circuit is similar in principle to, and can be mounted in the same box as, the 555 tester described elsewhere in this book. The opamp to be tested is connected as a simple square-wave oscillator.
When pushbutton S1 is closed, the non-inverting

input of the opamp is held at a reference voltage derived from the output voltage and the potential divider R2/R3. The current through R1 is used to charge capacitor C1 until the voltage level on the inverting input reaches that of the reference voltage. Since the opamp acts as a

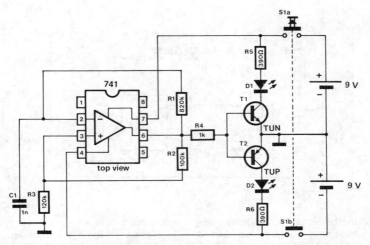

comparator, its output level will change state thereby producing a reference voltage of opposite polarity. The charge current for C1 will then flow in the opposite direction until the new reference voltage is reached and the whole cycle will be repeated.

When the output is high, transistor T1 will conduct and LED D1 will be on. Conversely, when the output is low T2 will conduct and LED D2 will be on. The transistors are included so that other opamps with the same pin-out as, but less current output than, the 741 can be tested.

The circuit requires a positive and negative power supply and will operate satisfactorily from two 9 volt batteries.

188 Automatic cycle lighting

This simple circuit (figure 1) ensures a great improvement in road safety for nocturnal cyclists. The light remains on when the cyclist stops at traffic lights — a battery supplies the current. During the trip with lights switched on (supplied by the bicycle dynamo) the battery, a parallel connection of four nicads, is charged across D1 and R1 and the relay is operated. When the bicycle stops, the relay drops out and it now connects the bulb to the battery. The one thing to remember of course, is to switch off the lights at the end of the ride, but even this can be electronicised. Figure 2 gives a suitably extended version of the circuit.

Forgetting the lights need now no longer be a problem with this luxury version, which switches the lights off automatically after about 3 minutes. The circuit is of course a little more elaborate than the standard model.

The battery is charged in the same way during the ride with the lights switched on. When the bicycle is halted at a traffic light the voltage is no longer supplied by the dynamo. The trigger input of IC1 (pin 2) then receives a negative pulse and the relay is energised. Now the lights

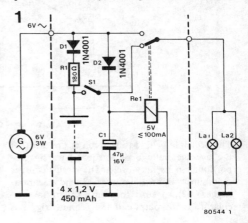

80544 1

209

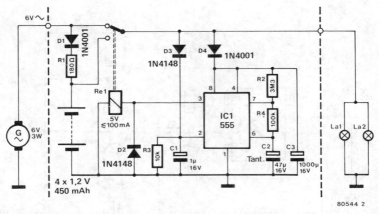

are supplied by the battery (through the relay contacts) until the voltage at pin 6 has reached the level of the internal reference voltage. Then the relay drops out again and the lights and the entire circuit are cut off from the battery. The time is preset by R2 and C2 to approximately 3 minutes. That is more time than a red light takes, believe it or not.

If this luxury version is used on bicycles with a hub dynamo and a switch in the headlamp, it may be useful to mount a switch between the dynamo and the input to the circuit. Not that it draws much power, but the relay clicking in and out could be a nuisance!

189 Voltage controlled duty-cycle

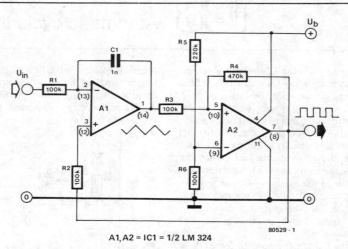

A1, A2 = IC1 = 1/2 LM 324

80529 - 1

The principle behind this circuit is the fact that the average voltage of a squarewave is proportional to its duty-cycle. The circuit consists quite simply of an integrator (A1) and a Schmitt-trigger (A2), together forming a squarewave oscillator. If the output of the Schmitt-trigger is low the output of A1 will gradually decrease until the lower threshold of A2 is reached. The output of A2 will then go high (just less than the supply voltage) causing the integrator output to rise until the upper threshold is reached and the Schmitt-trigger output goes low again.

By altering the voltage level on the inverting input of A1 the integrator's characteristics can be altered. As the trigger thresholds of A2 are fixed, the result is a change in duty-cycle. The average voltage of the squarewave output will always be equal to the input voltage, but the frequency will remain constant. In this way the duty-cycle can be varied between 0% and 100%. The control voltage may be anywhere between 0 V and 1.5 V less than the supply voltage.

When the LM 324 is used, the supply voltage may be anywhere between 3 V and 30 V. If another type of opamp is used, the control range may become limited.

190 Exposure meter and development timer

A great deal has been published about exposure meters and development timers in electronic magazines. However, it is very rare to find an article covering both devices at the same time. For this reason a combination design is presented here. As usual an LDR (light-dependent resistor) has been included in the bridge circuit of the exposure meter. The amount of light falling on the LDR determines the degree of imbalance in the bridge network. During measurement, relay Re1 is activated via S2e and the enlarger is turned on. Balance is then restored manually by adjusting potentiometer P1. The final value of P1 will correspond to the exposure time required.

Indication that the bridge is in balance is given by two LEDs (D7 and D8). Of course, this could also be indicated on a centre-zero meter but this could be difficult to read in the dark and would probably be more expensive than two LEDs. The circuit is in balance when both LEDs are extinguished.

Once the above procedure has been carried out switch S2 is changed to its other position. The circuit will now operate as a development timer. The value of P1, together with C3, now determines the pulse duration of the monostable multivibrator IC2. The timer is started when push-button S3 is pressed. The output then goes high activating the relay and lighting the enlarger lamp. LEDs D5 and D6 are optional and are used to illuminate the panel of the case in which the circuit is mounted. If a single pole double-throw relay is used then it is possible to switch the exposure lights off when switching on the enlarger lamp.

The role of potentiometer P2 has not yet been discussed. It enables the characteristics of the bridge amplifier to be altered to suit different kinds of paper, and should be provided with a suitable scale. The usefulness of the circuit will depend on how well it is calibrated.

Readers who wish to carry out spot measurements can simply mount the LDR into a cardboard tube. This is then placed inside a metal film can and covered by a piece of perspex which has been slightly sanded with emery paper. For details see figure 2. When measuring the exposure time the perspex can be removed and a larger piece placed directly under the enlarger lamp. No details of the negative will be visible when the enlarger is switched on. The perspex is, of course, removed during exposure.

The circuit is calibrated by making test strips. Potentiometer P2 is given a linear scale division numbered 1...20. With S2 in the 'time' position,

1

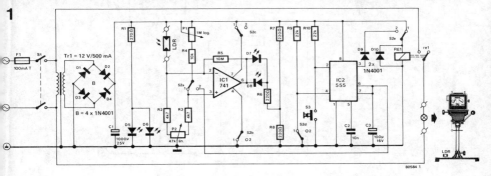

2

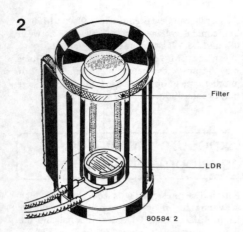

Filter

LDR

80584 2

P1 is adjusted until a set of whole numbers is obtained which correspond to the length of time the lamp is on. This will form the scale for P1. Once this has been done a test strip is made using the old method.

The same exposure time is then selected with P1. Test strips are made with P2 in various positions until the best results are obtained. The positions of P1 and P2 are then written on the test strips to provide the correct coding for all types of paper.

D.S. Barrett

191 AFC via the tuning diode

Some receivers have Varicap tuning, but no AFC. IF this facility is desired, it seems a pity to have to add yet another Varicap. The principle of the circuit described here is that the voltage on the Varicap tuning diodes in a receiver is automatically affected by the AFC voltage. This is achieved by connecting the common pin of an integrated fixed voltage regulator with the AFC control voltage, instead of to ground. This not only causes the total output voltage to rise, but also enables it to be controlled.

The AFC voltage from the demodulator is buffered with the aid of an opamp, after which it is fed to the voltage regulator. Part of the quiescent current of the regulator flows through R3,

and at the same time this resistor provides a defined terminating impedance for the opamp. The AFC voltage from most demodulators is roughly 4.5 V (within ± 0.5 V) and the quiescent current of the voltage regulator is approximately 3 mA. In order to control the output voltage over a large enough range and allow the circuit to behave in a stable manner, the opamp will have to sink 2/3 of the quiescent current. From this R3 may be calculated as follows:

$$R3 = \frac{4.5 \ (\text{volt})}{1 \ (\text{mA})} = 4500 \ \Omega$$

Therefore, 4k7 was chosen here.
To avoid oscillation the opamp is compensated

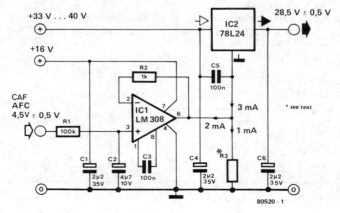

80520 - 1

by C3 and the voltage regulator is decoupled with C5. The LM 308 type was chosen as a buffer (IC1) because of its low input current (only 3 nA) and its very low drift.

The circuit's current consumption is approximately 300 µ A.

The AFC voltage is fed to the input by means of a low-pass filter (R1 and C2) which causes any interfering signals to be thoroughly suppressed. It also ensures quiet, stable AFC control. To switch off the AFC the input voltage of the circuit is preset to the average value of the AFC voltage.

S. Hering

192 Wind-o-meter

This device utilises the fact that an air current has a cooling effect on an object which is warmer than its surroundings. The object cooled in this case is a transistor (T2) which is connected as a diode. To make it warmer than its surroundings it has been thermally coupled to a transistor (T1) which has a current flowing through it continuously. The wind's speed is measured by comparing the voltage across the cooling diode with that across a reference diode (T3). These two voltages are fed to the non-inverting and inverting inputs respectively of an opamp.

This amplifier, which is preset for a gain of 1000, passes a current through the heating transistor via resistor R1. When the wind cools the diode, the forward voltage across that diode rises (2 mV/°C) causing the voltage at the non-inverting input of the opamp to increase. As a result, the output voltage of the opamp rises to provide more base drive current for T1 thereby generating more heat in this transistor. The opamp thus tries to compensate for the tempera-

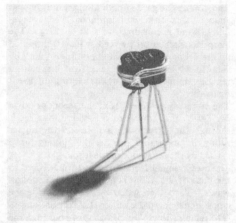

ture drop, which leads to an increase in T1's collector current.

A high sensitivity is obtained by making the temperature of T2 about 5 degrees higher than its

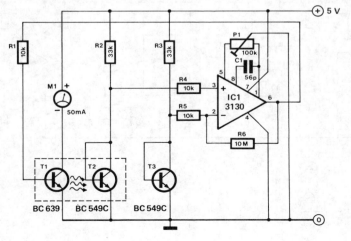

surroundings. This is achieved by presetting the meter to give an offset of about 5 mA when there is no wind blowing. Resistor R1 is selected so that the current through T1 is not excessive.

In the circuit, T1 is shown as a BC 639, but a BC 547 type may also be used: the maximum collector current must then be limited to 100 mA. If the circuit tends to oscillate, the gain of IC1 should be reduced − by increasing the value of R5.

The photograph shows the construction of the wind detector. The two transistors are coupled by glueing their flat sides together with a heat conducting adhesive.

193 Garden path lighting

Plant a new bulb in your garden! This circuit will lead you up the garden path at night in safety. It enables the path to be illuminated whenever required, and it consumes very little energy. The lamp is switched on by reed switches, mounted in the front door and in the garden gate. By using a 24 V lorry bulb, electrical installation remains simple and safe while ensuring sufficient light.

The circuit is powered from the secondary of a 24...30 V/5 A transformer. Where long leads through the garden are a necessity the higher rating is preferable due to the voltage drop caused by the resistance of the leads.

The 50 Hz signal from the transformer is fed to the base of T2 which converts it into a square-wave. This is then gated by N2 to provide the clock signal for the counter IC2, for as long as Q14 remains low. As soon as Q14 goes high the clock signal is blocked. Transistors T3...T5 form a zero-crossing detector which is also controlled by the 50 Hz signal. Each time the transformer

voltage crosses zero the collector of T5 is pulled low for 100 s. This pulse arrives at the base of T1 via the buffer N1. This transistor is used to control the triac which in turn switches the lamp on at every zero-crossing. The light will, of course, appear to be on continuously for as long as Q14 remains low. The path will be illuminated for nearly three minutes − long enough for someone to walk up the average path and open the front door.

The circuit is activated when the reset input of the counter is taken high. For this to happen, both inputs of N4 must be low. One of these inputs to N4 is controlled by an opamp whose output is determined by the amount of light falling on an LDR (light-dependent resistor). A certain amount of hysteresis has been incorporated in this part of the circuit. As long as there is sufficient daylight the output of IC1 will be high. The reset input of the counter will remain low thereby inhibiting the system. As darkness draws in the output of IC1 will go low (the actual level

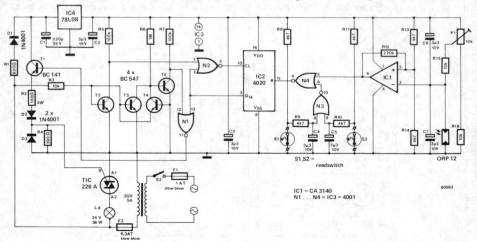

can be preset by means of P1) enabling one of the inputs to N4. The other input to N4 is taken low when one of the two reed switches (S1 or S2) opens and closes, when the garden gate or front door is opened and closed. This fulfils the condition that both inputs of N4 must be low and the inhibit is removed from the counter enabling operation (and illumination).

Thin twin-lead cable can be used for the reed switches, but thicker wire (about 2.5 mm²) is required for the lamp. Current consumption is approximately 100...150   A when the lamp is not on.

B.E. Kerley

194 Hybrid cascode

It is general knowledge that cascoding two or more transistors creates a new transistor with better characteristics than the individual ones (see figure 1). These include a very slight retroaction from point C ('collector') to point B ('base') and a higher collector impedance, thus a much better approach to current source operation at point C.

In the all transistor version of figure 1, the base of T2 will have to be fed a certain voltage with respect to the emitter of T1 -0.6 volts (D1 in figure 1) at least.

If T2 is replaced by an N channel FET, the DC bias of the cascode will be a lot easier to preset — see figure 2. As far as slope is concerned (i.e.

the ratio between collector current and base voltage) both versions are equally good.

195 Digital sinewave generator

More and more information is being generated by digital means, because of the good frequency and amplitude stability obtained. This particular circuit generates a sinewave, but if R1...R8 were to assume other values, different waveforms would also be possible.

After the supply voltage has been applied, the R9/C1 network ensures a short reset pulse: all outputs become logic zero. Since output 8 is also '0', the inverted level ('1') is offered at input D. With the aid of an external oscillator (not drawn) pulses are fed to the clock inputs. At every positive slope the information in the shift register IC1 moves one place further along. Thus, after the first clock pulse Q1 will be '1' and after the eighth Q8 will also be '1'. As soon as Q8 becomes logic 1 however, the information at input D will change to logic 0. Then zero's will be entered until Q8 also changes to '0'. The en-

tire operation is then repeated. By choosing suitable values for R1...R8 the output voltage is converted into a sinewave.

The output frequency is one sixteenth of the clock frequency. The CMOS IC can process up

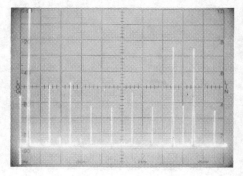

215

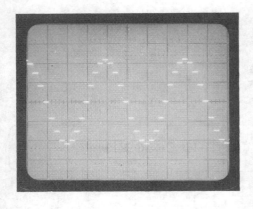

to 7 MHz so that the maximum output frequency is about 0.5 MHz. Gate N1 may be of any type provided that the signal is inverted.

The two photo's show the waveform and the frequency spectrum respectively. The most important harmonics, the third and the fifth, are almost 50 dB below the output level. Although the fifteenth and seventeenth harmonics are much larger, they can be nullified by a simple RC filter because they are further away from the main frequency.

A circuit using a 555 timer as an oscillator may be used for the clock pulses – see the synchronous FSK modulator described below. The sync output provides a squarewave, with the same frequency and phase as the sinewave, which can be used, for instance, to trigger an oscilloscope.

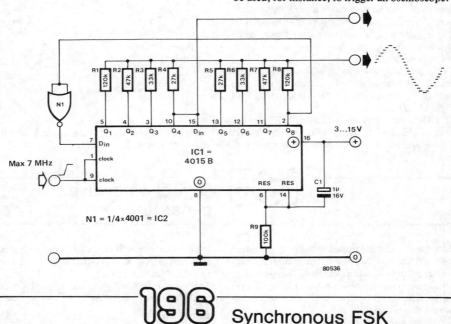

196 Synchronous FSK

A disadvantage of a number of popular FSK (Frequency Shift Keying) modulators is that the changeover between the 1200 and 2400 Hz frequencies often occurs at unpredictable times. A much better and neater solution would be to switch frequencies when the signal is at zero. If this is done then there is no phase shift in the FSK signal. Generally speaking, this is only possible when there is a definite relationship between the data and the FSK modulator. If there

isn't then the circuit given here should be of some help.

The actual FSK signal is obtained by means of the digital sinewave generator described previously (see above). At every zero-crossing the sinewave generator produces sync pulses which are used to clock FF2. The data level present at the 'D' input of this flip-flop determines which of the two output frequencies are selected. When a '1' is present at the input, the output frequency

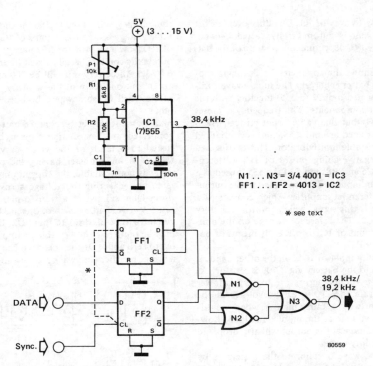

N1 ... N3 = 3/4 4001 = IC3
FF1 ... FF2 = 4013 = IC2

∗ see text

80559

will be 38.4 kHz, and when a '0' is present the output frequency will be 19.2 kHz. This output signal is then divided by 16 by the digital sine-wave generator to produce the correct FSK frequencies. The oscillator for the circuit is formed by the well known 555, albeit a CMOS version (that's why it has the slightly different 7555 type number). This IC's characteristics are practically the same as those of the 'ordinary' 555 with the added advantages of a much higher input impedance, less current consumption and its almost total 'spike' suppression during output level switching.

If the circuit is not used in combination with the digital sinewave generator, the sync input must be connected to the Q of FF1.

197 PWM battery charger

This circuit is designed to charge 6 V/3.5 Ah batteries similar to those often used in flash equipment. Of course, there are all kinds of methods to charge lead-acid batteries but what is special about this version is the fact that the charge current is continually corrected according to the state of the battery.

Figure 1 shows the block diagram of the PWM battery charger (PWM stands for Pulse Width Modulation). A1 is a squarewave oscillator which generates a frequency of around 2 kHz. A2 is a monostable multivibrator which is trig-gered by the negative-going pulses from A1. The pulse width from A2 depends on the control voltage which is derived from the differential amplifier A3. The latter constantly monitors the battery voltage. The output of A3 varies according to the difference in voltage between the pre-set reference level and the tested battery level. When both are equal the output voltage of A3 will be such that the duty-cycle of A2 will be 10%. This is enough to maintain trickle charge for the battery. The output of A2 controls the electronic switch ES1, so that current is fed to

217

the battery by way of R1. The duty-cycle of the output signal is automatically varied between 10% and 90%, depending on the state of the battery.

Figure 2 shows the complete circuit diagram of the PWM battery charger. The squarewave oscillator is formed by IC2 (a 555) together with the associated components. The frequency is preset at 2.27 kHz but this value is not critical. A2 is also constructed around a 555 and is configured as a monostable multivibrator. This is triggered by the negative-going pulses of IC2 differentiated by C5 and R8. Pin 5 of the 555 is used as a modulation input and is connected to the output of the differential amplifier which consists of a 741 IC. It is this signal which controls the duty cycle of IC3. The reference voltage on the non-inverting input of IC1 is preset by means of potentiometer P1.

The inverting input of IC1, on the other hand, is connected to the battery via a 100 k resistor. As long as the voltage across the battery is lower than the reference voltage, the voltage at the IC's output will be fairly high − when the difference in voltage at the inputs is reduced however, the voltage at the output will also drop and so will the duty-cycle.

The easiest way to calibrate the system is by using a discharged battery (about 2 V per cell) and a fully charged battery (about 2.4 V per cell). The discharged battery is first connected to the output of the circuit. The maximum presettable voltage is then fed to pin 3 of IC1 by means of P1. Now a resistor for R12 may be selected to obtain the correct charge current (in the case of a 6 V/3.5 Ah battery this will be 400 mA; in general about one tenth of the capacity). The value of R12 will be somewhere between 2.5 and 5 ohms.

Finally, the (completely) charged battery may be connected up. The charge current is now adjusted to a tenth of the value previously obtained. If an ammeter having the correct test range is not available, the current may be calculated by measuring the voltage across R12 and using Ohm's Law. If a transformer with only one 9 V/1 A winding is used, then a 3140 opamp will have to be used for IC1 and D2, D3, and C2 may be omitted. Pin 4 of this opamp is connected to zero volts. D1 then needs to be replaced by a bridge rectifier (full wave rectification).

1

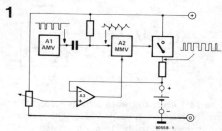

2

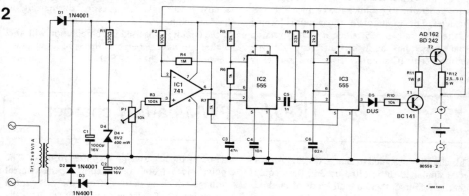

The level of water in a water tank can be measured in various ways, some of which can of course be more complicated than others. The circuit published here lights a LED whenever the

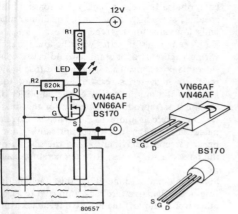

80557

level of water drops below the electrodes. With a high water level, the FET hardly conducts or not at all, because the gate is then connected to earth and there is no voltage difference between gate and source. When the water level drops, the gate/source connection is interrupted. The gate is then at a positive potential by means of the 820 k resistor, thereby causing the FET to conduct. The LED will now light. If the reverse operation is needed, that is the LED lights when the electrodes are short circuited by the water, just connect the 'earthy' electrode in the circuit to the positive and wire R2 between gate and source.

ITT Applications

199 Intelligent NICAD charger

Like all things, NICAD chargers are subject to human error, that is, the batteries can be placed in the holder in two ways, correctly and incorrectly. This charger will refuse to operate unless the cells are fitted correctly. The charger consists of a current source (T2) to maintain the output current at about 50 mA. The zener diode D2 and LED hold the base drive of T2 at a constant level and thus also the voltage across R3. The current through R3 is therefore also constant, providing the correct conditions for charging NICADs at the collector of T2.

The protection circuit includes T1, D1 and R1. The terminal voltage of an incorrectly fitted NICAD will turn off T1 preventing the charger from operating. An indication of this will be given by the LED − it will not light. When the battery is fitted correctly T1 will turn on and the charger will function normally.

Although the charger is capable of charging up to four penlight cells, it will not detect a single cell being the wrong way round if two or three others are connected correctly at the same time. A small transformer, bridge rectifier and electrolytic capacitor are all that is required for a power supply. The circuit works well providing the NICADs are not completely discharged.

200 Loudspeaker fuse

A loudspeaker protection circuit can be used to protect multipath loudspeaker systems effectively from users with destructive tendencies. It can be done simply by using an old-fashioned glass fuse in series with the loudspeaker wiring. The melting value (in A) of the fuse is based on a

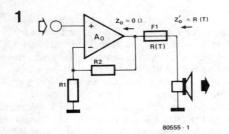

1

$$Z_o \approx 0\ \Omega \qquad Z'_o \approx R\ (T)$$

F1

R(T)

R2

R1

A₀

80555 - 1

2

$$Z_o \approx 0\ \Omega \qquad Z''_o \approx \frac{R(T)}{1 + A_0 \frac{R1}{R2}} \approx 0\Omega$$

F1

R3   R(T)

R2

R1

A₀

80555 - 2

compromise between a high value for the bass speaker, a less high value for the medium range and a low value for the treble speaker.

To place the fuse in series with the loudspeaker wiring (figure 1) as it stands would cause considerable problems. This is because a fuse has a relatively high series resistance. It is not too good for the muting factor of the amplifier or for the bass reproduction quality for that matter. But there is more to it. When a current passes through the fuse it gets hot causing non-linear thermal behaviour — and the quality of the bass will show a negative temperature coefficient.

Something can be done about this. Include the fuse in the negative feedback loop (figure 2), in other words, tap off the negative feedback voltage from a point behind the fuse. The fuse is by-passed by means of resistor R3 which is small compared to R2 (slight influence on the DC set-up of the amplifier), but large compared to the 4 Ω or 8 Ω load impedance. A value of 220 Ω (1 W) for R3 is fine.

201 Sawtooth synchronous to mains

This circuit is really meant to control a triac but it can also be put to other uses. The section around A1 forms an inverting Schmitt-trigger which 'squares up' the (low voltage) AC mains frequency input. This squarewave is fed to the differentiating network consisting of R5 and C1. The non-inverting input of A2 therefore receives two pulses for each period, namely, a positive and a negative pulse.

A2 is really an integrator which converts the signal into a 'sawtooth' waveform. The mixer reacts to the positive as well as the negative slope of the input signal. This is made possible by the

unusual internal architecture of the LM3900.

The opamp reacts normally to positive pulses. As soon as the non-inverting input becomes 'high', the inverting input will also have to become 'high' to maintain the balance. This can only happen if the output voltage is made to rise. The rise in voltage is then passed on through C2.

In order to be able to understand what happens to negative input pulses, it is important to realise that the input circuit of this opamp consists of a transistor whose emitter is connected to earth. For this reason the non-inverting input does not react at all. By way of D1 the inverting input is

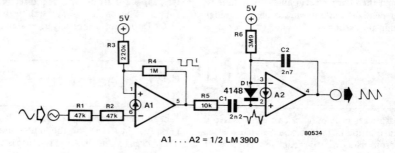

A1 . . . A2 = 1/2 LM 3900

80534

220

also cut off. When this condition exists the output voltage starts to rise as high as the supply voltage.

Resistors R1 and R2 have been included to limit the input voltage. If the circuit is not connected directly to the mains, it is better to use a single resistor of 100 k. The supply voltage is not critical and may be anything between 4 and 36 volts.

202 Plus or minus unity gain

This unity gain amplifier is capable of producing an inverted or a non-inverted output signal, as required, depending on the voltage level present at the control input (A).

The circuit works in a very simple manner. If the control input voltage is 0 V, the non-inverting input of the opamp (pin 3) will be connected to earth by way of the conducting FET. The opamp is now connected as an inverting amplifier causing the inverting input to constitute a virtual earth point (the opamp maintains the voltage level at pin 2 equal to that at pin 3, in this instance, ground). With the given values for R1 and R2 the gain will be − 1.

If the control input (A) is connected to − U_b the FET will turn off and will form a high impedance load for the rest of the circuit. Now the output of the opamp will *not* be inverted but the gain will remain the same. The input level must remain within 2 volts of the supply voltage extremes, (thus, $V_b + 2\,V \le V_{in} \le + V_b - 2\,V$).

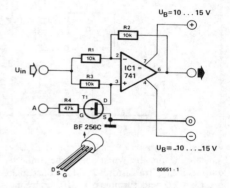

The impedance of the signal source should be as small as possible, since the input impedance depends on whether the FET is conducting or not. A source impedance of 500 Ω is recommended. The circuit may be used as an automatic polarity inverter for meters etc.

203 Enigma

Less energetic than musical chairs or charades, the use of this circuit can evoke just as much, if not more, humour from populous parties. The idea behind the game is to ask certain questions that can only have a 'yes' or 'no' answer and to produce answers which are hilariously incorrect. For instance, when the vicar is asked if it is true that the drinks fifteen pints of lager before breakfast the answer should be 'yes'. And 'no' must be elicited from the farmer's wife when asked to deny the rumour that she sleeps in the pig-sty. No doubt readers will be able to think of similar questions to put to their particular set of guests, but we cannot print the more obvious ones that spring to mind.

The circuit shown here produces a set series of 'yes' and 'no' answers by lighting one of two LEDs. This set sequence is, of course, only known to the questioner. Once a question has been asked the questionee presses the push-button S1. This triggers the timer contained in one half of IC1 to produce a pulse of around 4 to 5 seconds. The duration of this pulse can be varied by altering the values of R2 and C1 if desired. When the output of this timer goes high it clocks the divide-by-ten counter IC2 and removes the inhibit from the oscillator configured around the second timer IC1b.

This oscillator will produce a tone from the loudspeaker to indicate to all present that the button was in fact pressed.

Certain of the outputs from IC2 are connected

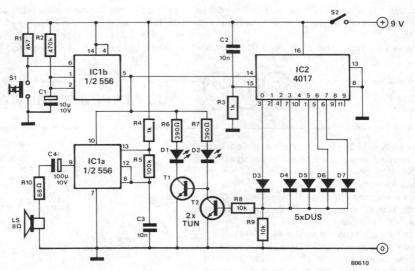

80610

via diodes to a pair of transistors and LEDs to indicate the answer. When one of the connected outputs is high transistor T2 will conduct, lighting LED D2 and turning off T1 thereby indicating a 'yes' answer. The LED will stay lit for the duration of the pulse from IC1a. When one of the unconnected outputs of IC2 is high T2 will turn off turning on T1 and D1 to indicate a 'no' answer.

The sequence of answers for the circuit shown is therefore: 'yes', 'no', 'no', 'yes', 'no', 'yes', 'yes', 'yes', 'no', 'no'. Any other sequence of ten answers can be selected by connecting fewer or more diodes as required. Once the sequence of ten is complete the cycle will be repeated.

Note: Capacitor C2 and resistor R3 are included to reset the counter on initial switch-on. This means that the first sequence will consist of *eleven* answers and the first answer will be 'no' for the circuit as shown – although it doesn't count, since no question has been asked yet!

204 Universal warning alarm

A device to attract one's attention when a certain condition is not being fulfilled would have a wide range of applications. The circuit presented here is versatile enough to provide an alarm for any application whether requiring immediate attention, or just reminding one that a certain function is not being properly accomplished.

The simplicity of the main circuit is immediately apparent (figure 1), consisting of only two CMOS squarewave oscillators and an output buffer. The circuit operates as follows: N1 and N2 form one of the CMOS oscillators. This oscillator is used to pulse a second oscillator (N5 and N6), which is set at an audio frequency. The mark space ratio of the first oscillator can be varied by means of P1 and P2. It can then be

seen that P1 determines the length of time that the second oscillator is enabled. Conversely, P2 determines the time that the second oscillator is *disabled*. The frequency of the second oscillator can be varied by means of P3 over the range of 40 Hz...15 kHz.

The output of the circuit will be a pulsed tone of the frequency determined by P3, the 'on' time determined by P1, and the 'off' time determined by P2. The circuit can be enabled in two ways:

1) A logic 0 on the A input
2) A logic 1 on the B input (provided N4 is omitted!)

Thus the circuit can be triggered by either logic state.

The output of N6 is fed to two inverters; N7 and

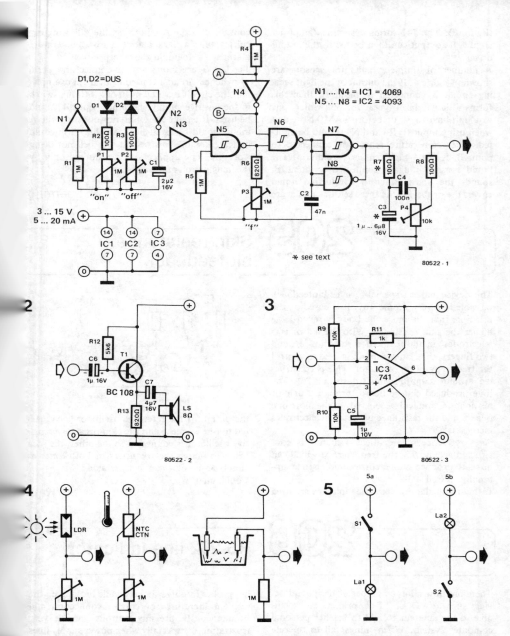

N1 ... N4 = IC1 = 4069
N5 ... N8 = IC2 = 4093

D1,D2=DUS

* see text

80522 - 1

80522 - 2

80522 - 3

N8. These feed a low pass filter formed by R7 and C3. These reduce high frequency harmonics and give the output a more pleasing sound. Potentiometer P4 is used as a volume control, and therefore the output is taken from the wiper.

If the circuit is to be used on its own, then the output can be fed directly to the positive side of C6 and to the output driver formed around T1 (figure 2). If more than one of these circuits is to be connected together, then all the 'out' terminals of the alarm circuits can be commoned and fed to the non-inverting input of IC3 (741)

223

(figure 3). The 741 forms a summer/amplifier circuit. Its output can then be fed to the output driver.

A number of simple circuits for sensors are shown in figure 4. If the output of the light sensing circuit is connected to input B, then this forms a dawn alarm (great for the winter, one wouldn't have to get up before 9 AM!) Note that when using input B, R4 and N4 should be omitted. The temperature sensor, if connected to point B, forms a high temperature alarm. The liquid sensor, if again connected to point B, sounds the alarm when a conductive liquid covers the probes. If the three sensor circuits are connected to the A input then the following circuits result: a dark alarm, a low temperature alarm and a no liquid alarm respectively.

The last figure shows how to connect the alarm to switched circuits. If used in a car for example, and the circuit is wired as in 5a, with the switch in the positive supply lead, then input B should be used. If circuit 5b is used however then the A input should be used. In a car, the alarm could indicate low oil, low petrol, seat belt not being worn etc. The applications are limited only by the imagination of the constructor.

B. Leeming

205 Skin resistance biofeedback

This device makes a special form of biofeedback possible in a very simple way. It is based on the principle that the more the body is relaxed the higher the skin resistance. With the aid of two 'electrodes' in the form of metal rings around two fingers, the skin resistance is used to control the frequency of an oscillator. This is constructed around a unijunction transistor (Ta). The tone produced can be heard through a pair of headphones and will become lower the more one relaxes and the resistance between the electrodes increases.

As a reference, an identical oscillator is constructed around T2, the frequency of which can be set to produce a tone, corresponding to an optimally relaxed state.

If (high impedance) stereo headphones are used

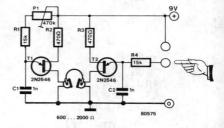

the output of the reference oscillator is connected to one earpiece and the skin resistance sensitive oscillator is connected to the other, the idea being to match the frequency of both tones as closely as possible merely by relaxing.

Cool it man!

S. Kaul

206 RS 232 line indicator

There are now a large number of peripheral devices such as VDUs, TTYs, printers etc. available to the amateur to add to his/her personal computer system. When things fail to operate correctly one of the first checks to be carried out is to make sure that the correct voltage levels are present on the RS 232 line interconnections. As many personal computer operators will testify, this is not a particularly easy task when the only test instrument available is a multimeter. Insert-

ing probes into live sockets while looking up the relevant literature for correct connection and simultaneously pressing buttons can be very frustrating — especially when power supply lines are shorted out accidentally! It would be desirable, therefore, to have a device that will check whether or not the signals are present and at the correct levels. The accompanying circuit is just such a device and can be built into the computer to provide a constant monitor of the RS 232 line.

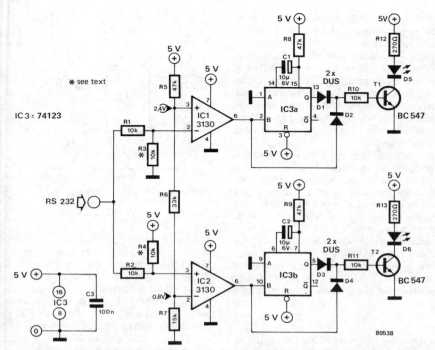

The circuit is very simple and consists mainly of two comparators and two pulse stretchers. Resistors R5...R7 form a potential divider chain to set the voltages on the non-inverting input of IC1 and the inverting input of IC2 to 2.4 and 0.8 volts respectively. The RS 232 input signal is attenuated by resistors R1...R4 and passed to the inverting input of IC1 and the non-inverting input of IC2. If the circuit is to be used with systems operating on TTL levels only then resistors R3 and R4 can be omitted. The output of IC1 will go high when there is a voltage level greater than 2.4 volts present at the input. Similarly, the output of IC2 will go high when the input level is less than 0.8 volts.

The outputs from the two comparators are fed to a pair of retriggerable monostable multivi-

brators contained in IC3 (the pulse stretchers). These provide a pulse with a fixed duration to turn on transistors T1 and T2 and light the respective LEDs. These pulse stretchers are included so that no matter how short the input pulse is it will still be seen by the human eye. The pulse duration is determined by the values of R8/C1 and R9/C2.

If the input signal is relatively long then the associated bypass diode takes over to ensure that the LED is lit for the length of the input pulse. In the circuit diagram, the upper LED (D5) indicates the presence of a positive pulse while the lower one (D6) indicates the presence of a negative pulse. Capacitor C3 is included to ensure correct power supply decoupling for IC3.

207 Simple 555 tester

The versatile 555 timer IC has the habit of turning up in wide variety of circuits. As it is such a useful little device it has become very popular over recent years. Although the 555 is generally

very reliable, there are occasions when malfunction does occur. The circuit shown here will provide a simple and effective method of testing suspect devices.

The timer to be tested, IC1, is connected as an astable (free-running) multivibrator. When the 'push to test' button (S1) is closed capacitor C1 will start to charge up via resistors R1 and R2. As soon as the voltage level on this capacitor reaches the trigger point of the timer the internal flip-flop is activated and pin 7 is taken low to discharge C1. The flip-flop is reset when the voltage on C1 reaches the threshold level of the IC. This takes pin 7 high and the charge cycle starts once more.

The output of the timer (pin 3) is connected to a pair of light-emitting diodes. When the output is high LED D2 will be on and D1 will be off. Conversely, when the output is low D1 will be on and D2 will be off. The LEDs will flash on and off alternately — provided, of course, that the IC under test is a good one.

For readers who may have other applications for the circuit and who wish to alter the frequency, the rate at which the LEDs flash is determined by the values of R1, R2 and C1. The frequency of oscillation can be calculated from the formula

$$f = \frac{1.44}{(R1 + 2R2) \times C1}$$

If, as in this case, the value of R2 is much greater than the value of R1, the frequency can be ap-

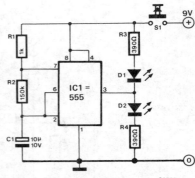

proximated from the following:

$$f \approx \frac{0.72}{R2 \times C1}$$

For the values shown in the circuit diagram the frequency works out to be around 0.5 Hz.

The tester can be made very compact by soldering all the components directly to the IC test socket, which is first mounted through a hole in the upper surface of the box or container to be used. Alternatively, the components can be mounted on a small piece of Vero-board or similar. Current consumption is minimal and the unit can be powered from a single 9 V battery.

208 State variable filter

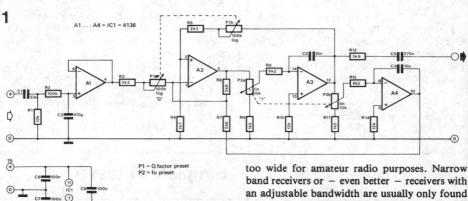

P1 = Q factor preset
P2 = fo preset

Many multi-band receivers and cheap communications receivers have a bandwidth compatible with the popular broadcasting stations which is too wide for amateur radio purposes. Narrow band receivers or — even better — receivers with an adjustable bandwidth are usually only found in more expensive systems.

In order to be able to listen to amateur radio transmissions (SSB and CW) without too much interference, on a broad band receiver, this ingenious audio band filter may provide a sol-

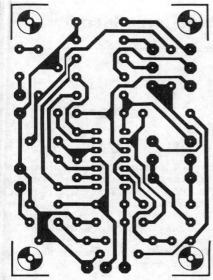

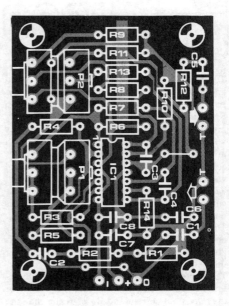

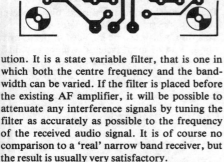

ution. It is a state variable filter, that is one in which both the centre frequency and the bandwidth can be varied. If the filter is placed before the existing AF amplifier, it will be possible to attenuate any interference signals by tuning the filter as accurately as possible to the frequency of the received audio signal. It is of course no comparison to a 'real' narrow band receiver, but the result is usually very satisfactory.

The input filter consisting of C1, C2, R1 and R2 is adequate to reduce the range of the available audio spectrum. The 6 dB points of this filter network are at 500 Hz and 3400 Hz. Opamp A1 acts as a buffer between the input filter and the state variable filter proper. The latter is constructed around the remaining opamps A2...A4. The Q of the filter and thus the bandwidth can be adjusted by means of P1 (control range: $1 \leq Q \leq 50$). The center frequency of the filter can be varied between 200 Hz and 2 kHz by P2. By manipulating these two potentiometers a very small area can be 'extracted' from the total audio spectrum.

Since wide band receivers and cheap communications receivers appear to be very popular at the moment, it seemed worthwhile to produce a printed circuit board for the state variable filter. Fortunately it is very compact as all the opamps in the circuit are contained in one IC (4136). The circuit requires a dual supply voltage (+ and − 15 V), but as current consumption is very low the supply need only produce a few milliamps.

Parts list

Resistors:
R1 = 10 k
R2 = 100 k
R3, R5 = 2k2
R4 = 2k7
R6, R7 = 5k6
R8, R13 = 8k2
R9, R11 = 1k5
R10, R14 = 12 k
R12 = 3k9

Capacitors:
C1 = 33 n
C2 = 470 p
C3, C4 = 10 n
C5 = 270 n
C6, C7, C8 = 100 n

Miscellaneous:
IC1 = A1...A4 = 4136
P1 = 2 x 100 k log.
P2 = 2 x 10 k lin.

227

209 Electronic fuse

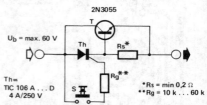

The electronic fuse shown here is a high speed and easily repaired direct current fuse. The thyristor (Th) is triggered by depressing pushbutton S for a brief period. The value of resistor R_g must be about 1 kΩ for every volt of supply voltage. The pushbutton may be released as soon as the thyristor has turned on. The anode current continues to flow — without further control voltage — until it drops below a certain 'hold' value. This will take place, for instance, if the current is conducted around the thyristor! This purpose is served by transistor T and resistor R_S. The thyristor current passes through resistor R_S and as soon as the drop in voltage across it is greater than the threshold level of the transistor this will conduct.

The value of R (minimum: 0.2 Ω) must therefore be chosen in such a way that the product of the maximum current and R_S is greater than the transistor threshold level (approximately 0.7 V).

When T is saturated, the collector base voltage falls, causing the thyristor current to drop below its holding value and the thyristor to turn off. The potential across R_S then falls below the threshold level of T so that the transistor also turns off thereby removing the supply to the load.

The initial situation is restored by depressing pushbutton S (reset).

This fuse, which can be included in the positive supply lead of most systems without any difficulty, causes no more than a drop of 1 volt.

210 Nicad charger

Now that the price of small nicad cells is relatively low the cost of the necessary charger is disproportionally high. It is hardly possible to find a less expensive method of charging 4 penlight cells than the one described here. Furthermore, the circuit offers low dissipation and provides a constant current for the cells to be charged.

The circuit uses two capacitors connected in parallel, instead of the usual transformer, to obtain sufficient current (a tenth of the batteries' capacity or 50 mA) from the mains supply. The voltage appearing at the 'cool' end of the capacitors is then rectified by means of four diodes.

The LED has been included to provide an indication that the circuit is actually charging. The resistors, R1 and R2, have been added as a measure of safety. This is because when the battery charger is switched off the capacitors may still be fully charged unless some form of discharge path is provided.

Safety is quite an important aspect for this circuit, since the main components are connected directly to the mains, and this could lead to acci-

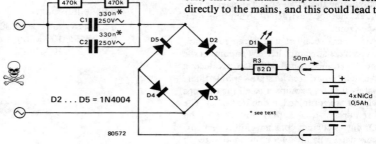

dents! For this reason a great deal of care must be taken during its construction.

The entire circuit can be mounted in the hinged part of a cassette case in such a way that it is impossible to touch the parts where a high voltage is present. The section containing the nicad cells has two solder pins which disappear into two holes when the box is closed and which don't make electrical contact until the box is almost completely shut. This eliminates any danger while the cells are being charged. Obviously,

adding a 1 A fuse and a double-pole mains switch wouldn't be a bad idea.

Note that capacitors C1 and C2 must be suitable for use at AC mains voltages − 250 V at least. Be warned: the DC working voltage gives no guarantee. It is no exception for a capacitor rated at 400 V DC to have an AC working voltage of only 200 V, or even less!

C.W. Brederode

---

211 High-frequency optocoupler

It is often necessary to ensure a 'safe' transfer of signals from one circuit to another. The desired AC signal must be passed, but even quite high DC voltages must be completely blocked − even AC *energy* transfer from one circuit to the other is often highly undesirable. Typically, this sort of situation occurs where mains voltages or high DC voltages occur in one circuit, whereas the other must be 'safe to touch'. A standard solution, nowadays, is to use a so-called optocoupler − the desired signal is passed as light.

In the circuit shown, the input signal is applied to T1. This transistor is biased to 20 mA by means of R1...R3. R3 is selected so that I_F (the current through the photodiode) varies from 15 mA to 25 mA as the input voltage swings 1 V peak-to-peak. Linearity can be improved at the expense of signal-to-noise ratio by reducing the I_F swing. This is accomplished by increasing R3 and adding a resistor from the collector of T1 to ground to obtain the desired quiescent current through the photodiode (20 mA).

The output transistor in the IC, T2, is connected

in a cascade circuit with T3. Feedback is applied through R4 and R6. R6 is selected for maximum gain/bandwidth product of T3. R7 determines the output swing; obviously, it should be selected to obtain maximum output without clipping. The closed-loop gain ($\Delta U_{out}/\Delta U_{in}$) is determined by R4, as follows:

$$\frac{U_{out}}{U_{in}} = \frac{I_d}{I_F} \cdot \frac{1}{R3} \cdot \frac{R4 \cdot R7}{R6}$$

In the unlikely event that the output amplifier (T2/T3) decides to operate as an oscillator, a capacitor of 27...100 p between collector and base of T3 should bring it back into line.

Typical data:
2% linearity over 1 V_{pp} dynamic range

Bandwidth:	10 MHz
Gain drift:	−0.6%/°C
Common mode rejection:	22 dB at 1 MHz
DC insulation:	3000 V

HP application note

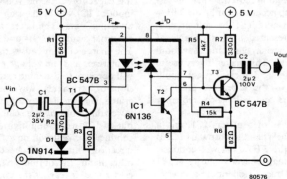

80576

212 Security rear light

Living in a temperate climate involves having to cycle with lights on every now and again. The trouble is that a bicycle dynamo can only produce energy for lighting while a steady rate of pedalling is kept up. As soon as you slow down before traffic lights, zebra crossings etc. the intensity of the rear light drops considerably, thus making it very difficult for vehicles coming up behind to see you. The safety rear light described here is an indispensable addition to the normal reflector. As soon as the dynamo is switched on and producing a voltage, the rear light will come on. The light will have a constant intensity no matter what cycling speed is kept up. Furthermore, it will continue to burn for about four minutes after the bicycle comes to rest, which is ample time to cross the busiest of crossroads.

Unfortunately, this circuit has a drawback – it relies on batteries and when these are dead the system will not work. One consolation is, however, that when 4 or 5 alkaline penlight cells are used there is enough energy available for 35 hours use.

The dynamo lead which is normally wired to the rear light is connected to the input of the circuit.

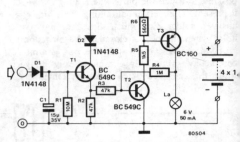

When a voltage is present, T1 is switched on which in turn provides base drive current for T2 and T3. The lamp will now light. When the cyclist stops and the dynamo no longer produces a voltage, T1 continues to conduct for a few minutes until capacitor C1 is discharged through R1 to such an extent that the Schmitt-trigger formed by T2/T3 turns out the light. The entire circuit is now inoperative and no current is drawn from the batteries.

If the system is to be used for long periods at a time, it is advisable to include 5 nicads (also the penlight size). With a capacity of 0.5 Ah and a rear light of 6 V/50 mA the batteries should last for about ten hours.

213 Precision VCO

According to the author, the linearity and synchronisation (when several VCOs are used) of this circuit is very good indeed. When the circuit is correctly set up accuracies of below 0.01% can be achieved! In addition, the voltage controlled oscillator presented here is capable of generating square, triangular and sawtooth waveforms as required. This makes it very useful for music synthesiser and measurement applications. Examples of the latter are precision waveform generators and voltage-to-frequency converters.

The oscillator consists of a mixer, IC1, and a Schmitt-trigger, IC2. When the output of IC2 is positive (+15 V), the FET (T1) will conduct; when the output voltage is negative, however, T1 will be turned off. Thus, T1 operates as an elec-

tronic switch. When T1 is conducting, a charge current flows through resistors R1 and R2 into the capacitor C1. The voltage at the inverting input of IC1 will be the same as that at the non-inverting input. The latter is determined by the potential divider R3/R4 and is equal to $1/3\ U_{in}$. The charge current causes the capacitor voltage to increase and the voltage at the output of IC1 will decrease to the same extent. The descending slope of a triangular waveform is therefore generated. As soon as the output voltage reaches the lower threshold of the schmitt-trigger, the output of IC2 will swing high and T1 will start to conduct. Current will now flow in the opposite direction and C1 will be discharged. On the other hand, the output voltage of IC1 will increase until it reaches the upper threshold of the

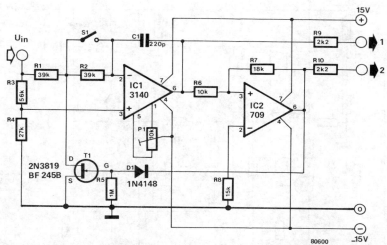

schmitt-trigger and the complete cycle can start afresh.

The triangular signal is available at output 1, while a symmetrical squarewave is available at 2. If the switch S1 is closed, the capacitor will be discharged very quickly. Then a descending sawtooth signal will be generated at twice the frequency of the original triangular wave. The second output will now provide 'needle' pulses. The amplitude of the triangular waveform will be ±8.3 V, while that of the squarewave will be ±15 V.

For maximum precision, 1% metal foil resistors should be used (except for R5, R9 and R10) and a ceramic capacitor is recommended for C1.
The frequency of operation can be calculated from:

$$f = \frac{U_{in} \cdot R6}{180 \cdot R7 \cdot R2 \cdot C1} \text{ Hz}$$

With the values shown, a conversion factor of 357 Hz/V is obtained. The circuit is set up by connecting both inputs of IC1 to ground then adjusting P1 to give 0 V out (pin 6).

A. van Ginneken

214 Ulp amp

At first sight, this amplifier design looks like any other. However, it boasts a number of highly interesting characteristics. To start with, the abbreviation 'ulp' stands for 'ultra low power'. This does not refer to the maximum power produced by the amp (100 mW), but rather to the quiescent current consumption which is approximately 1.5 mA. This makes this amplifier particularly suitable for use in a receiver which derives its supply from solar cells.

A further advantage is the wide choice of supply voltages. Apart from the maximum output power, of course, the other characteristics remain unchanged, regardless of whether a 3 V or a 12 V supply is used. The voltage gain is not affected either.

When the circuit in figure 1 is considered, an awful lot of components appear to be involved. However, they are all without exception 'normal' parts.

To enable the amp to work well at all supply voltages, a differential amplifier (T1, T2) has been used as an input stage with a current source (T3, T4) in the emitter lead. The input signal passes from T1's collector to the discrete darlington driver, T5 and T6. To ensure as much gain as possible, there is also a current source (T7) in the collector of T6.
In spite of the fact that the quiescent current of the output transistors is preset (there is only one diode, between the base of T8 and T9), crossover distortion is kept to a minimum by this type

231

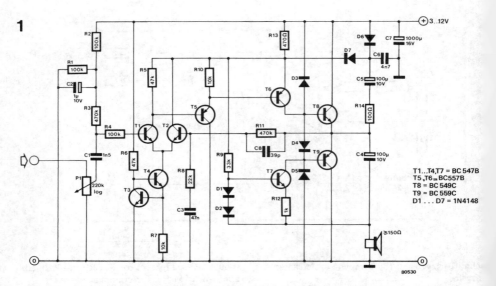

1

of current control. Negative feedback of course also helps. The feedback network is formed by R11 and C8 and is connected between the emitters of the output transistors and the base of T2. The voltage gain of the ulp amp is therefore determined by the ratio of R11 to R8 which is a factor of 22 in this case.

In order to obtain maximum output amplitude (almost supply voltage — a very rare phenomenon!), bootstrapping has been applied in two ways. As far as the negative half-signal is concerned the 'base' of the current source (junction

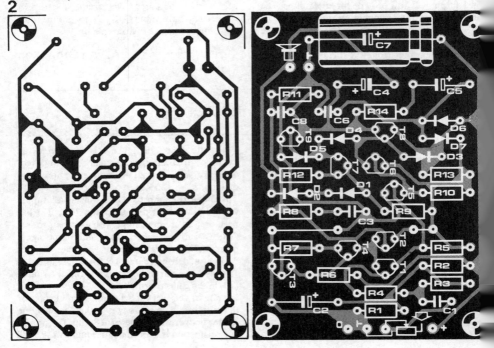

2

Parts list

Resistors:

R1, R2, R4 = 100 k
R3, R11 = 470 k
R5, R6 = 47 k
R7, R10 = 10 k
R8 = 22 k
R9 = 33 k
R12 = 1 k
R13 = 470 Ω
R14 = 100 Ω
P1 = 220 k log.

Capacitors:

C1 = 1n5
C2 = 1 µ /10 V
C3 = 47 n
C4, C5 = 100 µ /10 V
C6 = 4n7 (cer.)
C7 = 1000 µ /16 V
C8 = 39 p

Semiconductors:

T1...T4, T7 = BC 547B
T5, T6 = BC 557B
T8 = BC 549C
T9 = BC 559C
D1...D7 = 1N4148

D2/R12) is connected to the output capacitor instead of to earth. The peak-to-peak output range will now be greater because the output signal voltage is added to the supply voltage of the driver. Similar use has been made of the positive half-signal and, as far as we know, for the first time in history. The output signal is passed through R14 and C5 to diodes D6 and D7. After it has been rectified it is added to the positive supply voltage, the signal at the R13/D7 junction will therefore rise above the supply voltage. And of course this will increase the peak-to-peak output range of the driver during the positive half-signal. To prevent T8 and T9 from being over-driven, the driver output is limited by two diodes (D3 and D5).

Figure 2 shows the printed circuit board for the amplifier. It may not be the smallest but its low current consumption will certainly take a lot of beating.

215 Trigger with presettable thresholds

Most triggers with switch hysteresis (the schmitt-trigger included) have switching thresholds which cannot easily be preset (if at all) because the levels affect each other or the switching behaviour of the trigger. This particular trigger is an exception and consists of three opamps.

The switching thresholds can be preset between 0 and 83% of the positive as well as the negative supply voltage, independently of each other, by means of P1 and P2. It makes no difference which pot is used as the upper or lower threshold.

Only when the input voltage is higher than the highest preset threshold voltage, will outputs A1 and A2 both be 'low'. The voltage on pin 10 of A3 will then be lower than that on pin 9, causing the output voltage to become negative.

The trigger can operate with DC or AC signals.

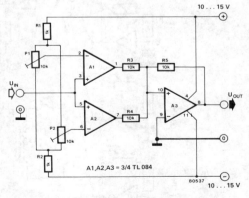

The peak values of the input signal must of course remain within the supply voltage's limits.

216 Simple L/C meter

With the aid of this device it becomes a simple matter to check the value of capacitors and inductors. When measuring an inductor (switch S2 in position a) the current flowing through the coil is interrupted periodically so that the self-induced voltage can be monitored. This is achieved by feeding one of the six squarewave signals (N1...N6) to the base of transistor T1. The base drive current to T1 is therefore constant in all cases which means that the collector current is also modulated to the same maximum value. The self-induced voltage U can be found from the formula:

$$U = \frac{-L\,\Delta I}{\Delta t}$$

where L = inductance
ΔI = change in current
Δt = time during which the voltage change takes place

The self-induced voltage will only alter when a different inductor is placed in the circuit. The average value of the voltage will then be:

$U_{ave} = L \cdot I_c \cdot f$ where
I_c = average collector current
f = control voltage frequency

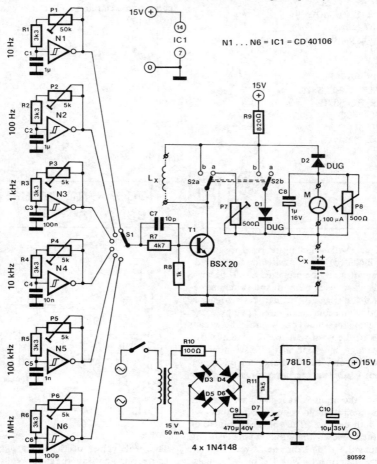

N1 . . . N6 = IC1 = CD 40106

4 x 1N4148

80592

The average voltage is a measurement of the self-induction. From the proportional relationship between the voltage measured U_{meas} and the inductance L it follows that the scale will be linear. Similarly, it can be proved that the average discharge current of the capacitor C_x (S2 in position b) in this circuit will be:

$I_{meas} = C \cdot U_c \cdot f$ where
U_c = the charge voltage on the capacitor
f = the control voltage frequency

Again the scale division for the capacitance meter will be linear.

The corresponding parameters are given in the table.

In order to calibrate the unit, the squarewave

f in Hz	1 M	100 k	10 k	1 k	100	10
L in H	10 μ	100 μ	1 m	10 m	100 m	1
C in F	100 p	1 n	10 n	100 n	1 μ	10

generators must first be adjusted to produce the correct frequencies. A capacitor with a known value is then connected into the circuit and P1 trimmed to give the right reading on the meter. After this, P2 is adjusted with an inductor of known value in the circuit. Accuracy will suffer if a supply voltage of less than 15 V is used. A suitable power supply is shown in figure 2.

Based on an idea by P. Herlitz

217 Sound effects generator

This 'black box' should prove quite popular with (electronic) guitar players. It offers all kinds of possibilities for enriching the sound. There are three controls; the effect of the most important of these (P3) is illustrated in figure 1.

The original input signal is shown at the top. With P3 set to zero, this signal is simply clipped as shown; as P3 is turned up, all kinds of other wave-shapes are obtained — including frequency doubling, even. As will become apparent when we come to the circuit, P3 determines the basic waveform; a further control (P2) determines the 'degree' of the effect; and a final control (P1) sets the sensitivity. As with most circuits of this type, the final effect depends on the input signal level (surprisingly, musicians seem to like it that way!), so that a sensitivity control is both necessary and useful. The overall gain of the circuit depends on the various control settings; it can be

anything between x3 and x30 (10 dB...30 dB). Note that it is not the intention to use P1 as a volume control — guitar amplifiers have one of those already.

The circuit is shown in figure 2. A1 is an input buffer amplifier; its gain is determined by P1. The output from A1 is fed to a x10 amplifier (A2) and to a variable-gain amplifier stage (A3), the gain of which is determined by P2a. At this point, things get a bit complicated... Two diodes, D1 and D2, are connected between the outputs from A2 and A3. If the gains of both stages are identical, their outputs will also be identical and the diodes will never conduct. However, as the gain of A3 is reduced, two things start to happen: the output from A2 is clipped at the input to A4, and the output from A3 is *boosted* at the peaks of the signal. The latter signal is inverted by A5 and, at the same

1

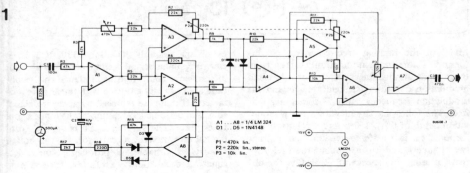

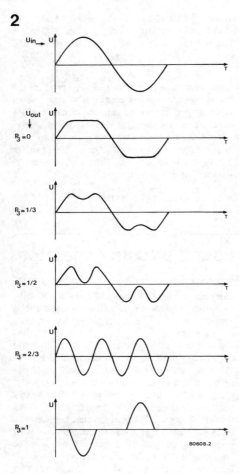

time, the gain in this stage is set by P2b to compensate for the gain difference between the two signal paths that was introduced by P2a. To achieve this, P2a and P2b are connected 'in opposite sense': as the value of one increases, the value of the other must decrease.

We now have two signals at the same basic level, but in antiphase. Furthermore, where one is 'flattened' at the signal peaks, the other is boosted at those points. These two signals are summed in A6. So what do you get? The basic, undistorted component in the two signals is identical and in antiphase, so it cancels. The distortion components, however, *add*: where the output of A4 is 'down' due to clipping, the output of A5 is at a negative peak level, because this stage inverts. The result of all this is that the output from A6 contains nothing but short peaks, that correspond to the peaks of the incoming signal when D1 and D2 conduct. Or, to be more accurate, short dips that correspond to the peaks and vice versa: when the output of A4 goes high, the output of A6 goes low. P3 can therefore be used to select any desired 'blend' of these two signals, producing the intriguing waveforms shown in figure 1.

A7 is used as an output buffer. Which leaves one unused opamp, if you're using quad opamp ICs. Pity... may as well do something useful with it: make a simple VU meter circuit (A8).

Using this level meter, it is a simple matter to set up the sound effects generator. The sensitivity control, P1, is set so that hitting one string causes the meter to reach approximately mid scale (40...70%). The basic distortion can now be set between 0 and 100% with P2, and the 'blend' is set with P3. By ear, of course — according to personal taste.

---

218 IC tremolo

Many of the familiar tremolo effect circuits (periodic amplitude modulation) suffer from three main disadvantages. Both distortion and modulation deviation frequently occur and the modulation frequency range is sometimes limited. The following circuit allows for a modulation depth of 0%...100% and is relatively distortion free. It is a stereo version, that is it has two channels, and it can simulate the Lesley effect (rotating loudspeakers). Basically, the circuit is quite simple. The TCA 730, IC2, is an electronic balance and volume control with built in frequency compensation. Balance and amplitude are normally adjusted with linear potentiometers. If these are replaced by a varying signal source, a periodic modulation of the input signal takes place. The varying signal is derived from the XR2206 waveform generator, IC1. Although this IC is capable of producing sinusoidal, square and sawtooth waveforms, for the pur-

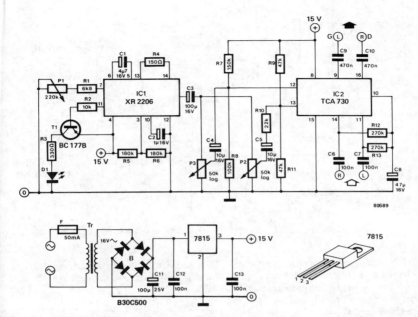

80589

B30C500

7815

poses of this circuit only the sinewave signal is of interest.

The modulation frequency can be varied with potentiometer P1 as required from 1 Hz to 25 Hz. The squarewave output of the XR 2206 is used to drive a PNP transistor, T1, so that an LED can provide an optical indication of the modulation frequency.

The internal frequency compensation of the TCA 730 (pins 1...7) remains unused. The sinewave amplitude level can be adjusted by P2, thus controlling modulation depth. The degree of balance can be adjusted with P3 (to produce the Lesley effect).

Little needs to be said about the power supply. The 7815 voltage regulator solves all the problems. It is not advisable to use an unstabilised supply as the modulation in the circuit would cause current fluctuations on the supply line. This will then cause deterioration of the modulating sinewave. The supply transformer should have a secondary winding of 15...18 volts at about 120 mA. The voltage regulator requires a heatsink in the form of an aluminium plate of about 10 cm².

T. Stöhr

219 Electronic magnifying glass

Rectification is usually a question of removing the negative half-cycle (during positive rectification) or the positive half-cycle (during negative rectification) of the alternating voltage. The reference for the resultant voltage then becomes 0 V. However, the reference level can be any other positive or negative voltage as required. This is done by removing everything above or below the reference level. An example of this is the circuit in figure 1. It is a precision rectifier which allows all of the input signal, U_i, through

unchanged provided it is above the reference voltage U_R (figure 2a). Negative rectification is also possible (figure 2b). All that is required is to change the polarity of diodes D1 and D2. The reference voltage can be preset by potentiometer P1. The circuit works accurately enough for frequencies up to 20 kHz.

What can you do with it? You can make an electronic magnifying glass. Supposing a relatively small portion of the alternating signal is to be examined in detail on an oscilloscope. Increasing

1

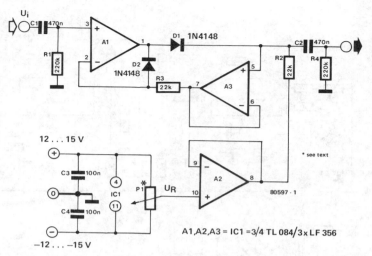

A1,A2,A3 = IC1 =3/4 TL 084/3 x LF 356

the gain of the oscilloscope may produce the required enlarged area, but — apart from unpredictable overdrive — the DC shift range could be insufficient to obtain a clear view of the signal in as much detail as needed.

Why not then just feed that part of the signal in which we are interested to the oscilloscope. In order to examine the amplitude stability of an oscillator, a positive rectifier is used with a reference voltage preset to a level just below the peak level of the signal. To look at negative extremes a negative rectifier is required. To 'magnify' an area somewhere between the two extremes a positive and a negative rectifier are connected in series.

The value of P1 may be anything between 1 k and 1 M. It is important that the reference volt-

age be sufficiently accurate and stable. If necessary, a multi-turn potentiometer can be used for P1.

2

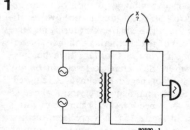

There are many instances where it is necessary to test electrical connections, for instance, cable networks, the wiring of connectors, and the various interconnections on a printed circuit board. These tests can be carried out with an ohmmeter, but it is often impossible to keep an eye on everything at once, for while watching the meter dial you have to make sure that the test probes do not short anything out.

One solution is to construct a simple test circuit which produces a sound when the connections

---

220 Acoustic ohmmeter

1

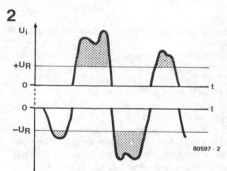

80590 - 1

are shorted and which remains silent when the test probes are an open circuit. This permits numerous possibilities. The simplest version which uses a small transformer and a bell is shown in figure 1. The problem with this circuit is that large amounts of current can be produced which could prove too much for the circuit being tested.

By replacing the bell with a small loudspeaker and suitable series resistor the current flow can be limited to below 1 mA. This is shown in the circuit diagram of figure 2. The transformer secondary voltage is full-wave rectified by diodes D1...D4 to provide a 100 Hz signal for the loudspeaker. When the base of T1 is connected to R1 (testing for a short circuit) the two transistors will amplify the signal to produce the required tone.

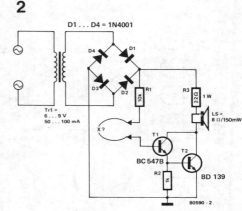

221 Armless bandit

For most of us, giving money away is very easy, all that is required is a car! For many others the odds need to be a little shorter. They use a 'one armed bandit', or 'fruit machine', or 'three in a row', or 'jackpot'. Call it what you will they all do the same job — part you from your money. A

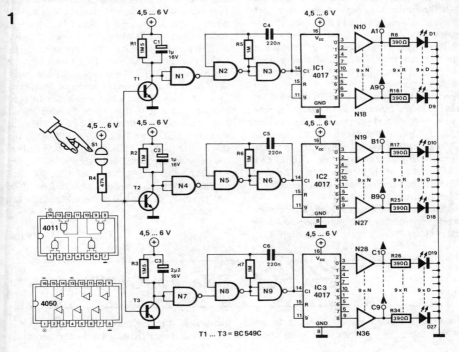

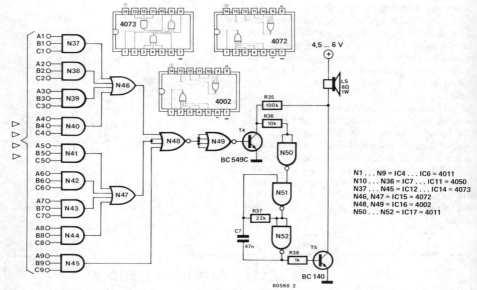

number of rolling drums induce a hypnotic trance in the victim reducing his number of movements to two, inserting coins with the left hand and pulling a lever with the right with only one known surefire cure — atmospheric pockets! Yes, we know that they pay out because the person before you proved it (and so will the one following you).

With this circuit it is possible to work out the sequence all day long without touching a single coin. We have even taken out the all too familiar ache in the right arm.

It operates with a total of 27 LEDs in three rows of nine. It might be advisable to mount the rows above each other and number the LEDs in each row 1...9. Touching the sensor plate cause the LEDs in the three rows to 'run'. Then, on releasing the touch plate, one random LED in each row will remain lit. If these happen to be three LEDs with the same number, a buzz announces that you have won.

Although the circuit diagram looks a little complicated, its operation is quite simple. If the touch contacts, S1, are bridged, transistors T1...

T3 start the three oscillators constructed around N1...N9 which provide the three decimal counters (IC1, IC2 and IC3) with clock signals. The outputs 0...9 of these counters will then go high one after the other. Although the drawing has been simplified, each output (except for output 9 which is used as a reset) is connected to a buffer/series resistor/LED combination such as N10/R8/D1 etc. Thus we have three rows of LEDs which run continuously until the touch contacts are released. When this is released, the oscillators continue for a certain period of time determined by the RC networks connected to each transistor collector before stopping. One output from each of the counters will remain high and (any) one LED from each row will light. If the three LEDs happen to have the same number, the comparator circuit built around N37...N49 will detect this and turn on transistor T4. The oscillator constructed around N51, N52 will than start up and, via T5, will cause the loudspeaker to 'buzz'.

B. Jouët

Selective CW filter

Certain requirements must be met when designing CW filters (CW = carrier wave — basically, unmodulated morse telegraphy). The response curve must be sufficiently narrow to permit as

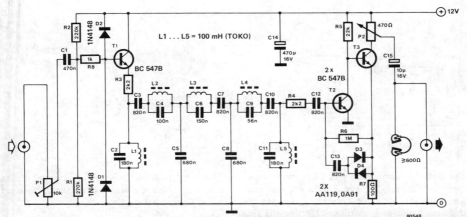

little QRM as possible, but must be wide enough to overcome receiver drift. It must also be phase linear within the bandwidth. Readily available filters usually have a bandwidth in the order of 500 Hz (6 dB points) and give approximately 60 dB attenuation at around 1 to 2 kHz.

In many instances CW signals are insufficiently filtered, so that ringing can often occur in the receiver. A filter with a very high Q allows for maximum selectivity, but is, of course, totally unsuitable for this application. The filter must also be easily reproducable, without any trimming if possible, and the cost must be kept to a minimum.

The circuit shown here fulfils all these requirements and has a comparatively low centre frequency thereby reducing any effect that component tolerances would have at higher frequencies. It was decided to incorporate LC filters in the design as they are superior in operation to RC networks. The coils used need not be of any special quality, virtually any 100 mH choke coils will suffice.

Differences in the signal amplitude of normal receiver filters can be considerable as they are usually more than one CW station 'wide' and the automatic gain control (AGC) may cause the filter to 'pump'. For this reason a limiting circuit (D1 and D2) is included at the input of the filter and a further logarithmic limiter (D3 and D4) is

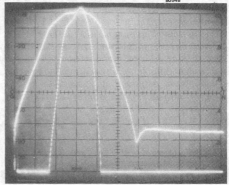

included at the output stage. The audio image signal still needs to be eliminated and this is only possible after the IF signal has had special treatment.

This circuit is virtually indispensable when it comes to displaying CW signals with the aid of a microprocessor and a TV. The filter then only needs a simple interface circuit.

The photo clearly shows the frequency characteristics of the filter circuit. The horizontal scale is 200 Hz per division for both curves. The centre frequency of the filter is around 600 Hz. The narrow curve has a vertical scale of 1 dB per division while the broader curve has a scale of 10 dB per division.

 Low-pass filter

Most communication receiver designers assume that 'anything above 3 kHz can be cut out' and

sometimes a series of four RC filters in a row are given in the receiver. It is obvious that frequency

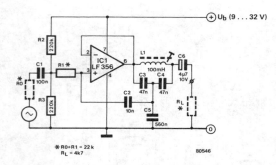

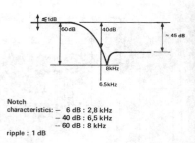

Notch
characteristics: — 6 dB : 2,8 kHz
— 40 dB : 6,5 kHz
— 60 dB : 8 kHz
ripple : 1 dB

characteristics dropping by 12 dB or more at frequencies between 2.5 and 3 kHz are far from ideal. The real object of the exercise is to remove the broadband noise without affecting the frequency characteristics within the range required. In other words, it is better to remain at 1 dB with as sharp a cutoff as possible after 2.5 or 3 kHz. The configuration described here already fulfils this function with only one section. The circuit contains nothing but a single IC and a few other components. Although it appears to be decoupled through C5, this is in fact not the case, because the input circuit is part of the star formed by C3, C4 and C5 (bootstrap principle).

TOKO manufacture coils with a presettable core and when these are used the notch can be tuned to the desired position.

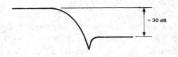

224 The STAMP

Super Tiny AMPlifier

It has nothing to do with the mail, but it is small enough to go through it. This circuit is a versatile, miniature amplifier and loudspeaker combination that can be used in the tightest of electronic corners. The Super Tiny AMPlifier uses only one IC, a loudspeaker and eight other components. It measures two square inches and has an output of 200 mW or more. As if this is not versatile enough, the gain can also be preset (or switched).

Frequently, small projects require an external amplifier of equally small proportions. Finding a suitably sized circuit can present some difficulty. This problem can now be 'STAMPed' out.

The circuit is so simple that it hardly needs any explanation. It is based on the LM 386, IC1. This is produced in a variety of specifications and table 1 lists the major differences, output power and supply voltage being the most significant factors.

The gain of the amplifier is set by the components between pins 1 and 8 of the IC. With

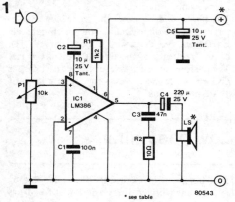

Table 1

Technical data of the LM 386

Operating supply voltage

LM 386N	4...12 V
LM 386N-4	5...18 V
Quiescent current (U_B = 6 V)	typ. 4 mA
Absolute maximum input voltage	± 0.4 V
Input resistance	typ. 50 k

Output power (THD = 10%)

LM 386N-1	U_B = 6 V		325 mW
LM 386N-2	U_B = 7.5 V	R_L = 8 Ω	500 mW
LM 386N-3	U_B = 9 V		700 mW
LM 386N-4	U_B = 16 V	R_L = 32 Ω	1 W

Absolute maximum package dissipation (at 25°C)

LM 386	660 mW
LM 386A	1.25 W

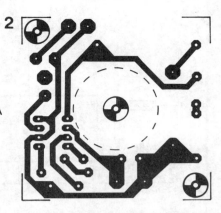

Parts list

R1 = 1k2 (see text)
R2 = 10 Ω
P1 = 10 k preset potentiometer
C1 = 100 n
C2, C5 = 10 µ /25 V Tantalum (see text)
C3 = 47 n
C4 = 220 µ /16 V
LS = loudspeaker 8 µ /0.2...1 W

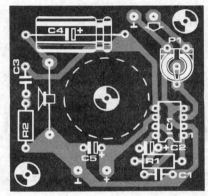

both R1 and C2 included (in series) the gain is set at 50. Excluding these two components sets the gain at 20. For the maximum gain of 200, C2 is included and R1 is replaced by a wire link.

The loudspeaker is the limiting factor of the output power if size is the major consideration. The printed circuit board was designed so that, after cutting the hole out of the centre, the board can be mounted over the magnet of the speaker. This of course, means that only the smallest of speakers would be suitable limiting the power output to 200 mW. However, there is no reason why a larger loudspeaker can not be used and the STAMP stuck (with double-sided tape) on or near it. Table 1 should be referred to in this case.

---

225 Cheap seconds

Miniature crystals for watches are almost invariably tuned to 32.768 kHz, and for a good reason − it is quite easy to derive a 1 Hz signal from this frequency.

Add to this knowledge the fact that the IC type 4060 contains a 14-bit divider stage and oscillator section, and you can put two and two together... The watch crystal is eminently suitable as frequency-determining element for the oscillator. If the maximum division ratio of the divider stage is used (2^{14}), the result is a 2 Hz output. Getting close... To bring this down to the mother of all timing intervals one-pulse-per-second, a single flipflop must be added; half of a

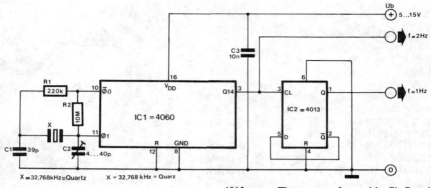

X = 32,768 kHz = Quartz   X = 32,768 kHz = Quarz

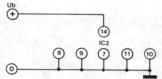

4013, say. The output from this flipflop is a 1 Hz signal, swinging between 0 V and positive supply.

Life would be beautiful, if it weren't for component tolerances. Crystals need trimming – which is where C2 comes in. For absolute accuracy, a frequency meter is required. Connected to pin 9 of IC1, it should read 32.768 kHz.

226 Variable pulse width generator

This simple little circuit will find a great many uses where pulse width is critical.

Opamp A1 is connected as a squarewave generator whose frequency can be adjusted by potentiometer P2. Let us assume that the output of the opamp goes high when the system is first switched on. Part of that output voltage is fed to the non-inverting input via the voltage divider R4, P2, R3. As long as C1 is not yet sufficiently charged, the voltage at the inverting input will be lower than that at the non-inverting input and the output will remain high. The moment that the capacitor is charged to such an extent that the voltage at the inverting input becomes greater than that at the non-inverting input, the output of the opamp will swing low. Capacitor C1 then starts to discharge until the voltage at the inverting input becomes lower than that at the other input, whereupon the opamp output will swing high once more.

The mark-space ratio (duty-cycle) may be varied with potentiometer P1 without affecting the frequency. This is done by making sure that the charge time is different (either greater or smaller) than the discharge time. Capacitor C1 is charged via part of P1, diode D2 and resistor

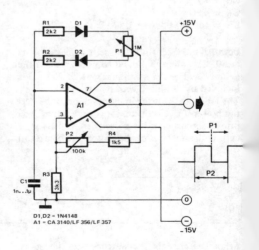

D1, D2 = 1N4148
A1 = CA 3140/LF 356/LF 357

R2, whereas it is discharged via resistor R1, diode D1 and the other part of P1. The sum of these two time constants will remain the same (as will the frequency) when P1 is used to alter the mark-space ratio.

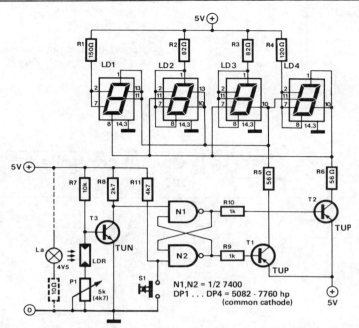

N1, N2 = 1/2 7400
DP1 ... DP4 = 5082 - 7760 hp
(common cathode)

Has the postman been yet or isn't there any mail today? This question is asked daily by millions of people. As a rule, the answer is to go to the letterbox to have a look. The farther you have to go to find out and the emptier the letterbox, the greater your disappointment.

The post indicator shows on four seven-segment displays whether it is worth the walk or not. Initially, the flipflop formed by N1 and N2 is reset and transistor T2 conducts causing the word 'NONE' to appear on the display. When the light beam to the LDR is interrupted (when a letter falls through the letterbox) T3 will conduct

briefly and trigger the flipflop. As a result, T2 will turn off and T1 will turn on. The display will then show the word 'POST'.

The circuit will remain in this state until the reset switch S1 is pressed whereupon it will revert to its initial state. For reliable operation it is advisable to mount the lamp and the LDR as close as possible to the actual aperture of the letterbox.

Further to requests by frenzied members of the staff we are now designing a 'bill detector' which will automatically eject unwanted mail.

W. Korell

Normally, a centre-tapped transformer and a bridge rectifier is used to construct a symmetrical power supply. This seems such a natural solution, that people forget it can be done in a much simpler way. The accompanying circuit

diagram shows the simpler version. A disadvantage is the single-sided rectification which makes it necessary to use a larger smoothing capacitor to prevent mains hum.

With the values shown, a maximum of 10 mA

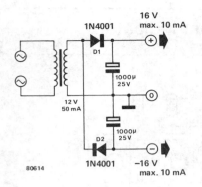

can be supplied at a ripple voltage of about 0.2 V_{p-p}. By using the formula below, values for other currents and ripple voltages can be calculated.

$$U_{ripple} = \frac{20 \cdot I}{C}$$

(U_{ripple} in volts (peak-to-peak), derived current I in mA and C in μ F)

229 Crystal controlled sinewave generator

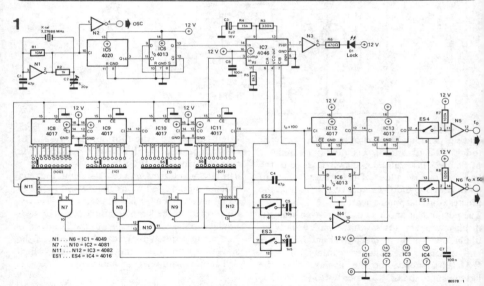

The applications of simple designs are not always restricted to those of a single circuit. A combination of two (or more) circuits can offer new perspectives. For instance, combining a crystal controlled frequency synthesiser and a digital spot sinewave generator produces a very stable sinewave generator. This 'hybrid' uses switches to select the output frequency in 1 Hz steps.

Figure 1 shows the crystal controlled frequency synthesiser section. The heart of the circuit is formed by a phase locked loop (PLL). A very stable frequency is fed to one input of the PLL

(IC7) and its output is passed through a variable divider chain before being fed to the other PLL input. The PLL will try to equalise both input frequencies and adjust its output frequency accordingly. Therefore, when the division ratio is set to the figure N, the output frequency will be N times greater than the input frequency. As the input frequency is derived from a crystal source, the output frequency will be very accurate.

The frequency of the crystal oscillator (3.2768 MHz) is divided by a factor of 2^{15} (IC5 and half of IC6) to provide the PLL with an input frequency of 100 Hz. The frequency divider for the

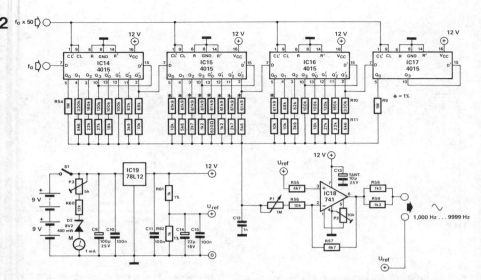

2

PLL is formed by IC8...IC11 and the desired division ratio (N), and hence the output frequency, is set up on switches S3...S6.

For optimum operation, the value of the capacitor connected between pins 6 and 7 of the PLL will have to be varied with frequency. This is accomplished with the aid of electronic switches ES2 and ES3. The remaining half of IC6 divides the PLL output frequency by two, while IC12 and IC13 form a divide-by-100 counter. This means that two signals are available at the output — one with a frequency fifty times greater than the other.

The circuit of the spot sinewave generator is shown in figure 2. It can be directly connected to the circuit of figure 1. Basically, the circuit consists of a 25 bit shift register and a resistor network.

The fundamental frequency, f_O (output of N5 in The fundamental frequency, f_O (output of N5 in figure 1), is fed to the data input of the first shift register (IC14). The higher frequency (output of N6 in figure 1) is fed to the clock input of each shift register. The signals at the outputs of IC14...IC17 are symmetrical squarewaves with a frequency of f_O. The voltages derived from two successive Q outputs are shifted in phase for the duration of one clock period. All 25 output signals are added by means of the resistor network consisting of R10...R54, so that a 50-step sinewave signal is generated across C12. The circuit around IC18 is an amplifier which acts as an output buffer.

The amplitude of the output signal can be varied between 50 mV_{p-p} and 5 V_{p-p} by means of P1. The frequency can be varied in 1 Hz steps between 1000 Hz and 9999 Hz. The sinewave is symmetrical around a reference voltage (U_{ref}) and any offset can be removed by P2. The output impedance of the amplifier is 600 Ω.

Both the 12 V stabilised supply and the reference voltage are derived from a pair of 9 volt batteries (or 4 x 4.5 V). Battery condition is monitored with the aid of the 1 mA moving coil meter, M. Finally, note that the resistors marked with an asterisk (61k9) are listed in the E48 range. If these are not available 62 k 1% resistors will be suitable from the E24 range will be suitable.

A.G. Hobbs

230 Variable power supply 0-50 V/0-2A

Because of its internal reference source, the LM 10 is eminently suitable for use in power supplies. By using two ICs both the current and the voltage can be made variable. An added fea

1

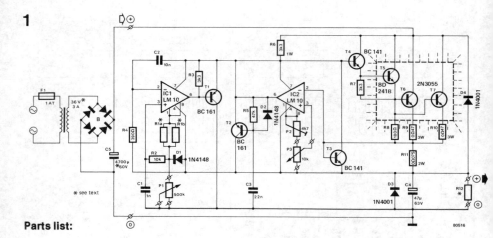

Parts list:

Resistors:

R1a = 2k2
R1b = empirically established (see text)
R2 = 10 k
R3, R7 = 3k3
R4 = 390 Ω
R5 = 47 k
R6 = 3k3/1 W
R8 = 180 Ω
R9, R10 = 0,47 Ω /3 W
R11 = 0,075 Ω /2 W (2 x 0,15 Ω in parallel or resistance wire)
R12 = 470 Ω /5 W
P1 = 500 k lin.
P2 = 4k7 preset
P3 = 10 k lin.

Capacitors:

C1 = 1 n
C2 = 10 n
C3 = 22 n
C4 = 47 µ /63 V
C5 = 4700 µ /80 V (see text)

Semiconductors:

T1, T2 = BC 161
T3, T4 = BC 141
T5 = BD 241
T6, T7 = 2N3055
D1, D2 = 1N4148
D3, D4 = 1N4001
IC1, IC2 = LM 10C

Miscellaneous:

Tr = 42 V (36 V)/3 A transformer
B = B80C2200 (200 V/8 A bridge rectifier)

ture is short circuit protection.

The output voltage is increased linearly by potentiometer P1, and the current (also linearly) by P3. The preset P2 is used to set the peak output current, up to a maximum of 2 A. The maximum output voltage can also be preset by a resistor connected in parallel with R1a. This method ensures better stability and less noise.

The output voltage is stabilised in the following manner. The inverting input of IC1 is connected to the output via R4 with the other input to the junction of P1/R2. The opamp will attempt to prevent any voltage difference by controlling T1. This will either increase or decrease the current through R6 which will consequently vary the voltage to the darlington output stage.

The voltage level at the junction of P1/R2 is generated as follows. Pin 1 of the LM 10 is the reference output. No voltage difference should occur between the two inputs of the opamp, in other words, junction R1/R2 is connected to the same potential as the negative connection (pin 4) of IC1. The reference voltage across R1 will be 200 mV at a current of approximately 100 µ A which will also flow through P1. This means that the potential drop across P1 will be equal to 10^{-4} (100 µ A) times its resistance. Otherwise, there *will* be a difference in voltage at the input of the opamp, so that it will adjust this until the output voltage has reached the exact value.

Current is stabilised by comparing part of the reference voltage (at the wiper of P3) with the voltage dropped across R11 (through which the output current passes). Since the LM 10 is not very fast, conventional current protection has been added with the aid of T3. This limits the current at a fixed threshold value.

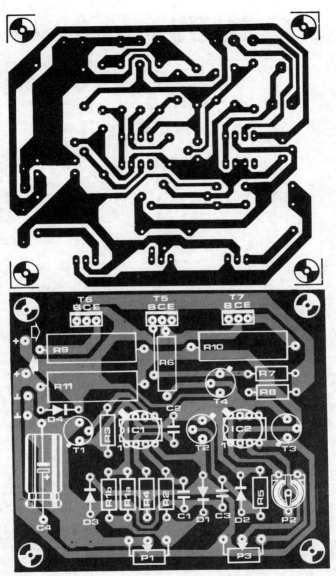

To a certain extent, the minimum output voltage will depend on the load. This is because the (small) supply current of the two opamps passes through the output. It is therefore always advisable to connect a fixed resistor across the output of the supply. With a fixed resistance of 470 Ω (5 W) a minimum output voltage of 0.4 V was measured in the prototype.

The maximum output voltage can be determined with R1b, as mentioned above, and should be no more than 50 V. In many cases however it is better to accept a lower value to work on and use a transformer of 36 V. The 4700 μ electrolytic capacitor may then be the common 63 V type.

Transistors T5, T6 and T7 will have to be mounted on a fairly large heat sink. Figure 2 shows the printed circuit board layout for the supply.

National application note

231 FSK PLL demodulator

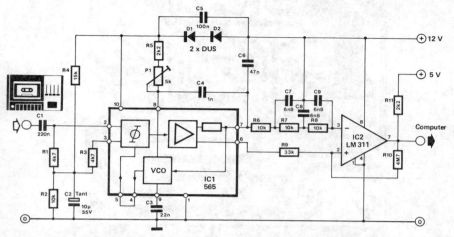

FSK (Frequency Shift Keying) signals can be demodulated in a simple manner with the aid of a PLL (Phase Locked Loop). Frequency shift keying is used regularly for data transmission, where a carrier wave is switched between two predetermined frequencies. The frequency shift is obtained by controlling a VCO with the binary data signal, so that the two frequencies are determined by the '0' and '1' logic states.

When a signal is present at the input of IC1 the VCO is locked in synchronisation with the input frequency. This involves an equal change in voltage at the output of the IC (pin 7). The loop filter capacitance (C6) is smaller than usual to eliminate spikes from the output pulse. At the same time, a ladder network of three RC sections is used to filter out the remains of the carrier wave from the output signal. The free-running frequency of the VCO can be preset with potentiometer P1 between about 1900 and 6200 Hz. The characteristics of the circuit (low pass filter R5...R8, C7...C9) make it suitable for speeds of up to 714 Baud.

232 Audio frequency meter

If your interest is primarily with audio, a commercial frequency meter, although very nice, is not strictly necessary since most of its range will be redundant. The simple circuit described here is used to convert an ordinary 10 k Ω /volt moving coil volt meter into an audio frequency meter.

The input signal is first amplified by transistor T1 (with a gain of about 40) and then passed through a Schmitt trigger formed by N4. This converts the signal to a square wave and the negative edge of this is used to trigger a monostable multivibrator (N1 and N2). Its output is

then inverted by N3 and fed to the multimeter which should be switched to the 2 volts (fsd) range.

The three ranges of the frequency meter are selected by S1. They are 200 Hz, 2 kHz and 20 kHz and are calibrated (with the aid of a frequency generator) by the three potentiometers P2, P3 and P4.

The circuit can be set to maximum sensitivity with P1. This potentiometer varies the DC bias through T1 and therefore the voltage to the input of N4. When this voltage is exactly centred between the two trigger threshold levels the sen-

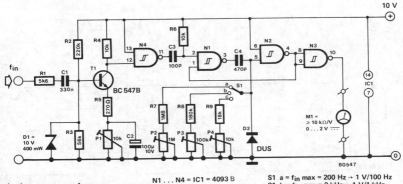

N1 ... N4 = IC1 = 4093 B

S1 a = f_{in} max = 200 Hz → 1 V/100 Hz
S1 b = f_{in} max = 2 kHz → 1 V/1 kHz
S1 c = f_{in} max = 20 kHz → 1 V/10 kHz

20 Hz ≤ f_{in} ≤ 20 kHz $U_{in\ min}$ ≃ 100 mV

sitivity is then at a maximum.

The input is able to withstand up to 50 volts peak to peak. For low input voltages, less than 14 volts peak to peak, the impedance is about 25 kΩ. At greater input voltages, D1 starts to conduct and the input impedance drops to about 5 kΩ.

The accuracy of the frequency measurement will be determined by the meter used since the accuracy of the circuit itself is better than 2%.

233 Deglitching remote control

1

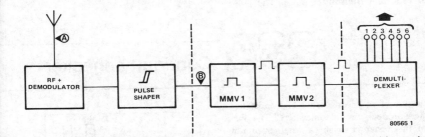

80565 1

Interference pulses in remote control receivers are a nuisance. Worse, when the control is for model planes they can be fatal... A quite effective interference rejection circuit can be built, using only two monostable multivibrators. Figure 1 illustrates the basic principle, as a block diagram; figure 2 gives a complete circuit for one common commercial system. The circuit is included in the receiver, between the pulse shaper and the demultiplexer.

In a normal system, interference at a level of only 10...30% of your own signal strength is enough to drive the servo's completely haywire. The 'interference susceptibility' of a given receiver depends, by and large, on its response speed. The faster it reacts, the more it tends to go wild. In general, the end of the 'burst' from

the transmitter is the most sensitive period. As illustrated in figure 3, interference spikes after the transmitter shuts down tend to extend the output from a pulse shaper – like MMV1 in figure 1. However, MMV2 in figure 1 is not 'retriggerable': it gives a brief pulse, after which it has

2

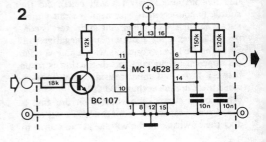

251

3

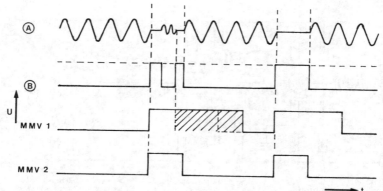

a considerable 'down time'. This second one-shot is triggered at each positive edge from the first MMV, so that it 'reconstructs' the original control signal – ignoring any interference spikes that occur after the transmitter closes down! If the interference is prolonged, MMV1 remains triggered; it doesn't produce any further pulses for MMV2, so that no further output pulses are produced. The servo's remain in their original position. Not that that is necessarily ideal, but it is better than having them run wild! The pulse length of MMV1 should be approximately twice that of a normal transmitter pulse. The pulse length of the second MMV is less critical: anywhere between 0.2 and 0.5 milliseconds should do.

The circuit given in figure 2 is a typical example of the principle. However, component values will vary from one system to another. Until manufacturer's standardise, we can't give one final 'recipe'! The principle is valid, however, for all similar remote control systems that use AM modulation.

A. Stampfl

234 Continuity checker

The question often arises – is it a high resistance or is there an open circuit somewhere? The purpose of this tester is to check whether or not there is a conductive path with a resistance of less than 5 MΩ between two points. A higher resistance than this is indicated as an open circuit. The results are indicated by two LEDs.

As the circuit diagram shows, the drain of FET T1 is directly connected to the positive supply line (consisting of two 1.5 volt cells) and the source is connected to the negative rail via resistors R2 and R3. The circuit under test is connected between the gate and the negative rail. Since the FET only conducts with a gate voltage (as opposed to current), no distinction is made between large and small resistance values (provided these are lower than 5 MΩ).

When open circuit, the voltage on the gate is +3 V with respect to ground and T1 will conduct thereby causing the voltage at the source to

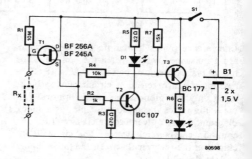

just about reach the supply voltage. This in turn provides transistor T2 with a base drive current and it starts to conduct, with the result that LED D1 will light. If the resistance is lower than approximately 5 MΩ , the gate voltage will drop, so that the FET will behave like a large resistance and the voltage at the source will also drop.

Transistor T2 will then turn off and, of course, so will D1. As far as T3 is concerned, the voltage on its base will also drop causing it to conduct and thereby lighting LED D2.

The value of R1 determines the resistance range which can be tested. With the value given here the highest resistance which can be tested is approximately 5 M Ω .

M.S. Dhingra

235 Pebble game

This circuit is based on the well known video game 'Break Out' where the idea is to shoot down as many bricks as possible in as few attempts as possible. In the version described here the bricks are represented by six LEDs.

Initially the reset key must be depressed for the six 'pebbles' to light up. The device is then activated with the 'LOAD' key whereupon the green LED (D1) will light up. If a point is scored with the 'FIRE' button, the pebble that was hit disappears and the corresponding LED goes out. Scoring a hit is pure coincidence and the system will have to be reloaded after each shot.

There are two methods of playing the game. Either each player has to hit all the pebbles and the winner will be the one to do this in the least number of shots, or the players fire shots alternately and he who hits the last pebble wins.

The operation of the circuit is quite straightforward. The shift register (IC1) is reset by switch S3. All the outputs will then be low and

the six pebble LEDs will light via the buffers N5...N10. Operation of the 'LOAD' key, S1, triggers several events. The 'standby' flipflop, FF2, is set so that its $\overline{Q}$ output goes low and lights LED D1. The oscillator formed by N2 is enabled for the length of time the 'LOAD' key is depressed and this will clock flipflop FF1. When the 'LOAD' key is released therefore, the Q output of FF1 will be either high or low depending on the frequency of oscillation and amount of time the key was depressed. No clock pulses will reach the shift register however as they are inhibited by N3.

Once loading is complete the 'FIRE' button can be pressed which will reset FF2 and the standby LED will go out. If the Q output of FF1 was high, the output of N3 will go low and the shift register will receive a clock pulse via N4. As the two serial inputs of IC1 are permanently held high, each of the shift registers outputs will go high (and remain high) in turn every time a clock

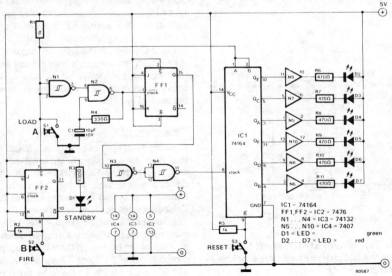

pulse is generated. The corresponding LED will, of course, go out to indicate a 'hit'. If the target is missed (the Q output of FF1 is low) the number of pebbles remains unchanged. In both instances the unit is prepared for the next LOAD and FIRE.

The Q̄ (or Q) output of FF2 can also be used to control a step counter to indicate exactly the actual number of shots fired. This makes scoring much easier. Power supply requirements for the pebble game are a measly 5 V/100 mA.

H.-J. Walter

236 NiCad battery monitor

keeps the cells 'topped up'

Now that an increasing number of battery-powered devices are being used in the home, it is much more economical to replace 'ordinary' batteries with NiCad cells. If such cells are to lead a long and healthy life, however, they will have to be correctly recharged from time to time. The question is, when is the right moment to recharge them?

More often than not, no indication is given on the electrical device itself and it isn't until the portable radio, the calculator, etc. stops working that its batteries are discovered to have run out, but then, of course, it is already too late... This article describes a small circuit that constitutes a very straightforward and yet highly effective method of keeping NiCads permanently 'topped up'.

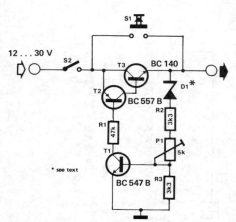

Figure 1. This circuit switches off the load whenever the battery voltage drops below a certain limit.

It would seem that batteries are specifically designed to go flat at the most inoportune moment, during an interesting radio programme or when the calculator is absolutely necessary. In either case, the answer is not simply to replace pen light batteries by NiCad cells, as these need recharging too every now and then. The trouble is, very few devices are equipped with some sort of monitor system, so it is very difficult to know when the cells need boosting. To sit back and wait until they run out won't exactly guarantee the cells a long lifespan — which, remember, was the reason why they were bought in the first place!

The author felt it was high time an end was put to this situation and designed a straightforward circuit to monitor the battery voltage. The circuit operates as follows: when the voltage drops below a certain pre-determined value, the current supply to the circuit is cut off to prevent the cells from discharging any further. Even when the battery voltage rises again because no current is being consumed, the cells will remain cut off. As a result, the monitor's own current consumption will be practically nil as well so that the entire circuit will use a minimum of current during normal operation.

The circuit

Looking at the circuit diagram, it can be seen that very few components are involved. The circuit is connected in series with the electrical device's power supply line 'after' the on/off switch as indicated in the drawing in figure 1. The battery voltage may be between 12 and 30 V. Transistors T2 and T3 from a PNP darlington pair, the base of which is linked to transistor T1 by way of a resistor (R1). When transistor T1 conducts, so will T2 and T3 and everything connected to the supply line will be provided with current. If, on the other hand, T1 stops conducting, T3 will stop too and the cells will no longer supply any current.

The purpose of the circuit is to allow T3 to conduct for the period during which the battery voltage (under load) is higher than 80% of the nominal voltage. This is done by connecting D1, R2, P1 and R3 in series, the junction of P1 and R3 being connected to the base of T1. If the base voltage of T1 drops below 0.6 V this transistor will stop conducting (and so will T3). The values of the zener diode and the resistors are chosen so that the voltage at the base of T1 is greater than 0.6 V when the battery voltage is 0.8 times the size of the nominal voltage. At the same time, the zener diode makes sure that a large share of the change in voltage on the supply line reaches the base of T1. The zener voltage is dependent on the battery voltage and can be calculated as follows:

$$U_z = 0.8 \cdot U_{nominal \ battery} - 1.5.$$

D1 may then be the lowest value closest to that result. The zener diode need only be a 400 mW type, as in this particular case the current passing through it will be very low (only about 200 A). Otherwise the true zener voltage will drop way below the level indicated and the calculation will no longer apply.

Pushbutton S1 plays a very important part in the circuit. If we were to construct the circuit without it, or the batteries for that matter, the circuit would never conduct. When the circuit is initially switched on, current is unable to reach the zener diode and the resistor chain, as a result of which the voltage at the base of T1 will prevent the transistors from switching on. If, however, S1 is pressed briefly, current will be able to reach the resistor divider chain via the zener diode. This will enable transistor T1 to conduct and thus switch on the rest of the circuit. It will be apparent that only a momentary operation of S1 is necessary.

The precise moment at which the circuit switches off can be determined with the aid of the preset potentiometer. First of all, the voltage of a fully charged cell that is under no load is measured with an accurate voltmeter. After this, 80% of the measured voltage is fed to the input of the circuit by means of an accurate power supply. P1 is then adjusted very carefully until the point is reached where T3 stops conducting (don't forget to press S1).

The circuit can produce a maximum current level of 1 A. The current consumption is very low. When the circuit is switched on this will be less than 0.5 mA at 12 V and less than 1 mA at 30 V. In the 'off' state, the amount of current consumed will be negligible.

W.-D. Roth

237 RF-test generator

a 'mini test generator' for the 2 metre, 70 cm and 23 cm wave bands

This straightforward little circuit will be an extremely useful tool for high frequency enthusiasts. It is a kind of 'harmonic generator' that can be modulated and which will produce test signals in 9 MHz steps up to the giga hertz range. It can be used both for FM and SSB receivers and is a fairly inexpensive circuit to build.

At one time or another, Ham radio operators who built their own sets are going to need a generator for receiver alignment. A commercially available test transmitter would, of course, be ideal, but they tend to be rather expensive and rather over-sophisticated. In nine cases out of ten a much simpler device will do the job, provided it produces a reliable, stable test signal within the required frequency range.

There is, however, one snag: an absolutely stable generator with an output frequency that is continuously adjustable is almost impossible to obtain. This plus the fact that we are looking for an economic alternative meant that another solution had to be found. A crystal generator was therefore designed that was capable of producing a wide frequency range without having to be tuned. The secret is for it not to be a 'clean' oscillator, but one with an output signal that contains many harmonics. Even though it includes an ordinary transistor, the oscillator produces

1

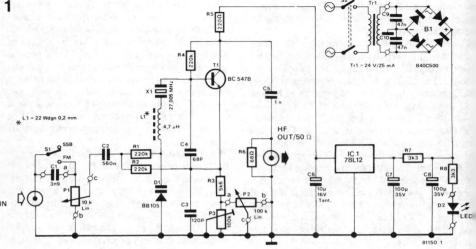

powerful harmonics of gigahertz proportions in addition to its 9 MHz fundamental frequency! This means that the test generator could also be used for reception and transmission on VHF and UHF. The generator's third harmonics are on the 27 MHz wave band (CB), its 16th harmonics

Figure 1. The test generator circuit diagram. It is straightforward and purely functional.

Figure 2. The printed circuit board for the 'mini test generator' is very compact.

2

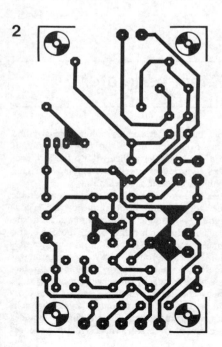

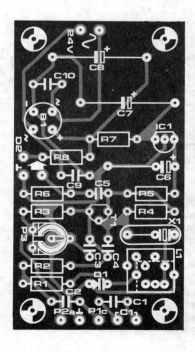

are at 144.08 MHz (2 metre wave band), its 48th harmonics are at 432.24 MHz (70 cm wave band) and its 144th harmonics are at 1296.72 MHz (on the 23 cm wave band).

The circuit is also ideal for testing speech processors.

The circuit

The remarkably simple circuit diagram is shown in figure 1. Around T1 there is a colpitt-like oscillator using a 27 MHz crystal. This does not make use of the third overtone of the crystal but rather the fundamental frequency, this being 9 MHz. This happens to be a very favourable frequency for our present purpose, since its harmonics extend over a range that is very practical for radio amateurs.

Parts list

Resistors:
R1, R2, R4 = 220 k
R3 = 5k6
R5 = 220 Ω
R6 = 68 Ω
R7, R8 = 3k3
P1 = 10 k linear
P2 = 100 k linear
P3 = 100 k preset

Capacitors:
C1 = 3n9
C2 = 560 n
C3 = 120 p
C4 = 68 p
C5 = 1 n (cer.)
C6 = 10 μ /16 V (tantalum)
C7, C8 = 100 μ /35 V
C9, C10 = 47 n

Semiconductors:
T1 = BC 547B
D1 = BB 105
D2 = LED
IC1 = 78L12
B1 = B40L500 round version

Miscellaneous:
X1 = 27.005 MHz crystal
L1 = 4.7 μ H coil (see text)
Tr1 = 24 V/25 mA transformer
S1 = SPDT switch
S2 = DPDT switch

When a crystal is used at the fundamental there is always a considerable difference between the theoretical and the measured frequency. The required frequency (here: 9005.000 kHz) must therefore be tuned precisely with coil L1. With the aid of the varicap diode D1 the oscillator can be frequency modulated. The usable modulation level (presettable with P1) is not particularly high, but high enough to test narrow band FM amateur and other special band receivers.

SSB receivers can be 'whistled through' with the generator. In order to obtain intelligible modulation level for such receivers, the frequency modulation (FM) should merely be converted into a phase modulation (PM). This can be done quite simply by connecting a small capacitor (C1) in series with the modulation input − thus, S1 can now switch between FM and SSB.

In most test generators a separate attenuator is used to measure a receiver's behaviour at very low signal levels. In this particular case this was found to be superfluous since the oscillator continued to be reliable even when barely operating. It is therefore quite a straightforward matter to built an attenuator by making the emitter resistor belonging to T1 adjustable. Pots P2 and P3 have a fairly wide range: at a frequency of 144.08 MHz (2 m wave band) the maximum output signal is around 1 mV and a minimum of around 30 nV (or 0.03 μ V)!

Construction

Obviously, building the board (figure 2) is a simple matter. Even the coil L1 should be no problem; just 22 turns of enamelled 0.2 mm copper wire wound around a Kaschke core, type K3/70/10. If readers happen to dislike this chore, an adjustable 4.7 μ H inductor coil obtainable from Toko will also be suitable.

With the exception of the mains transformer, the simple power supply shown in figure 1 is included on the printed circuit board. Since the circuit consumes very little current (and therefore the transformer can be quite small) the test generator and its power supply can be a highly compact instrument. When putting it into a case, be sure to provide a metal screen between the mains transformer and coil L1, otherwise there will be a lot of hum − a type of modulation that is not always to be desired!

238 Telephone amplifier

makes distant callers loud and clear

'Keeping in touch' is easier said than done, despite the modern telephone networks that stretch to the four corners of the globe. For one thing, a pound for a minute seems a lot of money to hear Granny's faint voice ten thousand miles away and then not understand a word she's saying. The solution is in the form of an amplifier which, when connected to the telephone, enables the whole family to listen in to the conversation.

Some callers, of course, don't need amplifying, as anyone blessed with an old aunt who bellows hearty greetings down one's ear at eight o'clock on a Sunday morning will agree. Here an attenuator would be more appropriate! But then that is

an exception. Distant and sometimes even local lines can be very poor indeed, so that an amplifier is really practical. For instance, when relatives ring up from South Africa, say, or Australia, it would be much more economical if the whole family could listen instead of having to 'queue up' to say a few costly words. What's more, the amplifier drowns any interference caused by crossed lines and thousands of 'clicking' relays, so that the once distant voice sounds as loud and clear as if the person were sitting in the same room.

Now that we know what the amplifier is for, we can study the circuit diagram in figure 1. Looking at the drawing from left to right, the circuit starts with a pick-up coil, the centre contains an amplifier and at the other end there is the loudspeaker. The pick-up coil operates according to magnetic principles: any alteration in the mag-

1

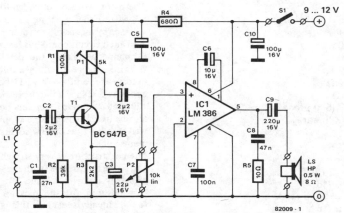

82009 - 1

netic field that is radiated by wires in the telephone set or in the receiver will be fed to the amplifier. This slightly roundabout system is necessary, since a direct electrical connection to the interior of a telephone is forbidden.

The rest of the circuit diagram in figure 1 comprises very few components. L1 represents the telephone pick-up coil which is specifically designed for this type of application. A very low AC voltage is induced across the coil and this is amplified by transistor T1 and the amplifier IC1 and then fed to the loudspeaker.

Figure 1. The circuit diagram of the telephone amplifier.

Figure 2. The printed circuit board track pattern and component layout for the telephone amplifier.

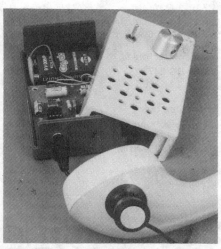

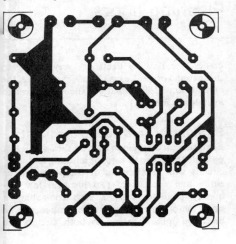

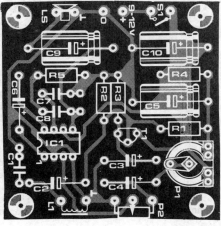

259

Parts list

Resistors:
R1 = 100 k
R2 = 39 k
R3 = 2k2
R4 = 680 Ω
R5 = 10 Ω
P1 = 4k7 (5 k) preset
P2 = 10 k linear

Capacitors:
C1 = 27 n
C2, C4 = 2μ2/16 V
C3 = 22μ /16 V
C5, C10 = 100μ /16 V
C6 = 10μ /16 V
C7 = 100 n
C8 = 47 n
C9 = 220μ /16 V

Semiconductors:
T1 = BC 547B
IC1 = LM 386

Miscellaneous:
L1 = telephone pick-up coil
LS = 8 Ω /1½ W miniature louaspeaker
S1 = on/off switch

There are two ways in which the volume can be adjusted: either by using P1 to set the threshold value or by means of the volume control P2.

A printed circuit board has been designed for the telephone amplifier, the details of which are shown in figure 2. Using a miniature Japanese loudspeaker and a 9 V PP11 battery, the whole circuit will easily fit into a plastic case of roughly 120 x 65 x 40 mm. A mains power supply may also be used, provided the supply voltage is very well stabilised, as otherwise there could be some mains hum.

The construction is very straightforward indeed and so we can proceed with the setting-up, which primarily involves L1 and P1. First of all, the best position for the pick-up coil has to be found. Ideally speaking, this is underneath the telephone, but this would mean having to raise the 'phone a little, since the coil is about 3 centimeters high. Another solution is to fit L1 onto the side of the telephone so that it is close to the amplifier. Readers should decide for themselves what the best practical solution is.

Now for the preset P1. This adjusts the maximum volume. Above a certain level, the sound reaching the amplifier input will be so loud that acoustic feedback ('howl round') will occur. This is a kind of echo that has got out of hand and produces a high-pitched tone. After setting P2 to maximum, P1 is adjusted so that this just does not occur. It would of course be feasible to omit all the components to the right of P2 and use HiFi equipment to reproduce the caller's voice, but then, that is up to the reader.

---

239 Flashing lights

The flashing lights described here can be fitted to an inexpensive (plastic?) toy car to provide an effect very similar to the warning lights seen on ambulances, fire engines and police vehicles. When used with the Hi-Fi siren it will, at minimal cost, add new dimensions to a toy, which any child will find fascinating.

Toy cars are always appreciated and, provided they are not too small, can usually accommodate a small circuit board and a couple of batteries. This particular circuit adds a special touch to the 'common or garden' toy car. As mentioned

earlier, the flashing lights are very similar to those found on police cars etc. What is more, the effect is so well simulated that there is no need to include any moving parts.

Straightforward and to the point

As the circuit diagram in figure 1 shows, it is still possible to design all sorts of amusing and 'fun' circuits with a minimum of components. The entire unit consists of two identical low frequency oscillator circuits each controlling a small lamp. The principle of operation can be described quite briefly. As both circuits are

identical, only one need be described. The oscillator (astable multivibrator) is constructed around the Schmitt trigger N1. Capacitor C1 is connected between the inputs of the gate and ground. The output of N1 is fed back to the input via resistor R1 and potentiometer P1. The capacitor is either charged or discharged by way of these resistors, depending on the logic level at the output of N1. Whenever the voltage across the capacitor reaches one of the trigger levels, the output of the gate 'toggles'. Thus, the multivibrator produces a squarewave output signal, the frequency of which is determined by the relationship between the capacitor value and the total resistance of R1 and P1. The frequency can be altered by adjusting P1.

The RC network C2/R3 connected to the output of N1 acts as a differentiator. Since R3 is connected to the positive supply rail, the network is only sensitive to the negative-going edges of the squarewave signal. These short 'spikes' are then converted to usable pulses by gate N2 to drive the darlington transistor T1. In turn, this transistor switches the lamp connected to its collector on for a short period of time. A resistor (R5) has been included across the emitter and collector of the transistor to ensure that the lamp remains at the correct temperature. This has the advantage that the initial current through the lamp is much

Figure 1. The circuit consists of two identical multivibrators. Depending on the effect required, there are three methods of linking the two circuits.

1

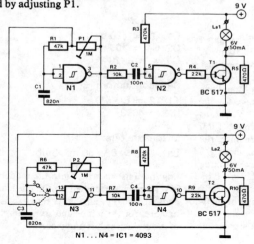

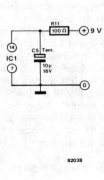

82038

261

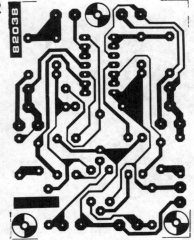

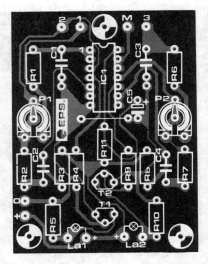

2 82038

less than normal and therefore the lamp will have a much longer life span. To make the lamp light up brightly, a 6 V type can be used with a (recommended) supply voltage of 9 V.

The only difference between the first and second sections of the circuit is the fact that the second one can be 'programmed' to perform in one of three different ways. This is accomplished with the aid of a wire link on the board. By linking points 3 and M, two completely independent flashing lights are obtained. By linking points 2 and M, the lamps light alternately. The frequency can then be adjusted by means of P1. Finally, if points 1 and M are linked, the two lamps will light simultaneously. Again, the frequency is determined by means of P1.

The printed circuit board

The two oscillator circuits can both be mounted on the printed circuit board shown in figure 2. The frequency controls, P1 and P2, can be either normal potentiometers or preset types. Do not forget to make the link between point M and one of the points 1...3. The supply voltage for the circuit can be anything between 3...15 V, but, as mentioned before, a 9 V battery supply (PP3) would be ideal. For optimum performance, the voltage rating of the lamps should be about 2/3 of the supply voltage, while the current rating should not exceed 400 mA. The values of resistors R5 and R10 should be chosen empirically so that the lamps are just on the verge of lighting.

We do not intend to give any details about installing the finished article into the model car. This is very much dependent on the particular model chosen. Usually, all that is required is a couple of holes for the lamps and some simple method of mounting the bits and pieces.

Figure 2. The printed circuit board and component overlay for the flashing lights circuit. The unit is so small that it can be built into a toy car quite easily.

Parts list:

Resistors:
R1, R6 = 47 k
R2, R7 = 10 k
R3, R8 = 470 k
R4, R9 = 22 k
R5, R10 = 470 Ω (see text)
R11 = 100 Ω
P1, P2 = 1 M preset
All resistors ⅛ W

Capacitors:
C1, C3 = 820 n
C2, C4 = 100 n
C5 = 10 µ /16 V

Semiconductors:
T1, T2 = BC 517
IC1 = 4093

Miscellaneous:
La1, La2 = 6 V, 50 mA bulb

240 Continuity tester

It is possible that after etching a printed circuit there is a break or short circuit in the copper pattern. The chance of this sort of fault occuring increases as the tracks and the insulation between them become narrower. The method of manufacture of printed circuits used by the amateur do not always allow very accurate detailing of the copper layout. A detailed inspection of the results is therefore necessary. This can, of course, be done using a normal resistance meter (a multimeter), but this has the disadvantage that you must keep one eye on the meter. An audible indication can make the testing much quicker and easier leaving both eyes free to check suspect tracks with two test prods. The continuity tester gives a tone when there is a connection, and is silent when there is an open circuit.

The circuit diagram (figure 1) shows that the tester is a very simple design consisting only of a two transistor astable multivibrator. When the

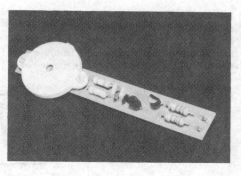

two test points are connected, the two transistors conduct alternately causing a square wave voltage to appear across the buzzer, at a frequency of a few kHz. The tone produced by the buzzer indicates the connection.

The circuit operates from a supply of only 1.5 V, and draws no more than 1 mA. Because of the small load, even the smallest 1.5 V battery will have a long life.

The continuity tester is built on the printed circuit board shown in figure 2. This includes space for the buzzer as well. The complete circuit and battery can be fitted into a plastic tube, so that the tester fits easily into the hand.

Parts list

Resistors:
R1, R2 = 2k2
R3, R4 = 470 k

Capacitors:
C1, C2 = 470 p

Semiconductors:
T1, T2 = BC 547B

Miscellaneous:
Bz = buzzer PB-2720 (Toko)
2 test probes
1.5 Volt battery

1

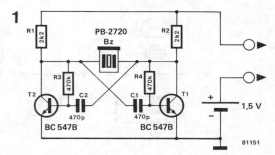

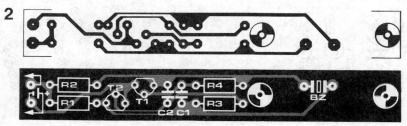

This scoreboard featured in this article is intended for use in quiz type competitions where competitors can both gain and lose points. Scoring can sometimes become quite 'confused' in the heat of the moment therefore simple oper-

ation is essential. In this design a point is awarded or deducted by the process of pushing one of two buttons — one push, one point. When for instance the scorer has already awarded points and the referee reverses the de-

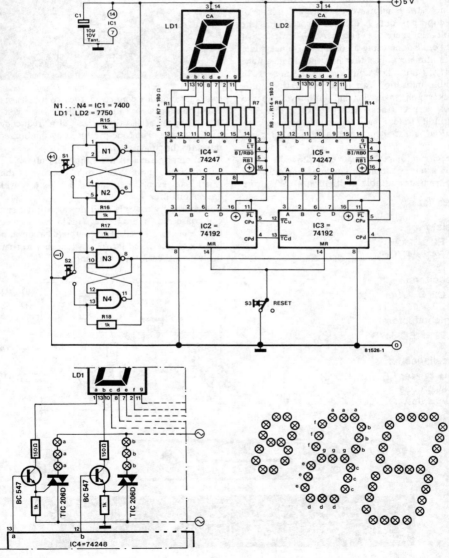

cision the correction can be carried out easily.

The circuit of the scoreboard is shown in figure 1. The counter IC chosen is the well known 74192 decade counter. This has two clock inputs, one for counting up and the other for counting down. The count (or clock) pulses are created by either of the two flipflops formed by gates N1, N2 or N3, N4 which are triggered by switch S1 or S2. The two counters are connected in series to provide a maximum count of 99.

The 74192 presents the information at its output in BCD (Binary Coded Decimal) format and therefore some form of decoding is necessary for the 7 segment displays. For this purpose the 74247 (an updated version of the 7447) BCD to 7 segment decoder/driver is used. This IC carries out all the functions required between the counters and displays which are in fact connected directly to its output via current limiting resistors. Virtually any type of common anode 7 segment display can be used. Switch S3 is included to reset the score and when pressed both displays will revert to zero.

It will be apparent that the LED displays will be altogether too small where a larger audience is concerned and for this purpose the design for a very much larger display is included to the right of figure 1. This uses 240 V bulbs and should be bright enough to be visible from a few hundred yards away. The complete display can be as large as required by carefully spacing the bulbs. The wiring must be as shown in the illustration. Each segment of each display requires a triac and a driver transistor. The bulbs are 15 or 25 Watt and can be obtained in various colours for a more 'professional' appearance. The triac used must have a turn on gate current of 5 mA.

If the mains version is built a 74248 must be used for both IC4 and IC5. The LED display can still be retained for use by the scorekeeper in case he is unable to see the larger one.

LS devices can be used to replace all of the TTL ICs but the two types cannot be mixed. The supply current for LS ICs will be about 350 mA while TTL will require up to 450 mA. .

WARNING: Readers who have no wish to renew their aquaintance with the physical properties of 250 V AC when connected with their person should take extra care when constructing the mains display version.

242 Loudspeaker peak indicator

Nowadays, any decent loudspeaker unit is, fortunately, pretty resistant to rough treatment. However, problems can arise in the living room when the volume is turned up high enough for clipping to occur. At that point substantial distortion and higher harmonics can be generated. This does not only spoil listening pleasure but it can actually damage the tweeters. A measure of protection can be acheived by the use of a clip or peak indicator, an extra not yet normally included in the majority of audio amplifiers.

The peak indicator described here can be connected directly to the output of the amplifier or even fitted into the speaker since a separate power supply is not required.

The circuit will respond even to very short peaks making it highly suitable for determining when the amplifier is about to peak (in other words, it

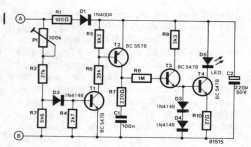

is not just an overload indicator). The peak power level at which the circuit is expected to respond (that is, the peak voltage) is adjustable between 15 and 125 Watts with an 8 ohm speaker (14...45 V). The circuit will light a LED when the amplifier just delivers its peak power enabling the listener to actually see when things begin to go wrong. If the LED only occasionally lights everything is fine. When the LED begins to light continuously then it is time to turn the volume down a little.

The circuit diagram for the indicator is shown in figure 1. Its power supply is derived from capacitor C1 which is charged via R1 and D1 from the speaker output of the amplifier. Half-wave rectification was considered suitable since 'normal' 45 V transistors can be used.

With no signal input all transistors are switched off and therefore current drain from C2 is vir-

tually nil. When the input signal level exceeds a certain value (dependent on the setting of P1), the voltage at the junction of R2 and R3 will reach a point at which T1 will start to conduct.

Components required:

Resistors:

R1 = 100 Ω
R2 = 27 k
R3 = 5k6
R4 = 2k7
R5 = 8k2
R6 = 39 k
R7 = 220 Ω
R8 = 1 M
R9 = 3k3
R10 = 27 Ω
P1 = 100 k adjustable potentiometer

Capacitors:

C1 = 100 n
C2 = 220 μ F/50 V

Semiconductors:

D1 = 1N4004
D2, D3, D4 = 1N4148
D5 = LED
T1, T3, T4 = BC 547B
T2 = BC 557B

2

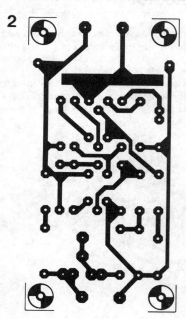

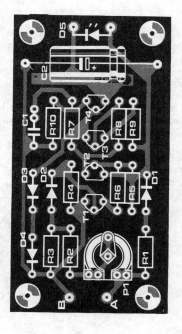

This switches on T2 causing C1 to charge rapidly. Resistor R7 has been included to prevent the maximum permitted collector current of T2 from being exceeded. Both transistors T3 and T4 will now conduct and LED D5 will light. The current through the LED will be maintained at 20 mA by C2, independent of the speaker signal level. When the input voltage then drops below the preset level, T1 and T2 will switch off. However, the LED will remain lit for a few moments longer while C1 discharges via R7 and R8.

Construction should not present any problems if the printed circuit board shown in figure 2 is used. It would probably be advisable to use the larger type of LED for maximum 'visibility'. Calibration is carried out in the following manner. If the peak power of the amplifier is known, its peak voltage can be calculated with the formula:

$$V_{peak} = 2 \times P_{peak} \times R_{speaker}$$

Connect the indicator circuit to a stabilised power supply (positive to point A), and set the DC supply level to the calculated value. P1 should then be turned back until the LED just begins to light. During this operation care should be taken to ensure that the LED does not remain lit for too long because it may cause the dissipation limit of T4 to be exceeded.

Once the clipping level has been set, the circuit may be connected to one of the speaker outputs of the amplifier or, if desired, to one of the speakers. It may be possible to modify the circuit to operate a relay that rings a bell... or fires a cannon perhaps?

243 6 Watt stereo amplifier for a car radio

The TDA 2004 from SGS-Ates contains two balanced class B power amplifiers. The IC was designed especially for use as an in-car stereo amplifier, and for this reason it is housed in a strong package and protected against all kinds of overload. For example, output short-circuits or disconnection of the loudspeaker, overheating of the chip, peaking of the power supply or even briefly reversing the polarity of the supply connections are unable to destroy the device.

With the component values shown and with a supply voltage of 14.4 V (a fully charged car bat-

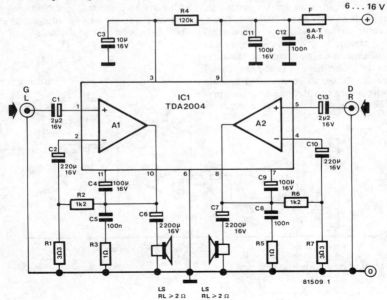

267

tery), the stereo amplifier is capable of delivering a power output of at least 6 W, typically 6.5 W with a load impedance (RL) of 4 Ω . It can also handle a load impedance of 2 Ω , in which case the output power is a minimum of 9 W, but typically 10 W. Power outputs of this order are subject to about 10% distortion, however, if lower power outputs are acceptable, 4 W with a load impedance of 4 Ω or 6 W with a load impedance of 2 Ω , distortion is only in the order of 0.3%.

The voltage gain of the left-hand channel is determined by the ratio of R2 to R1, and that of the right-hand channel by the ratio of R6 to R7. With the values given, this will be 50 dB. Therefore, a signal of about 50 mV is required at the input to give the maximum output. If this input sensitivity is too great, a 50 kΩ stereo potentiometer can be included at the input. The impedance of the non-inverting amplifier input is minimally 100 kΩ .

The network consisting of resistor R3 and capacitor C5 (and R5/C8) is included to prevent

the amplifier oscillating at high input frequencies. The bandwidth of the circuit is more than adequate for use as a car radio amplifier. The frequency response of the amplifier is 40 Hz to 16 kHz (3 dB points).

Obviously, the IC must be kept sufficiently cool. However, the well thought-out design makes it a very simple task to mount the device on an adequate heatsink. The thermal resistance of the heatsink should be at least 4°C/W.

2

244 Polarity converter

Analogue or digital voltmeters (or both!) are a very important requirement for the electronics laboratory, be it amateur or professional. Therefore, the easier it is to measure voltages, the better. In the case of most analogue meters and some digital ones, it can be something of a nuisance when the probes have to be changed round every time the voltage to be measured assumes the opposite polarity to the one measured previously. Forgetting to do this could result in

rather disastrous consequences!!

The circuit presented here helps matters considerably, as the output voltage will always be positive irrespective of the polarity of the input

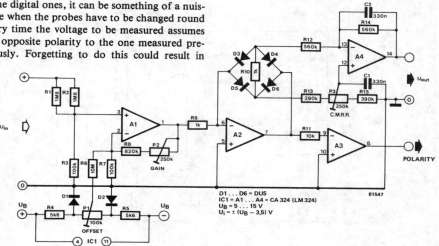

voltage. The circuit also has a 'polarity' output which will produce an output of $+U_B$ when the input voltage is positive and $-U_B$ when the voltage to be measured is negative. Provided the circuit is calibrated correctly, the overall accuracy is guaranteed to the better than 0.5% of the maximum input voltage (U_i).

The calibration procedure for the circuit is as follows. Resistors R12 and R13 are disconnected from R10 and linked to each other. A level of $+1$ V is then applied between the junction of R12 and R13 and ground (0 V). The output voltage (A4) is then adjusted to a minimum level by means of preset potentiometer P3. This is called the common mode rejection ratio (CMRR) preset. The polarity of the 1 V test voltage is then reversed (-1 V). A certain voltage (several millivolts) will now be measured at the output and P3 is adjusted once more to reduce this level to about half.

The above procedure is repeated by alternately reversing the polarity of the test voltage and adjusting P3 until the measured output voltage is the same in both cases (at $+1$ V and at -1 V). The CMRR will then be set to its maximum level. (The low output voltage is due to the offset of A4 and can not be completely eliminated.)

The next step is to connect resistors R12 and R13 as shown in the circuit diagram. The input is then short circuited and the overall offset of the circuit can be reduced to a minimum by means of preset potentiometer P1.

Once this has been accomplished, a known input voltage of, say, $+1$ V, is applied to the input and the gain of the unit is adjusted by means of P2 so that the output voltage is equal to the input voltage. The circuit will now be correctly calibrated and ready for use.

Last, but by no means least, the circuit should be provided with a stable power supply. This is because fluctuation in supply voltage level would mean having to calibrate the unit all over again.

245 Temperature recorder

This circuit, together with a certain amount of mechanical ingenuity, makes it possible to construct a relatively inexpensive piece of equipment which can be used to record a temperature curve. An ordinary radio control servo is used to operate the pen. It uses a negative temperature coefficient (NTC) resistor as the sensor. The circuitry around N1, N2, T1 and T2 forms an oscillator whose pulse width is determined by the instantaneous value of the NTC resistor. The resultant signal is fed directly to IC2. This IC (the SN 28654) is specifically designed as a servo

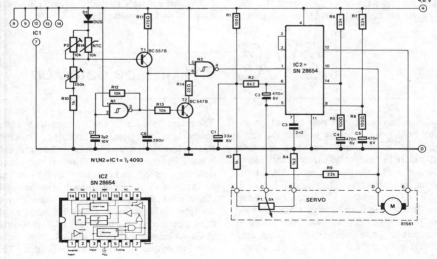

amplifier, which is abundantly clear from its specifications:
- an output current of 400 mA with no external transistors
- change of direction is accomplished with a single supply voltage
- the 'dead space' − the degree of input change required before a change in the output occurs − is dependant on the value of C3
- a maximum dissipation of around 800 mW.

The pulse width modulated signal is fed to pin 1 of IC2. The control output for the servo appears at pins 10 and 12 of the IC. Readers who would like to know more about this particular device than we have room for here are advised to obtain the data sheet from the manufacturers or from one of their distributors.

The non-linear course of the resistance value constitutes a bit of a problem when using NTC devices as temperature sensors. This can be solved, however, by utilising only a small portion of the temperature characteristic. This is accomplished here by the 'sensitivity' potentiometers P2 and P3 which effectively set the amount of deflection of servo per degree of temperature change and the lower limit of the range respectively. This achieves a reasonable degree of accuracy, but of course, we are not trying to construct a piece of laboratory equipment. In reality, the circuit is only intended to record a change in temperature over a period of time rather than measure actual temperatures.

The mechanical parts can be constructed quite simply. The servo can be mounted on a clip over the roll of paper. The holder for the recorder pen can be glued or screwed to the arm of the clip. As a holder for the pen, what better than part of

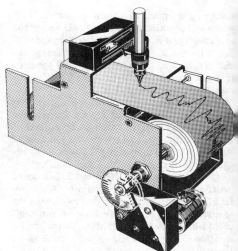

an old pair of compasses? This has the advantage that the pen can be easily removed for cleaning or replacement. The paper can be the type used in printing calculators, but the roll should move at a slow and constant speed when the equipment is in operation. The paper drive can be made with the aid of motors and gears that are normally used by model boat builders, available from any good model shop. Failing this, geared motors, for a variety of voltages, are readily available from surplus stores such as Proops and J. Bull.

To prevent the NTC resistor from heating up on its own, care should be taken when adjusting P2 and P3 to keep the voltage across the NTC below 0.5 V. If the voltage rises above that value, accuracy will suffer considerably.

246 End of tape detector

This design incorporates a new type of photo-detector which has a large number of applications such as detecting breaks in magnetic tapes. Before the output of the detector reaches the outside world, the signal passes through the following internal stages. The photo-diode is followed by a linear opamp which feeds a Schmitt trigger. In turn, the Schmitt trigger controls a so-called 'totem-pole' output stage. Sensitivity to fluctuations in power supply levels is reduced considerably by the use of the Schmitt trigger.

The totem-pole output enables the user to install several photo-detectors in parallel. Basically, this is how the circuit works: When the light beam is interrupted, the output of the photo-detector goes low and transistor T1 is turned off so that the relay is deactivated. The normally closed contact of the relay keeps the motor of the tape player running. However, when something goes wrong, the beam from the transmitter (a Ga-As infra-red diode) reaches the receptor so that the output of the device goes high. This

270

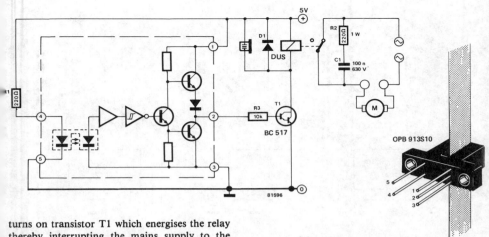

turns on transistor T1 which energises the relay thereby interrupting the mains supply to the motor. A dc buzzer has been connected in parallel with the relay to give an audible warning when there is a break or tear in a tape being inspected.

The circuit has numerous applications as long as the object examined has dimensions which fit through the slit of the detector. As mentioned above, one of the most obvious applications is the end, or break detector in magnetic tapes.

The circuit is completely TTL compatible, so that the power supply can be of the simple asymmetric 5 V type. When the unit is used in conjunction with a tape recorder, it should be kept in mind that the photo-detector should be positioned as closely as possible *before* the magnetic heads. This is to ensure that if a break occurs, no pieces of tape get wrapped around the heads and drive wheels before the break is detected.

247 CMOS pulse generator

A pulse generator can be extremely useful when designing digital circuits. To make the most of its possibilities it must be as flexible as possible. The clock frequency must be variable over a fairly wide range and of course the pulse width must be variable also. An automatic output level control would be a major advantage. All these and a few other features are combined in the circuit given here.

The use of CMOS ICs throughout has two advantages. In the first place it is possible to power the circuit from batteries. Furthermore, the large supply voltage range afforded by CMOS, from 5 to 15 V, makes it possible to provide the automatic output control mentioned above. This is clear from the fact that if the pulse generator itself is powered from the circuit under test, the supply voltage will equal that of the circuit and the output logic levels must therefore be compatible whether it is CMOS or TTL (output buffers

are included). Furthermore, the low current requirement of the generator input results in a very low current drain on the circuit being tested.

The description of the circuit begins at the clock generator, IC1. This IC is wired as an astable multivibrator and its frequency is adjustable between 2 Hz and 1 MHz (depending on supply voltage) by potentiometer P1 and switch S1. With S5 closed and S4 in the 'high' position, IC1 will run continuously. With S5 opened an external signal can be used to trigger IC1 via the 'gate in' socket. Switch S4 can then be used to select the required polarity for pins 4 and 5 of IC1 from the external source.

The output signals of the clock generator appear at pins 10 and 11 of IC1. The Q output (pin 10) is passed to the trigger input of IC2. This IC is used as a pulse shaper to provide a narrow sync pulse output for external trigger purposes. The Q output of IC1 is also fed, via S6 (duty cycle

271

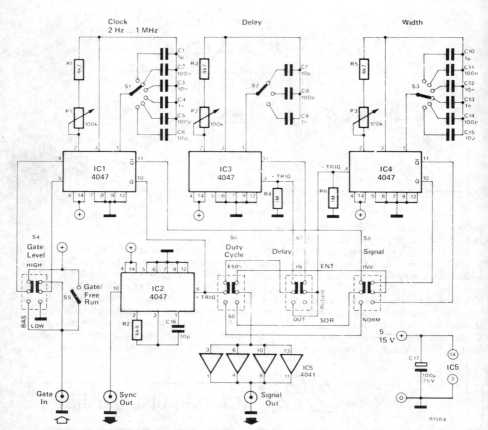

50%) and S8 (signal normal), to the output buffer stage, IC5.

ICs 3 and 4 are also wired as triggerable monostable multivibrators. With S6 in the 50% position and S7 set to delay out, the Q output of IC1 will be passed to the trigger input of IC4. Any required pulse width can now be achieved by the adjustment of both P3 and S3. This provides a variable duty cycle output at pins 10 and 11 of IC4. Depending on the position of switch S8, either the normal or the inverted signal can be passed via the buffer stage to the signal out socket.

A further modification to the signal can be carried out with IC3 when S7 is switched to the 'delay in' position. IC3 will now be triggered by the clock output signal of IC1 (S6 still in the 50% position). Now, by adjusting P2 and S2, it is possible to delay the output signal from 1.5 s to 250 ms with reference to the sync out trigger pulse. The output of IC3 is now used to trigger IC4. The pulse width can still be modified

as required. It should be noted that the delay circuit does not alter the output signal but varies its timing relative to the sink output. By setting the delay to a suitable value, it is possible to move the leading edge of the output signal but varies its timing relative to the sync output. By setting the delay to a suitable value, it is possible to move the leading edge of the output signal pattern to a more central position on the oscilloscope screen enabling the complete waveform to be studied.

The prototype generator was constructed using Veroboard since very little layout work is required. Virtually all of the wiring concerns the controls on the front panel. All of the range capacitors can be mounted on the switches S1, S2 and S3 if two wafers are used for each switch. Mounting resistors R1, R2 and R3 between the potentiometers and switches leaves only five components and the five ICs for the board. However, there are quite a few interconnections to be made between the board and the front panel so care should be taken. Ribbon cable may prove to be useful for this purpose.

Power for the generator can be derived from the circuit under test or from batteries. If the latter are used, the input and output levels may not be totally compatible.

RCA application note ICAN 6230

248 Fuse protector

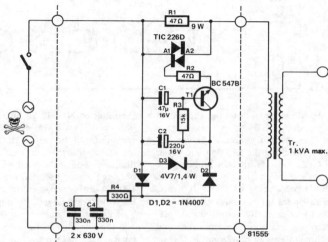

In recent times, the requirement for higher power hi-fi equipment has grown to such an extent that it has now become necessary to protect even the domestic house fuses from being blown too often. The solution is a 'soft start' circuit − a circuit which maintains the initial surge current to within acceptable limits.

Normal domestics fuses are rated at 13 A and many readers may express some surprise if we venture to suggest that the transformer in their equipment could conceivably draw this seemingly excessive amount of current. The short answer is yes, it can and it does! It should be realised that these large transformers can easily withstand powers of up to 1 kW in some cases. The 'turn on' current of the transformer goes into a very low impedance, both in the primary and the secondary winding. Furthermore, the smoothing capacitor on the dc side can be so large that when it is still discharged it can virtually have a zero impedance. Effectively, therefore, the fuse in the primary side of the transformer is presented with a short-circuit and it is not at all surprising that the mains fuse does blow on occasion. The fuse protector alleviates

this problem by limiting the surge current via resistor R1. Only after approximately 100 ms (two mains periods) will this resistor be shorted out by the triac. The delayed input voltage is obtained by the drive to the triac gate via transistor T1. The mains voltage is reduced by a capacitive series impedance, C3/C4, to the point that after rectification by diode D2, stabilisation by D3 and smoothing by capacitor C2, a dc voltage of 4.7 V appears across the zener diode. Transistor T1 is then turned on via capacitor C1 and remains on. This in turn drives the gate of the triac causing it to turn on and provide a short across resistor R1. The full primary current will then flow through the triac.

The circuit can be constructed with the triac type TIC 226D (as shown) with transformers with a rating of up to 1 kVA. Larger transformers will obviously require larger triacs.

The fuse protector can be used for a variety of applications such as hi-fi equipment (as mentioned), domestic appliance motors (washing machines etc.) and heavy duty lamps - especially ultra-violet and infra-red types.

249 Miser - LED

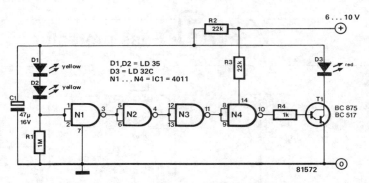

The circuit described here allows the amount of energy consumed by LEDs to be reduced to a fraction of the normal value. This is accomplished by switching the LED on and off at intervals of 0.625 seconds, thereby reducing the average current through the LED to around 200 μ A with a peak value of about 100 mA. This is quite sufficient for normal 'viewing'.

Mainly due to continually more dense integration, electronic circuits are becoming less and less demanding on energy consumption. However, this does not hold true for LEDs which are used for a variety of indicator functions. Most LEDs consume a minimum current of around 20 mA, which in many instances is several times more than that used by the rest of the circuit. This is an especially unsatisfactory situation where the equipment in question is battery-powered.

The circuit operates as follows: Capacitor C1 is charged via resistor R2. Once the potential across this capacitor is sufficient to overcome the bias presented by (yellow) LEDs D1 and D2,

the input of N1 will go high. Consequently the output of N4 will also go high providing a short steep pulse to the base of the Darlington transistor which will then turn on rapidly so that C1 discharges through the LED D3. The current passing through the LED reaches a maximum of 100 mA during the short discharge period. When C1 is fully discharged, the input to N1 goes low. This means that the output of N4 also goes low and the Darlington transistor will turn off. Capacitor C1 will then start to charge up again and the entire cycle will be repeated.

If preferred, several 'ordinary' diodes in series can be used instead of the two yellow LEDs D1 and D2. As the 4011 has a very critical threshold value, it may be necessary to experiment with several different diodes in order to obtain the correct switch-over point. The IC receives its power via resistor R3 which ensures that the current to the IC is restricted to a minimum. The actual physical size of the complete unit is so small that it will cause no problems if it is to be installed into existing equipment.

250 Zero voltage indicator

This zero voltage indicator uses two LEDs to show whether the input voltage lies within a specified small voltage range, which is symmetrical about zero. If the voltage is within the range, the LEDs flash. If it is outside, one of them

lights continuously. Within the specified range there is also an indication of whether the voltage is at the edge of the range, or near the centre (i.e. near to zero). At the centre of the range the LEDs flash regularly, but towards the edges they

1

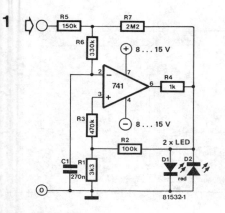

81532-1

become irregular.

The operation of the circuit is actually quite simple, although it may not at first appear so from the diagram. If you imagine the circuit without some of the components (R3, R4, R5, D1 and D2), you have a normal opamp oscillator. However, by including the potential divider, R7, R5, we ensure that the voltage fed back to C1 is no longer equal to the supply voltage. (It is also limited by D1 and D2.) If R5 is not now connected to earth, but to a DC voltage (the input voltage), the DC level of the feedback voltage will be changed. When this level is so high that the voltage across C1 falls outside the hys-

teresis loop of the Schmitt trigger, the circuit stops oscillating and one of the LEDs lights continuously.

If the input voltage is exactly 0 volts, then the DC level across C1 is zero, and the LEDs will flash regularly. However, if the input is not exactly 0 volts, (e.g. slightly positive), then one LED (D2) will be on slightly longer than the other.

The sensitivity of the circuit is about 50 mV, i.e. the LEDs change from flashing to a continuous light at plus and minus 50 mV. This can be changed readily by altering the value of R7. A higher resistance increases the sensitivity ($R7_{max}$ 3M3). You must bear in mind that if R7 is reduced, C1 must be increased.

The source impedance of the voltage which is connected should not be greater than 10 k, otherwise a buffer-amp must be interposed.

2

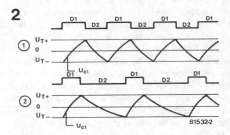

81532-2

---

251 Auto theft alarm

Readers who are in the habit of parking their cars close to lampposts at night may presume that the vehicle is considerably safer in a well lit area. However, it could be mentioned that car thieves, as a rule, like to see what they are getting! Further precautions are, therefore, very necessary, or your car could still be found to be gone. Alarm circuits for this purpose must be:
a. reliable; b. easy to operate, and c. failsafe.
After all, if the neighbours have been woken up several times on previous occasions due to false alarms, it may not be easy to maintain good relations with them and they may therefore be less likely to inform yourself or the police when a genuine break-in occurs.
The alarm circuit described here has a number of good features. It uses very little current, it has delayed turn on and delayed alarm, it has repeti-

tive as well as continuous alarm and it will automatically re-arm itself once it has been triggered. All this complexity means that the circuit itself needs to be fairly complex. The actual operation of the unit will become clear as we describe the circuit diagram.
When the alarm circuit is switched on, by means of the (hidden) keyswitch S1, capacitor C1 begins to charge via preset potentiometer P2. This charge time is actually the delay which allows the driver and passengers to leave the car and shut the doors. When the base/emitter voltage of T1 (in series with D1) is sufficient to turn the transistor on, the alarm is activated and is in the 'standby' state. If a door is now opened, the door switch, S2 will make and operate relay Re1. Once the alarm has been triggered, that is, a door has been opened, it can only be switched

275

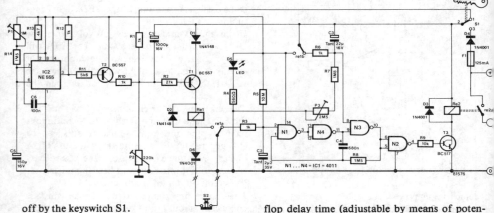

off by the keyswitch S1.

Now to the next function performed by the circuit. Once the alarm has been armed by means of S1 and a would-be thief opens the door, relay Re1 pulls in and latches on via contacts re1a, which bridge the door switch S2. If required, the interior (courtesy) light can be made to remain lit by replacing diode D6 with a wire link. A point worthy of note is the fact that no matter how fast the would-be car thief opens and closes the door, the alarm will remain active since the relay has operated.

The other contact of the relay, re1b, enables the charge path for capacitors C2 and C3. At the same time, an indication that the alarm has been triggered is given by LED D5. The charging of capacitor C2 via resistor R5 results in the alarm delay time, in other words, the thief still does not know that an alarm is present in the vehicle. This time delay is long enough, about ten seconds, for the driver of the vehicle to enter and disarm the alarm.

Only when C2 is fully charged will the voltage level at pin 2 of N1 become logic '1'. This level is fed through gates N4, N3 and N2 to the relay driver transistor T3. Relay Re2 will therefore be activated and the alarm will sound continuously. Capacitor C3 will also start to charge at the same time as C2, but this charge time is significantly longer and is adjustable by means of preset potentiometer P3 up to approximately thirty seconds. After this period, pin 8 of N3 will go low, as does the output of N2 and the relay Re2 will drop out again.

The 555 timer, IC2, is connected as a monostable multivibrator and its purpose is to provide the repetitive feature of the alarm circuit. This IC is enabled by relay contacts re1b and is triggered at pin 2 via resistor R13. After the mono-

flop delay time (adjustable by means of potentiometer P1) has elapsed, transistor T2 is turned on via the output of the 555 at pin 3. Capacitor C1 then discharges through resistor R10 and transistor T1 turns off when the voltage across C1 is reduced to about 1 V. This causes relay Re1 to drop out and capacitors C2 and C3 discharge rapidly via resistors R3 and R6 respectively. At the same time the timer IC is disconnected from the supply. The alarm is now in the original active standby state.

The 4011 (IC1) containing gates N1...N4 also serves another purpose besides that already mentioned. It also functions as a squarewave generator with a frequency of 0.8 Hz. This gives an intermittent alarm signal to the vehicle's horn and/or lights operated by Re2.

Warning: The horn relay in general use in cars usually has a very low impedance and therefore requires a relatively large amount of current. Transistor T3 must, obviously, be capable of supplying such a current. It may be preferable to incorporate a separate horn for the purposes of the alarm since certain car thieves are aware of the fact that the ordinary car horn is often used for alarms and therefore promptly disconnect it before opening the car door.

It is common sense to conceal the alarm unit and the operating switch as much as is practical for obvious reasons. The current consumption of the circuit is a mere 4 μ A in the standby condition.

R. Rastetter

252 Objektor

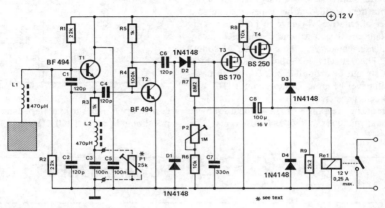

The aim of this circuit is to detect the presence of a conductive object, provided the object is within a certain range. The operation of the circuit is totally independant of the condition of the object (dead, alive, static or moving), as long as it remains within this range. The sensitivity of the circuit can be set remotely, by adjusting the preset potentiometer P1. This is to avoid wearing out shoe leather during the initial (trial an error) alignment procedure − repeatedly walking up and down to obtain the optimum setting for that particular range.

A rather innocent application of the circuit is its use as an invisible doorbell sensor, as the sensor could be located inside the house. The most important part of the circuit is the Clapp-oscillator constructed around transistor T1. The capacitor that should be connected in series with the coil L1 is formed by the sensor plate and the object to be detected. Due to the losses of this capacitor, the output from the oscillator is rather low, therefore a single amplifier stage (T2) has been

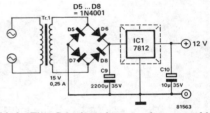

added. The Schmitt trigger and monostable functions are performed by transistors T3 and T4. VMOS FETs have been chosen for the sake of simplicity and the fact that less components are required with respect to bipolar devices increases the reliability factor ('what you don't fit don't go wrong!'). This does of course mean that the cost of the project will be somewhat higher.

Another application is fluid level measurements in noisy environments. As the sensor does not require physical contact, the fluid could possess agressive qualities (for instance, fuming sulphuric acid).

253 High input impedance voltage follower

It is common knowledge that Field Effect Transistors (FETs) feature a very high impedance − well within the Giga-ohm range, in fact. As shown in the circuit diagram, one FET is quite enough to construct a buffer amplifier with an input impedance of 1 G Ω . The circuit is simply an impedance converter (source follower) with a gain of 1 and can be used for a variety of applications, such as a buffer for high impedance (capacitor) microphones, as an oscilloscope

277

probe etc.

One way to obtain the required input impedance is to connect a 1 GΩ resistor between the gate of the FET and ground. Unfortunately, such high value resistors are not only difficult to obtain, but they are also rather expensive and so a cheaper alternative will have to be found. This particular circuit gets around the problem nicely by utilising capacitor C2 as a form of 'bootstrap'. Theoretically, the input impedance of the circuit should be around 2.2 GΩ, but in practice will never be greater than about 1 GΩ due to leakage currents.

The frequency response of the voltage follower extends from 30 Hz to 750 Hz (3 dB points). For

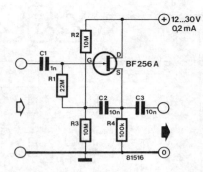

correct operation, the load impedance at the output should be at least 100 kΩ.

254 Power MOSFETs in the car

1

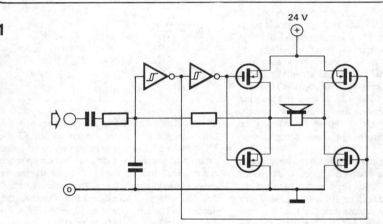

Due to the recent breakthrough in power-semiconductor technology it has become relatively simple to construct high power equipment for use in the car. Examples of two possible applications for power MOSFETs are a 50 Watt booster and a 12 V to 24 V converter as shown in figures 1 and 2 respectively.

A booster amplifier intended for use in vehicles should at least meet the following requirements:

1. The output power should be greater than 10 Watts, thereby providing sufficient audio output to overcome the level of ambient background noise (engine, wind etc.).
2. The amplifier needs to be compact without putting any constraints on cooling.
3. Performance must be acceptable even under

2

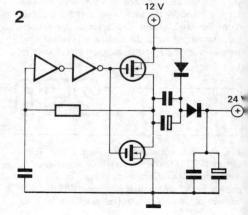

conditions of large fluctuations in power supply voltage.

The circuit shown in figure 1 meets these demands quite adequately. It is a bridge version of the self-oscillating PWM amplifier with an output power in the order of 50 Watts.

If such a high power audio amplifier has to be supplied from a 12 V battery, one of the following possibilities may be chosen:

1. The amplifier operates at 12 V in combination with a low impedance load.
2. The amplifier operates at 12 V and a step-up transformer is connected to the output.
3. A voltage converter is used to increase the supply voltage so that the amplifier can deliver the rated output. (The converter may or may not include a transformer).

The advent of the power MOSFET makes the third possibility especially favourable. The simplicity of the design is very apparent from the circuit diagram shown in figure 2. In fact, the entire converter is just a CMOS power astable multivibrator. After rectification and smoothing, the output voltage is added to the battery voltage.

Obviously, the circuit diagrams only reveal the basic principle of operation of the two designs. However, both the 50 Watt booster and the 12 V to 24 V converter are likely to receive further, more extensive treatment in a future issue of Elektor.

255 Six hour timer

This control unit was originally designed to turn off stereo equipment automatically at night, so that music lovers who drift off to sleep in their easy chairs no longer need to worry about the cost of the next electricity bill. As the switching unit controls a relay, the circuit can be used for a multitude of other applications as well.

The heart of the timing circuit is a 4060 CMOS device, which contains an oscillator and a 14 stage divider. The frequency of the oscillator can be adjusted by means of potentiometer P1 so that the output at Q13 is approximately one pulse per hour. The duration of this clock pulse will be very short (about 100 ns), as it also resets the entire 4060 IC via diode D8.

The 'once per hour' clock pulse is fed to the second (divide-by-ten) counter, the 4017 IC. One of the outputs of this counter will be high (logic one) at any one moment. As soon as the 4017 is reset, output Q0 will go high. After an hour, output Q0 will go low and output Q1 will go high, etc. Switch S1 therefore enables the operator to select a time period of from one to six hours. As soon as the selected output goes high, the transistor will stop conducting and the relay will be deactivated (thereby switching off the

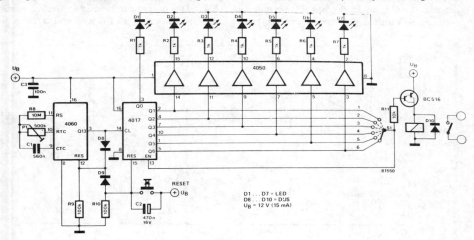

D1 ... D7 = LED
D8 ... D10 = DUS
U_B = 12 V (15 mA)

radio/record player etc.). As the enable input of the 4017 is also connected to the wiper of S1 any subsequent clock pulses will have no effect on the counter. The unit will therefore remain in the 'off' state until the reset button is depressed.

The 4050 CMOS buffer IC and the seven LEDs have been included to give an indication of the number of hours that have actually passed. These components can, of course, be omitted if an elapsed time display is not required. The supply voltage for the circuit is not critical and may be anywhere between 5 and 15 V. The current consumption of the circuit, not including the relay, is in the order of 15 mA. It is best to choose a supply voltage that is equal to the rating of the relay, so that any trouble is avoided. The BC 516 transistor can pass a current of 400 mA. If desired, two BC 557 (or similar) transistors may be connected as a darlington-pair instead.

K. Siol

---

256 VOX for PA systems

An annoying problem with PA systems is their tendency to whistle or 'howl' due to feed back phenomena. There are a number of methods of avoiding the problem, the most obvious being the repositioning of the speakers in relation to the microphone. However, this is not always possible and the object of this article is to provide an answer for those difficult situations where feedback appears to be 'built in'.

It is well known that lowering the frequency between the microphone and the PA amplifier by about 5 Hz will reduce feedback in many situations when all else seems to fail, but a 'frequency shifter' is an expensive piece of equipment and even then, its effectiveness is not always on a par with its cost. Since feedback requires time to build up, a simple solution to the problem would be to keep the microphone switched off for as long as possible, in fact, right up to the point at which speech begins. In other words, a voice operated switch or VOX.

This design is based on a National IC, the LM 346. This contains four programmable op-amps which can be used in a variety of applications. Briefly the circuit works as follows: The speech signal from the microphone is amplified by opamp A1 and then fed to two further op-amps, A2 and A3. The latter is simply a unity gain buffer for the PA amplifier. Opamp A2, together with diode D1, is used as a rectifier which converts the amplified microphone signal into a positive DC level. Any ripple voltage is smoothed out by capacitor C3. When the voltage across this capacitor is higher than the level set on the inverting input of A4 (with potentiometer P1), the output of the comparator (A4) will go high. This output can be used to control a relay or similar device. This DC level is also fed to the

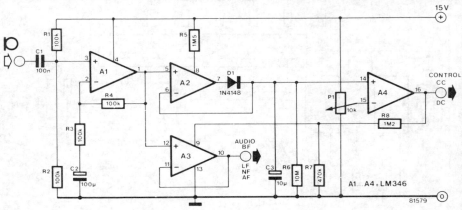

280

control pin (9) of opamp A3 via resistor R8. This opamp will only operate while this pin is held high. Therefore, when speech into the microphone ceases, A3 no longer operates and the main power amplifier remains inactive.

A high value resistor (R6) has been included in parallel with C3 to ensure that this capacitor discharges very slowly. This is very important because the signal path to the amplifier must remain open when the speaker pauses for a few moments. As mentioned previously, the output of A4 can be used to control a number of devices via a relay etc. This should find a number of applications especially in discos and the like.

257 Hi-fi pre-amplifier

Nowadays, there are quite a number of amplifier modules on the market, which usually contain the complete final output section and all the necessary protection devices. All that is normally required is to mount the module on a heatsink and connect the device up to a suitable power supply. Of course, a preamplifier is needed and this article sets out to describe such a preamplifier.

The entire preamplifier is constructed around a single IC (the TDA 1054, which is designed for this application). The circuit diagram for the

1

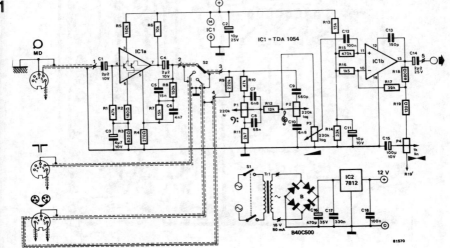

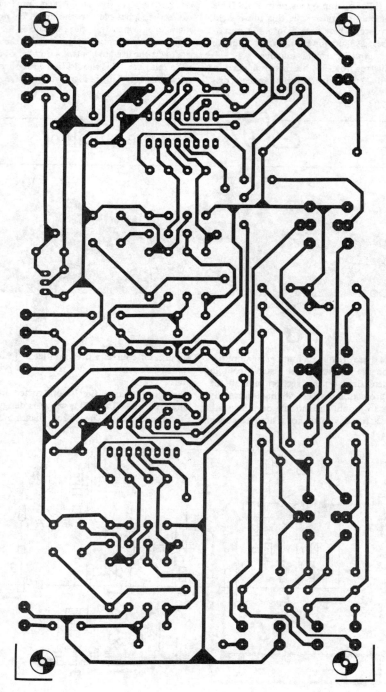

2

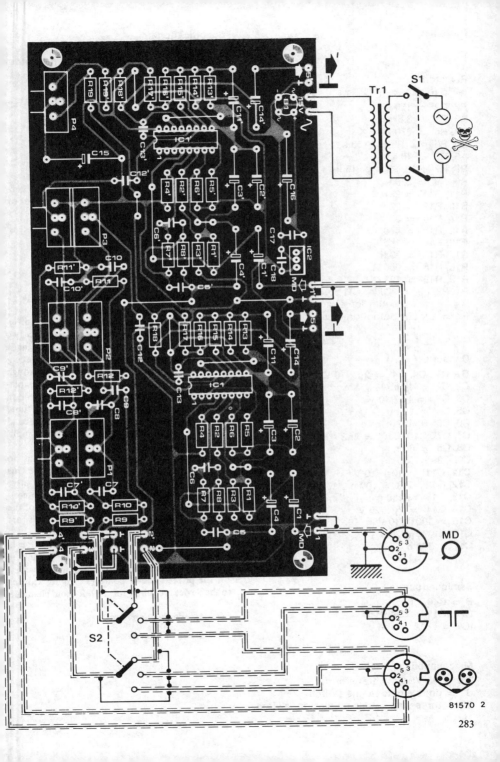

81570 2

283

Parts list

Resistors:

R1, R1', R10, R10' = 47 k
R2, R2' = 180 Ω
R3, R3' = 820 Ω
R4, R4' = 270 Ω
R5, R5', R8, R8' = 150 k
R6, R6' = 10 k
R7, R7', R13, R13' = 15 k
R9, R9' = 220 k
R11, R11' = 2k7
R12, R12' = 12 k
R14, R14' = 33 k
R15, R15' = 470 k
R16, R16' = 1k5
R17, R17' = 39 k
R18, R18' = 680 Ω
R19, R19' = 120 Ω
P1, P2, P3 = 220 k LOG stereo
　　　　　　　potentiometer
P4 = 1 k LIN potentiometer

Capacitors:

C1, C1', C4, C4' = 2µ2/10 V
C2, C2' = 10 µ /25 V
C3, C3' = 4µ7/10 V
C5, C5' = 15 n
C6, C6' = 4n7
C7, C7', C10, C10' = 6n8
C8, C8' = 68 n
C9, C9' = 560 p
C11, C11' = 10 µ /10 V
C12, C12', C18 = 100 n
C13, C13' = 150 p
C14, C14' = 2µ2/25 V
C15 = 100 µ /10 V
C16 = 470 µ /35 V
C17 = 330 n

Semiconductors:

B = B40C500
IC1, IC1' = TDA 1054
IC2 = 7812

Miscellaneous:

Tr1 = 15 V/50 mA transformer
S1 = double-pole mains switch
S2 = three-way double-pole rotary switch

Specifications:

input sensitivity to give 775 mV rms output
at a frequency of 1 kHz:

magnetic cartridge	– 3 mV
tuner	– 220 mV
tape input	– 220 mV
input impedance:	50 kΩ
balance control variation:	12 dB
bass boost/cut:	± 13 dB (100 Hz)
treble boost/cut:	± 13 dB (10 kHz)
harmonic distortion:	< 0.05% (f = 1 kHz at an output level of 775 mV)
frequency response:	20 Hz...24 kHz (± 3 dB, tone controls in the midposition)
signal to noise ratio (at 775 mV):	> 65 dB

left-hand channel of the preamp is shown in figure 1. The first section of the IC contains two transistors which are used to form a magnetic cartridge preamplifier with RIAA compensation. This is the 'standard' straight-through type and is not likely to need further explanation. It is followed by the input selection switch, S2, which connects either the tuner socket or the tape recorder socket to the second half of IC1 in addition to the cartridge preamplifier.

The tone control section is passive so that no problems can arise from too much control. This is followed by the volume control, P3, after which the signal is boosted by the opamp contained in the second half of IC1. The gain of the opamp is determined by the ratios of resistors R16/R17 as well as R18/R19 + P4.

The required 12 V supply for the preamplifier is provided by an integrated voltage regulator (7812). The asterisks on the component overlay for the printed circuit board (see figure 2) refer to the devices required for the left-hand channel.

SGS-Ates application note

258   Variable power 'resistor'

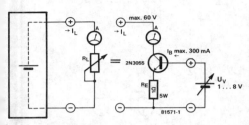

A major difficulty encountered when testing power supplies is the availability (or non-availability) of a suitable load. Usually, the problem is solved by a lash-up of resistors which, although not particularly elegant, will enable tests to be carried out. However, resistors with a power rating of 10 Watts and upwards can be rather expensive and certain values difficult to obtain. Furthermore, this type of load will not be variable. The simple circuit described here can overcome these problems effectively and economically.

A 2N3055 transistor with a variable gain controlled by an independant supply will form an infinitely variable load 'resistor'. This circuit will have a power capability of up to 50 Watts if a suitable heat sink is used. The ability to maintain a fixed load current when the power supply output voltage is varied is an added advantage.

The maximum dissipation of the transistor should be borne in mind. As figure 2 shows, a current of 2.5 A at 20 V is only 50 W but 2.5 A at 50 V is 125 W which may prove to be a little high for the 2N3055.

The base voltage for the transistor can be obtained via a voltage divider across an external power source. If this is not available the circuit shown in figure 3 can be used. In this case, the BD 139 is used as a driver transistor in order to keep the battery supply current drain as low as possible.

The power level can rise fairly steeply with a rising voltage and for this reason some indication of current and voltage levels in the circuit are essential. By using the graph shown in figure 2 it can be easily determined whether the maximum allowable power is being exceeded.

The circuit can also function as a current limiter. This facility will be useful when charging batteries with a constant current. The battery should be placed in the circuit between the ammeter and the collector of the 2N3055. It should be remembered to ensure that the voltage does not rise to a level high enough to cause damage to the plates of the battery.

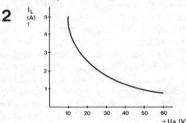

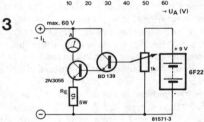

259   Auto reminder

The headlights in the majority of motor vehicles are unaffected by the ignition switch. This means that it is possible to leave the headlights turned on after leaving the car. In many instances, this is also true of auxiliary equipment, such as car radios etc., which have been wired directly to the car battery. For the forgetful driver, this can be something of a nuisance when trying to start the car the following morning. This circuit is intended as a warning to the driver that there is still something switched on which is consuming an unacceptable amount of power. The problem can be solved with a bit of logical thinking. After all, what is more obvious than to

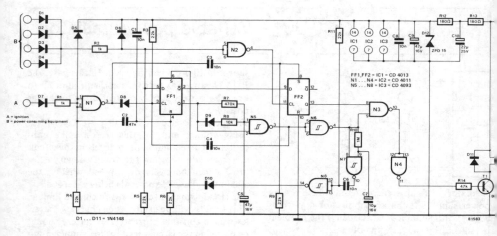

apply a little digital technology?

At first glance, the circuit looks a lot more complicated than it actually is. It only requires three ICs. The switched supply rails of the equipment to be monitored are connected to diodes D1...D4 (or more if desired), the coil side of the ignition switch is connected to D7 and the battery leads are connected to ' + 12 V' and '0'.

Let us first see what happens when the ignition switch is turned on and off, but there are no power consuming devices switched on. Effectively, nothing seems to happen! When the ignition switch is turned on, FF1 is reset via capacitor C2, the output of N1 goes low taking the clock input of FF1 low. As this flipflop only reacts to positive-going pulses, the Q output remains low and, via N5, N6 and N3, the output of N4 remains low. This means that transistor T1 is turned off and no sound is emitted via the buzzer.

When the ignition switch is turned off, the output of N1 goes high and FF2 will be set via capacitor C3. The Q output of this flipflop will therefore go high to enable N3. However, although FF1 receives a clock pulse via R3, the information at the data (D) input is low as there are no items of equipment on and so the outputs of FF1 remain as they were. The end result is that the output of N4 remains low and T1 stays off.

Now let us take the case when one or more auxiliary circuits are turned on. When the ignition switch is turned on the end result is the same as that previously described. When the ignition switch is turned off, however, things start to happen! Flipflop FF1 receives a clock pulse via R3 as before. This time, as the data input is

high, the Q output will also go high. Capacitor C5 is charged up via resistor R7 and, when sufficiently charged (charge time = R7 x C5), the output of N5 will go low. This signal is differentiated by C4/R3 to provide a further clock pulse for FF1.

During the period that C5 is charging, the driver still has the opportunity to turn off the relative equipment, thus preventing the warning signal from being sounded. If this is the case, the Q output of FF1 will again go low at the second clock pulse and C5 will discharge via R8 and D9. The output of N5 goes low thereby resuming the original condition. If, on the other hand, the driver neglects to switch off certain items, the output of N6 will go high when C5 is charged. This, in turn, takes the other input of N3 high (N3 was enabled when the ignition was turned off as described previously) so that the output of N3 goes low, the output of N4 goes high and transistor T1 turns on to sound the buzzer. At the same time, capacitor C7 charges up via resistor R10 over a period of about ten seconds. After this time the output of N7 goes low. This pulse is differentiated by C6/R11 to provide a reset pulse for FF1 via N8 and D10. Once reset, the Q output of FF1 goes low and the warning is cancelled.

It is possible, of course, to interrupt the alarm by switching the ignition back on. The circuit also allows for the possibility of deliberately leaving a particular item (such as sidelights) on without the alarm sounding. This is accomplished by first turning off the ignition with the desired piece of equipment switched on. This equipment is then switched off and back on again before the alarm sounds. This means that the output of N2 will go high when the item is switched off, providing a clock pulse for FF2. As the $\overline{Q}$ output of FF1 is low at this time, the D input of FF2 is also low therefore the Q output of FF2 will go low, so that N3 is disabled and transistor T1 is turned off. When the desired item is turned back on, the clock input of FF2 goes low, but the outputs remain the same. Although FF1 and gates N5...N8 go through their cycle, the alarm will not be operated.

It must be admitted that simpler alarm systems do exist. However, this circuit incorporates some interesting ideas and is simple to use. Nevertheless, the device does have one drawback. If, for instance, two items of equipment are left on inadvertantly and only one is switched off when the alarm sounds, the unit will not indicate this fact. Care must be taken, therefore, to have a good look round the dashboard when the alarm sounds!

W. Gscheidle

260 Adjustable square-wave edges

1

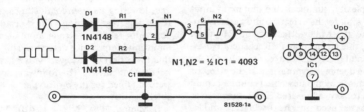

N1,N2 = ½ IC1 = 4093

81528-1a

The ability to delay the leading and trailing edges of a square waveform will find many applications in digital circuits. The diagram in figure 1a shows that only a very few components are required to do this. The circuit makes use of the fact that the output of a Schmitt trigger gate will not change state until the voltage level on the input reaches a certain critical point known as the trigger threshold.

During a rising edge at the input, capacitor C1 is charged via D1 and R1. This increases the time it takes for the voltage level at the input of the gate to reach the trigger threshold point. With a logic 1 at the input to the circuit, the potential across C1 will continue to rise until, for all practical purposes, it reaches the supply voltage level. When the input returns to zero C1 will discharge via D2 and R2, again delaying the time at which the trigger threshold is reached. A clear understanding can be gained from figure 1b which shows the waveforms at various points in the circuit.

It must be remembered that the trigger threshold point of a Schmitt gate is highly dependant on the supply voltage. The following figures are quoted for the RCA 4093:

U_{DD}	U_T^+	U_T^-
5	3.3	2.3
10	7	5.1
15	9.4	7.3

The leading edge delay can now be calculated with the equation:

$$\Delta t^+ = -R1 \times C1 \times nat.\log. \left(1 - \frac{U_T^+}{U_{DD} - 0.7}\right)$$

2

81528-1b

287

The delay in the trailing edge amounts to:

$$\Delta t^- = -R2 \times C1 \times nat.\log. \left(\frac{U_T^-}{U_{DD} - 0.7} \right)$$

Therefore, the choice of values for R1, R2 and C1 will give any required delay to the leading and trailing edges of the square-wave. However,

the maximum delay for either edge should not be more than 80% of the pulse duration.
Nothing in this world is perfect and different manufacturers of IC1 quote rather large trigger threshold tolerances. This means that the actual delay times can be quite different from those calculated.

261 Simple short-wave receiver

The most notorious effects of regenerative TRF receivers are radiation and unwanted coupling between the antenna and the LC circuit that is acted upon by the regeneration. Apart from the extra complexity, tuning of the (antenna) input adds quite a bit to the effect of unwanted coupling, due to the Miller-effect of the RF stage. Invariably, this means that TRF regenerative design, especially on shortwave, is only fit for those with a degree in gymnastics. If the effect of detuning caused by the unwanted coupling could be reduced to, say, a hundred Hertz, the receiver could also be used in the oscillating mode, thereby providing the owner with the possibility of product-detector reception modes, such as CW, RTTY and SSB. It should be stated at this point that this feature is positively enhanced when a frequency counter is added.

In order to achieve a minimum of pulling, the RF stage of the circuit shown consists of a bipolar transistor and an FET in cascode. As can be seen, the input is aperiodic. The disadvantage of input overload is more than compensated for

by the high sensitivity (even a tiny whip antenna can be used). A smooth control of regeneration is obtained by D1, which starts supplying a negative bias for T3 on reaching the threshold voltage, lowering its transconductance, thus 'counter-acting' regeneration. The detector is able to cope with relatively strong input signals, as it is an infinite impedance detector. This also means that distortion is low, even with a heavily modulated (AM) carrier. The following specifications were obtained for the prototype:

single sensitivity
  (AM mod. 30%, S/N = 10 dB): 1 μ V
single signal sensitivity
  (SSB, S/N = 10 dB): 0.3 μ V
frequency range with a 500 p
  tuning capacitor: 4.4...17 MHz.

The term single signal sensitivity may need some

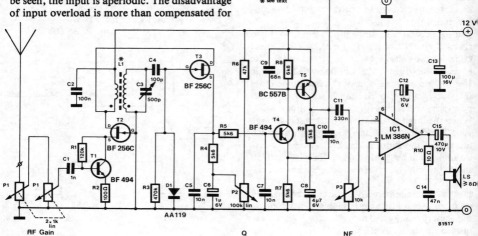

explanation. It is the figure obtained by measuring the sensitivity with the aid of a signal generator in the absence of all other signals. Due to input overloading (of the wideband RF stage) and envelope detection taking place on strong adjacent channel signals, the full benefit of this sensitivity will never be obtained, except perhaps in countries like Australia, where the spectrum is not yet polluted by OTHR's and BC jammers.

In the product detector mode, the suppression of AM will be in the order of between 40 and 60 dB, depending on tuning. The lower figure refers to the highest tuning frequency. Improvement can be made by reducing the L/C ratio.

The primary winding of L1 consists of 6 turns of 0.25 mm enamelled copper wire on an Amidon ring core type T94-6. The secondary winding consists of 25 turns of 0.68...0.8 mm enamelled copper wire over the complete length of the core. The primary winding should be situated at the 'cold' end and layed between the turns of the secondary.

262 Universal measuring amplifier

An analogue multimeter is, by now, one of the more 'standard' items of equipment owned by electronics enthusiasts. Even digital multimeters are now becoming quite common. However, it is not uncommon to find that the capabilities of the measuring instruments available are nowhere near as extensive as one would wish. Either the input sensitivity is not high enough (in other words, it can not measure low voltages) or else the input impedance of the instrument is too low. The second disadvantage is the worst, in fact it is often the reason why measurements taken are totally inaccurate. In general, interpretation of incorrect results will lead to incorrect conclusions!

The simple circuit described here, which uses only a few components suffers from none of these disadvantages. The circuit consists of a discrete differential amplifier constructed around transistors T1 and T2. A separate constant current source is connected in series with both emitter leads. The current source for transistor T1 consists of D1, D2, T3 and R6 and that for transistor T2 consists of D1, D2, T4 and R7. The constant emitter currents make the measuring amplifier independant of supply voltage variations.

The differential amplifier (T1 and T2) is followed by an integrated differential amplifier (the LM 301 from National Semiconductor). This opamp is connected to give unity gain. Its output is therefore an analogue measurement signal and

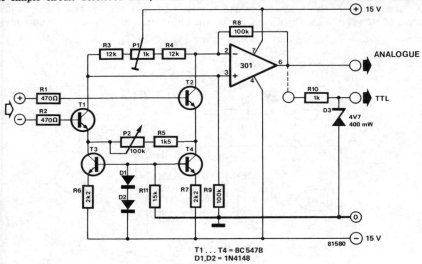

T1 ... T4 = BC 547B
D1,D2 = 1N4148

81580

can be used directly as such. Two further components, R10 and D3, convert the analogue output to a TTL-compatible signal.

Now that we have described the basic circuit, what can it be used for? Two possibilities have already been mentioned: It can be used as a pre-amplifier for a normal (analogue) multimeter and it can also be used as a preamplifier for a digital multimeter. Furthermore, the circuit can be used as an AF preamplifier for frequency counters or similar devices. In this case, potentiometer P2 can be used to set the trigger level. Finally, it is also possible to use the circuit as a preamplifier for an inexpensive oscilloscope.

Regardless of the actual application for the circuit, the only main calibration is the same in all cases. This is the 'zero offset' and is adjusted by means of preset potentiometer P1. This potentiometer must be set so that when the inputs are shorted (in other words, when the left-hand sides of R1 and R2 are connected together) the output from the opamp is exactly zero volts. In normal applications, potentiometer P2 adjusts the input sensitivity. With the aid of this potentiometer, it is possible to adjust the gain of the circuit over a wide range; from a gain of 2 to a gain of 130. It may therefore be useful to provide this potentiometer with a calibrated scale.

263 Digital sinewave oscillator

The circuit consists of two sections, each of which could have many useful applications on its own: an oscillator constructed around a pair of EX(clusive) OR gates and a divide-by-three circuit constructed around two ordinary flipflops.

The oscillator is made up from both a non-inverting gate (N1) and an inverting gate (N2). If only inverting gates had been used, at least three would have been required — as a non-inverting gate can be made up from two inverting gates connected in series.

The circuit works as follows. Let us assume that, initially, the input of N1 (pin 2) is low. This means that the output of N1 will also be low and the output of N2 will be high. Capacitor C1 will

then be charged via resistor R2. After a short while, the input of N1 will go high via R1 and the whole procedure will be reversed. Readers interested in this type of oscillator are referred to the National Semiconductor Application Note No. AN-118, which is included in their current CMOS data book.

The divide-by-three section consists of two flip-flops which both divide by two, in other words, it would be expected that together they would divide by four. However, another EXOR gate (N3) has been included between the output of FF2 and the input of FF1. This effectively inverts the clock input signal each time the output of FF2 changes polarity. If N3 was not present

1

$$N1, N2 = \frac{1}{2}\,4070 \qquad f \approx \frac{0.6}{RC} \quad (R1 = R2)$$

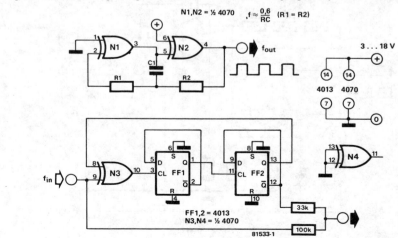

the output state of the flipflop would not change until the end of the current clock period. With the addition of N3, the clock signal is inverted and the positive-going edge triggers the flipflop after every half period. Therefore, the dividing factor here is three, not four.

The sinewave signal is generated via a pair of resistors (R3 and R4). When the input to both resistors is low (logic zero) there will be no output voltage. When the input to both resistors is high (logic one) the output voltage will be high. When one input to the resistors is low and the other high the output voltage will be either ¼ or ¾ of the supply (high) level.

Obviously, this can be proven mathematically, but a simpler method to justify it is to examine a single sinewave period diagrammatically. A small rectangle may be drawn in the centre of the sinewave to represent a logic one level. Two further rectangles of the same size can then be drawn to each side of the first. The area inside the sinewave of the last two rectangles will be half that of the first. The digital simulation technique generates a signal with the same areas as the above.

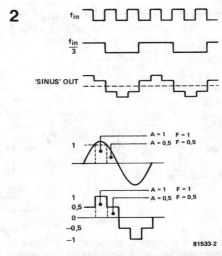

2

When constructing the circuit it should be noted that CMOS inputs should never be left 'floating'. In other words, pins 12 and 13 of the EXOR chip (N4) should be connected to ground (0 V).

264 Battery supply timer

A need often arises for battery powered equipment to be switched off after a certain period of time. Although timing circuits are legion, it is not such a simple matter to switch a power supply off after some hours of use. The circuit featured here will do this at the expense of a current drain of only a few nano amps.

A look at the circuit diagram will show that not many components are involved. Switch S1 is the 'on' button and, when pressed, supplies a base drive current to the darlington transistor T1 which will then conduct to supply power to the equipment in use. Transistor T2 will now also switch on to act as a latch across S1 maintaining the base current to T1.

Capacitor C1 will now start to charge via R4. When the voltage across R4 drops to about 1.2 V, T2 will switch off. This in turn will switch off T1 and therefore the supply. The only current now flowing will be the leakage current through both transistors but this will only amount to a few nano amps at most. To all intents and purposes, the battery supply will be

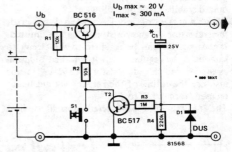

switched off.

The time period for which the supply will be switched on can be calculated from the rather horendous formula:

$$t = -22 \cdot 10^4 \cdot C1 \cdot \text{nat.log.} \frac{1 \cdot 2}{U_B} \text{ s (C1 in Farads).}$$

For those in doubt the 'try it and see' method may take longer but will work just as well. If required, the two darlingtons can be substituted by discrete transistors.

291

265 Power stabiliser

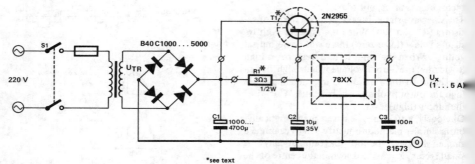

*see text

This power supply circuit consists of a three-pin voltage regulator IC in conjunction with a buffer transistor. This combination is a result of the fact that the 78xx series of voltage regulators are only capable of delivering a current of 1 A. In this design, when the output current exceeds about 200 mA, the buffer transistor takes over the task from the voltage regulator IC thereby allowing currents up to 5 A to be drawn.

The 78xx IC is available for a range of different voltages. By selecting the required regulator in the series, the circuit can be adapted for any voltage, provided of course the transformer output voltage is at least 4 V greater than the required stabilised output voltage.

Where a current of only 1 A (or less) is required, the transistor T1 and resistor R1 can be omitted. If desired, R1 can be retained in the circuit to safeguard the regulator IC. It will then function as a so-called 'bleed' resistor. However, in this instance the rating of the resistor should be increased from 0.5 W to 5 W.

The 78xx regulator is protected internally against overheating, but in practice the demand on this protection circuitry is not altogether satisfactory. To obtain a stable design, two measures have been taken in the circuit shown here: The current through the regulator IC can never exceed 300 mA except when there is a short-circuit on the output. The buffer transistor has a more than adequate current rating.

Provided the heatsink used is sufficiently large, both the voltage regulator and the buffer transistor should be able to survive momentary short-circuits, when the peak current may well exceed the maximum output current of 5 A. However, the actual amount of short-circuit current will be limited as the voltage regulator limits the amount of base drive current to transistor T1.

Capacitor C1 will smooth out any AC ripple, but its value should be modified to cope with the maximum flow of current. For a current flow of up to 1 A, a value of 1000 µ F should be sufficient, but for a current of 5 A the value should be increased to 4700 u F.

266 Constant current LED

It is normal nowadays to use a LED as a panel indicator whenever possible. However, in keeping with all electronic devices, they do have limitations and their operating parameters can make life difficult at times. For instance, if the supply voltage varies by any great degree the brightness of the LED will follow suit. Should the voltage level become too high it will result in the LED giving a permanently off indication! The ingenious circuit here can get around these problems quite effectively.

The maximum current capability of a LED is normally about 50 mA but brightness will not significantly increase above 20 mA. This figure is about the optimum economic current level and the purpose of this circuit is to maintain this value irrespective of fluctuations in supply voltage levels.

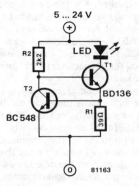

5 ... 24 V

R2 2k2
LED
T1
T2
BD136
BC 548
R1 39 Ω

81163

The two transistors, T1 and T2, form a constant current source and will maintain the current level to within the acceptable limits of 15 and 27 mA with variations in voltage level between 5 and 24 V.

Operation is relatively straightforward. A rising supply voltage will cause the collector voltage of T1 to rise. This in turn will increase the base drive current to T2. The subsequent drop in potential at the collector of T2 will reduce the base current to T1 and therefore counteract the rise in current to the LED. The circuit will now be stabilized.

The table below gives an indication of the LED current at various supply voltages.

5 V – 15 mA	15 V – 22 mA
9 V – 18 mA	18 V – 24 mA
12 V – 20 mA	24 V – 27 mA

267 Kansas City demodulator

The most popular form of FSK (frequency-shift keying) modulator used by computers nowadays is the 'Kansas City Standard' where digital information is transmitted sequentially by means of carrier pulses of constant amplitude and two different frequencies (1200 Hz and 2400 Hz). A logic low level generates a frequency of 1200 Hz whilst 2400 Hz is generated by a logic high level. Obviously, for every modulator there has to be a demodulator.

As can be seen from the circuit diagram, the Kansas City demodulator described here is quite straightforward. Opamp A1 acts as a Schmitt trigger and simply converts the output of the tape recorder into a perfectly symmetrical squarewave signal. Opamp A2 is configured as a 'charge pump' and converts the incoming fre-

quency into a low or high logic level. The output of A2 is fed to a low pass filter constructed around opamp A3 and the decoded, filtered signal is then fed to a second Schmitt trigger (A4) to 'clean up' the final digital output.

Transistor T1 and LED D2 are included to indicate whether or not the input (FSK) signal is of sufficient amplitude to drive the system.

The LM 3900 contains four opamps which are slightly unusual in that they react to differences in input *currents* rather than *voltages* (this type of device is commonly called a 'Norton amplifier'). This means that the output of the first Schmitt trigger (A1) is zero under no-signal conditions, because the current flowing through the inverting input (via R2) will be greater than that flowing through the non-inverting input (via

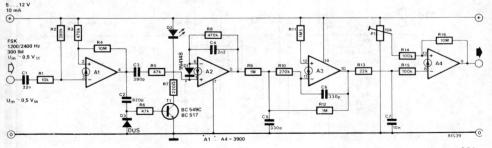

R3).

The charge pump works as follows: When there is no input signal, capacitor C4 is discharged via R8, so that the output of A2 is virtually zero. If at this point a positive-going pulse is received from A1, a brief current pulse will flow into the non-inverting input of A2 via capacitor C3. This means that an identical current must pass through the inverting input for the circuit to remain in equilibrium. This can only be achieved via C4 which is therefore charged a small amount. As a result, the output voltage of A2 will rise whenever a positive-going signal edge is present at the input. Afterwards, capacitor C4 will be discharged via resistor R8 and the output voltage will drop once more. The more pulses at the input, the higher the output voltage.

The circuit around opamp A3 is a conventional low pass filter. The turn-over frequency of the filter depends on the *baud rate* of the incoming signal. At 300 baud the maximum frequency at this point will be 150 Hz therefore the turn-over frequency must be slightly higher.

The output of the low pass filter has rather poor edges and is too low in amplitude to be processed by logic circuitry. For this reason the signal is passed through a second Schmitt trigger constructed around A4. This ensures that the final output pulses are sufficiently fast to drive CMOS ICs. If the phase of the output signal is not correct, the connections to R14 and R15 may be reversed.

Current consumption of the circuit is only a few milliamps and partly depends on the actual supply voltage. Ideally, this should be the same as that of the following logic circuitry.

The only adjustment for the demodulator is preset potentiometer P1 which is set so that the duration of logic zero and logic one pulses are the same when the input signal consists of eight cycles of 2400 Hz and four cycles of 1200 Hz.

268 Signal injector - tracer

A signal injector must certainly be one of the cheapest and most useful pieces of test equipment in the hobby workshop. The design described here doubles as a signal tracer and features an audio output enabling both eyes to be kept on the work in hand.

The circuit is very simple and consists of three main parts; a signal generator (IC3); a pre-amp

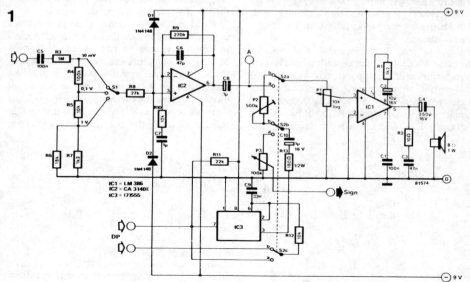

2

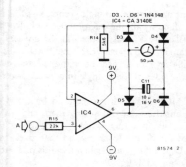

D3 ... D6 = 1N4148
IC4 = CA 3140E

81574 2

---

will attenuate the signal and a transistor will usually amplify it.

In order to detect changes in amplitude, it is important not to overload the loudspeaker. A simple switched attenuator is therefore included at the input to the pre-amp to provide three different input levels. To avoid loading the circuit under test a high impedance input is ensured by C5 and R3. The probe signal is amplified by IC2 and fed, via C8 and S2a, to P1 which is used to adjust the input level to the pre-amp, IC1.

Some readers may prefer a visual output indication and for this purpose a moving coil meter can be used as shown in figure 2.

Because of the high input impedance of the pre-amp it is necessary to use a screened lead and probe for this input. Failure to do this will result in plenty of noise at the output.

A design for an easily constructed probe is shown in figure 3. Normal test leads can be used for the signal output.

(IC2); and a main amplifier. The signal generator, IC3, is a 555 connected as a 1 kHz oscillator. With S2 in position b, this acts as a simple continuity tester. Since the test points DP are in series with the oscillator's RC network, the circuit will only oscillate when there is continuity between these points. Two test probes connected to the DP points can therefore be used to establish continuity between two points in the circuit under test. The output of the oscillator is fed via P2 to the main amplifier and a tone will be heard from the loudspeaker when there is a short circuit between the probes. Nothing will be heard if the probes are open circuit of course.

With switch S2 in position a, IC3 will oscillate continuously. Its output level is then controlled by P3 and fed directly to probe Ⓑ to be injected into the circuit under test. Capacitor C10 and resistor R13 are included to prevent the oscillator from being loaded by the test circuit. Probe Ⓐ is then used to trace the signal through the stages of the test circuit. A resistance or potentiometer

3

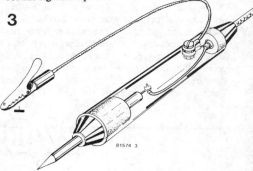

81574 3

2̳6̳9̳   American billiards

The popularity of American Pool continues to increase and this electronic game is played in a similar manner to the original table billiards. However, the billiard balls are symbolically represented here by six LEDs.

The circuit is based on a random generator. When the reset switch is depressed, all the LED's light up, and when the 'hit' button is pushed a number of random occurrences take place so that either one of the LED's goes out or everything stays as it was. One of the LED's going out, means that one of the balls has been pocketed.

The game can be played in two ways. In the first game, each player must pocket all the balls whereby all the LEDs are extinguished, and the person who can do that with the least number of 'hits' is the winner. In the second variation of the game, the number of players is restricted to only two. One player starts: if the first ball he hits is a red one, then he is obliged to pocket also all the other red ones. The second player then does the same with the green balls. As long as the first player continues to hit his own colour, it remains his turn. Only when he fails to hit a ball or hits one of his opponent's colour, is it the turn of the other player. As soon as three balls of one colour have been pocketed, the player of that colour has won the game. This makes it impossible for the game to end in a draw, and is a good way of deciding the winner of the first type of game that was drawn.

Let us now have a look at the circuit. To start, all six flipflops, FF1...FF6, are set to zero with pushbutton S2 so that all LEDs light up. The multivibrator, constructed with N1 and N2, delivers a clock frequency of about 800 Hz to the Johnson-counter, IC2, of which the outputs deliver '1' in sequence. The gates N5 to N10 are wired as latches and connect the counter outputs to the D-inputs of the flipflops.

Operating the 'hit' button S1 will supply a pulse to all the flipflops. The counter outputs which are high will then, via the latches, set the flipflops that were not already set, and the relevant LED goes out. The feedback from the Q-output of the flipflop to the gate at the D-input forms the latch and sees to it that a 'set' flipflop remains in that position even when further clock pulses arrive. As Q6 of the counter leads nowhere, it is possible for even the first shot to be a 'miss'. If so desired, this can be avoided by connecting the reset input of the counter to Q6 instead of Q7.

The best way of arranging the LEDs is in the form of an isosceles triangle, represented in the circuit diagram by the open diode symbols. The red LEDs are actually placed at the corners of the triangle. The green LEDs (the black ones in the diagram) can then be mounted half-way along the sides of the triangle in between two red ones.

The CMOS 4050 can be replaced by the 4049 which has the same pin arrangement and which contains six inverting drivers. This causes the state of the diodes to change so that after reset all LEDs are dark, but 'when a ball is pocketed' the relevant LED lights up.

The two sets of rules for the games described earlier are not the end. There are other possibilities. One ball can be designated as the 'black' in snooker which means that it is the last one to be pocketed. Another variation consists of, prior to 'hitting a ball', deciding which colour it is going to be. No doubt it will be possible to think up further variations, once the circuit and its possibilities have become familiar. When the game is played a lot, it is best to supply the power via a small mains supply or a nicad. The power consumption is 90 mA when all the LEDs are on. When the game is played less frequently it will be sufficient to use two 4.5 V dry cells.

H.J. Walter

---

270 Constant pulse width oscillator

Switching oscillators on and off can sometimes give rise to problems due to the fact that the first or last (or both) pulses can vary in width from maximum down to almost non-existent. In most cases, it is probably true to say that the very narrow pulse or 'spike' will be the one to cause the problems. It all stems from the fact that the oscillator switch off time is invariably not synchronised with oscillator output.

Figure 1B shows the usual simple gate oscillator that is often found in digital circuits, probably chosen for its simplicity and economy as much as anything. However, it does suffer from the problems mentioned above as can be seen from the waveform illustration in figure 2 Ⓑ. The variation in pulse width is readily apparent. The last pulse in the second set may prove to be too small for some gates to 'see' while others in the system can. The result could be an extensive 'red

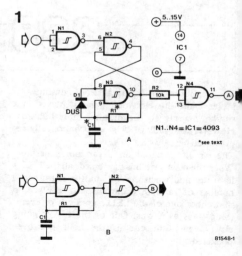

N1..N4 = IC1 = 4093

*see text

81548-1

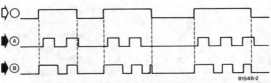

81548-2

...erring' chase.

An effective solution to the problem is shown in the circuit in figure 1A where the simple gate oscillator is coupled to an RS flipflop. Diode D1 prevents capacitor C1 from charging during the time that the oscillator is switched off. This ensures that the first pulse at the output has the same width as those following. This is illustrated in figure 2 Ⓐ . The sacrifice of two extra gates may well be worth the benifits that this constant pulse width oscillator can provide.

271 Single IC siren

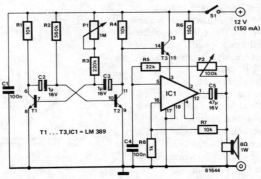

Circuits that produce some sort of noise appear to be highly popular with many readers. A possible reason for this is that correct circuit operation is verified audibly and without the need for test equipment, in other words, the circuit does something in a physical sense.

This particular siren is very simple and easy to construct since it is built around a single IC, the LM 389 from National Semiconductors. This IC contains an audio power amplifier, similar to the LM 386, together with three uncommitted NPN transistors.

The two transistors T1 and T2 form the basis of an astable multivibrator with a frequency variable between 1 and 7 Hz. The preset P1 is used to adjust this. The amplifier is also configured as a squarewave oscillator and its output drives the loudspeaker at frequencies variable between 250 Hz and 1500 Hz. The amplifier, however, is switched on and off by the multivibrator via transistor T3. The result is a pulsed siren like sound. The frequency of the audible tone is adjusted by the preset P2.

272 Pulse generator with variable duty-cycle

A single 4093 CMOS IC is eminently suitable for constructing a simple pulse generator. The IC contains four Schmitt-triggers. By adding a resistor, two diodes, a capacitor and a potentio-

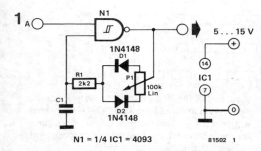

1

1N4148 D1
R1 2k2
P1 100k Lin
D2 1N4148
C1
N1

5 ... 15 V

IC1
14
7
0

N1 = 1/4 IC1 = 4093

81502 1

meter, one of the four gates can be used to produce an oscillator with a set frequency and a variable duty-cycle. The pulse duration is determined by the RC time-constant of the network consisting of capacitor C1 and resistors R1 + P1. When the wiper of the potentiometer is in the mid position a perfectly symmetrical squarewave signal is obtained at the output. If, however, the setting of P1 is altered, the capacitor (C1) will take a different time to charge than to discharge. As a result, gate N1 will be triggered either sooner or later on either the positive-going or negative-going edge of the signal depending on the direction in which P1 was rotated. This effectively means that the pulse width varies.

As far as R1 is concerned, this acts as a protective measure in case P1 is turned fully clockwise (minimum resistance). This means that the duty-cycle is not 100% variable, but, after all, a 2... 98% range should be perfectly acceptable!

The frequency of the oscillator is dependent on the value of capacitor C1, since the sum of the

RC time-constants is the same for both half-periods. If several different frequencies are required, a multiway switch with a corresponding number of capacitors may be included to replace C1 (see figure 2). This enables the pulse duration to be varied in stages.

Using the control input (A) the entire unit can be incorporated in a logic circuit. If the input voltage is logic zero, the output will be logic one; if, however, the input level is logic one, the oscillator will start to operate. If the control input is not required, this may be omitted by either linking the input to the junction of R1/C1 or to the positive rail of the power supply (logic one).

Although the edge of the output pulse is fairly steep already, it can be further improved by connecting one of the other gates in the same IC to the output. The second gate will then act as an inverter.

2

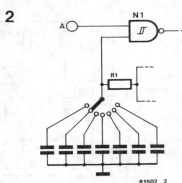

N1
A
R1

81502 2

---

273 Differential switch

There is virtually no doubt that interest in this particular circuit will increase as the price of electricity – and of energy in general – continues to rise. The differential switch is able to measure the difference in temperature between two points and, depending on the temperature difference, it will switch a relay on or off. The relay can then be used, for example, to activate a circulation pump. There are numerous applications for the circuit. It can be used in combination with solar heating panels or solar collectors and it can also be used to control the pump in central heating systems. In the latter case, one sensor is placed in the return pipe while the other

is situated in the hot water outlet pipe close to the boiler. As soon as the boiler switches on, a temperature difference is created and the pump also switches on.

The attractive feature of this design is the fact that both the temperature difference and the hysteresis of the unit can both be set independently, so that they do not affect each other. Moreover, the adjustments are virtually linear, therefore the potentiometer settings can be relied on to give consistent results. A LED has been included in the circuit to give an indication of when the relay is actually on.

The temperature sensors are two LM 335s

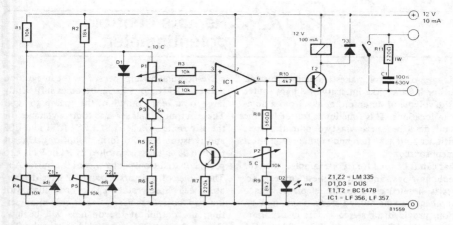

(National Semiconductor). This IC can be looked upon as being a zener diode whose voltage increases by 10 mV per °C. Therefore, at room temperature the zener voltage is equal to: $(273 + 20) \times 10\,mV = 2.93\,V$.

The temperature transducers incorporate calibration connections, which make it possible to set the output voltage (at 20 °C) to the value mentioned above. In the same way, undesirable differences between the sensors can be corrected. It is also possible to disregard the adjustment input of one of the sensors (by not connecting it) and to adjust the other sensor to give the same characteristics as the first. This can make construction and setting up considerably simpler.

The principle of operation is as follows: The voltages from the two sensors are directly compared by IC2. When the temperature − and thus the voltage − of Z1 becomes greater than that of Z2, the output of IC2 goes high lighting LED D2 and activating the relay via transistor T2. If potentiometer P1 has not been turned fully up, a higher input voltage is required to operate the comparator and the relay will therefore be activated at a higher temperature difference. There is a potential drop of about 0.6 V across diode D1. Approximately 100 mV of this remains across P1 (the actual voltage drop across P1 can be adjusted by means of P3). The 100 mV corresponds to about 10°C, so in effect P1 can be adjusted over a range of 10°C. Sensor Z1 must therefore be 10°C warmer than Z2 with P1 at the lowest setting in order to activate the relay.

Once the pump has been switched on by the relay, the temperature of the sensor close to the boiler will drop due to the circulation of the water. This could result in the circuit switching itself off almost immediately. Obviously, this

LM 335

situation is undesirable and for this reason potentiometer P2 has been included to adjust the amount of hysteresis by a maximum factor of 5°C. With P2 set in the centre position the circuit has a hysteresis of 2.5°C. This means that if P1 has been set to, say, 5°C, the relay will be activated when the temperature difference reaches 5°C, but will not turn off until the difference in temperature is $5°C - 2.5°C = 2.5°C$.

LED D2 should be a red one with an operating voltage of about 1.3 V. The supply voltage for the circuit is not critical and can deviate by a few volts. The circuit diagram shows a supply voltage of 12 V because relays operating at this voltage are readily available. Transistor T2 is only allowed to dissipate a maximum of 100 mA and for this reason the current rating of the relay should not exceed this value.

The actual temperature at which the circuit operates can be calculated from the voltage across Z1 and Z2, if a thermometer is not available.

274 Remote control potentiometer

This type of control makes it possible to regulate, for instance, the intensity of a light source or the volume of an amplifier etc. from a number of locations. This function is fulfilled by the circuit described here via two potentiometers which act both as switch and regulator for direct current sources.

What can it be used for? For example, when the telephone rings, and one of these controls devices is situated close to the telephone, stereo equipment can be turned down from that location, provided the stereo system incorporates dc-controlled ICs such as the TCA 730 or TCA 740. As already mentioned, the circuit can also be connected, via opto-couplers, to a light source and therefore act as a dimmer control. No doubt inventive readers can think of many more applications for the unit.

When the potentiometer setting is altered, an electronic switch will automatically close allowing the dc voltage level on the wiper of the potentiometer to be passed through to the output.

How does it work? The 'hot end' of the two potentiometers (P1 and P2) is kept at about 12 V by means of zener diode D1. As the input range of opamps A1 and A2 is 0 V to 13.5 V, this gives sufficient protection against input overload. When the setting of one of the potentiometers is altered, the potential difference between the inverting input and the non-inverting input of the corresponding opamp, caused by the integration networks R1/C1 or R2/C2, becomes sufficiently large to make the output of the opamp go high. These output signals serve as control voltages for the electronic switches ES1...ES4 (ES1 and ES2 and resistors R3...R6 form a flipflop). One of the two dc voltages controlled by P1 or P2 is also passed on to the output by way of the buffer A3.

The values of resistors R1 and R2 have deliberately been chosen rather high in order that, with the two potentiometers at their minimum setting, the output of the opamps will be low. Diodes D2 and D3 are included so that the flipflop does not return to its original state during the actual transition.

One of the not so good aspects of the circuit should also be mentioned at this stage. This is the fact that when it is necessary to set the previously unadjusted potentiometer to a low dc output, it must first be quickly turned up and then down. This may appear slightly awkward at first, but it will not take long to get the hang of it.

If the connecting leads to the circuit are rather on the long side, it will be necessary to include a 10 µ /16 V capacitor between the 'hot' ends of the potentiometers and ground.

R. Behrens

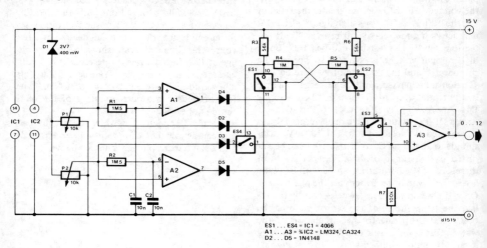

ES1 . . . ES4 = IC1 = 4066
A1 . . . A3 = ¾ IC2 = LM324, CA324
D2 . . . D5 = 1N4148

275 Long-period timer

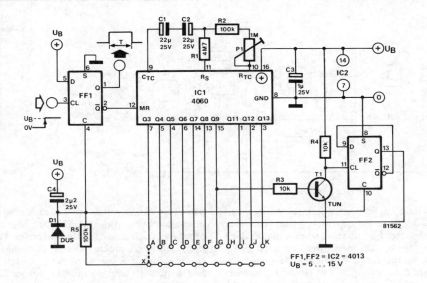

This monostable multivibrator can be seen as a long-period alternative for timer circuits which incorporate the well-known 555. It allows the user to obtain on-off periods varying from 20 seconds to about 60 hours.

The design is quite simple. It consists of a start/reset part, a 'slow' oscillator and a series of flip-flops. Most of this can be found, ready for use, in IC1. For the internal oscillator of IC1, only a further two capacitors (C1, C2), two resistors (R1, R2) and potentiometer P1 are needed. The output signals of the counter in the IC can be reached via the Q outputs. Rather curiously, Q10 is not included and a 'Q10' is constructed by the addition of T1 and FF2. The timer is set in motion by the leading edge (positive-going) of the clockpulse to pin 3 of FF1. The Q̄ output (pin 2) then becomes '0', and the oscillator in IC1 starts. The Q outputs of IC1 will then become 'high' in turn to the timing of the oscillator frequency which is adjustable between 2.5 and 25 seconds by rotating P1. Depending on which one of points A, B, C...K is connected to point X, a logic '1' will be sent to the clear input (pin 4) of FF1 via R5 after a short or very long period. This way, the flipflop is cleared, the Q̄ output becomes '1', and the oscillator stops. The 'timer' will start up again only after a new start

pulse reaches pin 3 of FF1.

Due to the very large number of possibilities, there is a formidable choice of periods to chose from. When points A and X are connected, the time set with P1 can be varied to range from 20 sec. to 3.5 min., with connection B-X this range becomes 40 sec. to 7 min., and so on.

The period can be calculated exactly with the help of a simple formula:

$$T = (M - 0.5) \times 25 \cdot 10^{-6} \times (R2 + P1),$$

in which T is the time and M the selected dividing factor. This factor is 2^3 for connection A-X, 2^4 for B-X, 2^5 for C-X, and so on. For connection K-X, the dividing factor is 2^{13} and, substituting this value in the formula, the respectable period of about 60 hours is obtained.

301

276 Novel clock control

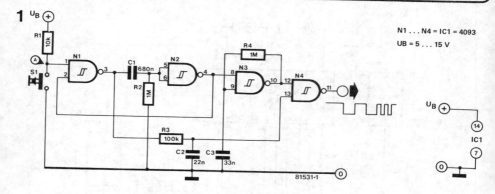

N1 . . . N4 = IC1 = 4093
UB = 5 . . . 15 V

81531-1

In certain applications it is often necessary to generate a series of clock pulses by using switches etc. For instance, when a digital clock has to be adjusted. More often than not a digital clock has two function buttons. When one is depressed a clock frequency of several Hz is generated enabling the clock to be set to roughly the correct time very quickly. When, on the other hand, the second button is depressed, only one clock pulse is generated so that the clock can be set accurately. Why then two buttons if they both appear to perform what amounts to the same function?

As a matter of fact, there is no real need to have two buttons. The circuit described here fulfils the same task by only using one. Everything now depends on how long the button is depressed for. If the switch is held down for less than half a second, only one clock pulse will be generated. If, however, it is depressed for longer, a clock frequency of 30 Hz will appear at the output of the circuit.

The circuit works as follows. When switch S1 is open the clock generator constructed around N1 will oscillate at a frequency of 30 Hz. However, since the output of N1 is logic zero, as is also

true of pin 13 of N4, the output of the circuit will be constantly high (logic 1). If switch S1 is now depressed the monostable multivibrator (one-shot) constructed around N1 and N2 will be triggered, causing the output of N2 to go low for half a second thereby inhibiting the oscillator N3. The output of N1 will now be high, so that the two inputs of N4 are also high. This means that the output of the circuit (N4) will be low (the first clock pulse). If S1 is still depressed after the time delay of the monostable has elapsed, the output of N1 will remain high, the output of N2 will be high, therefore N3 will now oscillate and the pulse train thus produced will be fed to the output of the circuit. If, on the other hand, S1 had been released before the end of the half second period, Pin 13 of N4 would have become logic zero the moment that N3 started to oscillate again. As a result, the output would go high once more.

The waveforms involved are shown in figure 2. The vertical lines in signal A represent the contact bounce caused by switch S1. This contact bounce is suppressed by the RC network R3 and C2.

2

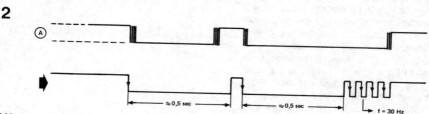

≈0,5 sec   ≈0,5 sec   f = 30 Hz

277 Novel flashing light

As you may have already guessed, this circuit represents no more or less than a method of illuminating a series of LEDs. The diagram shows five LEDs, but this can be extended to a maximum of ten by connecting the reset line (shown connected to output 5) to the next output, or, if ten LEDs are used, by omitting the reset line altogether. Of course, for each extra LED a corresponding output stage consisting of a transistor and a resistor will also have to be added. What can the circuit do?

In the simplest configuration, all the LEDs light up in turn. The rate at which this happens is determined by the setting of potentiometer P1. Other sequences can be found by incorporating some clever little 'tricks'. However, the basic configuration can certainly be useful, for example, in the case of a model of a road obstruction where they use those yellow warning flashers which light up one after the other. The illustration at Ⓐ shows how the LEDs can be made to light and remain lit in sequence by simply including a diode between each output stage. The cathode of the diode is connected to the base of T1 and the anode is connected to the emitter of T2. A second diode is connected between the base of T2 and the emitter of T3 and so on. This simple arrangement is quite adequate to produce the desired effect.

LEDs which light up in a 'to-and-fro' fashion

can be obtained by connecting the bases of the transistors to the outputs of IC2 in the following manner: The cathode of the first diode is connected to the base of T1 and the anode is connected to pin 3 of the 4017. Two diodes are connected to the base of T2, one goes to pin 2 and the other to pin 6. Similarly, T3 is connected to pins 4 and 5, T4 is connected to pins 7 and 1, and finally T5 is connected to pin 10.

By altering the pin numbering a totally 'random' display sequence can be obtained. Remember that if more outputs are to be used the reset connection must be moved to the next, unused output.

The effects can also be combined: all sorts of 'weird and wonderful' sequences can be obtained by placing diodes between the outputs of IC2 and the transistor bases and between the base of one and the emitter of the next.

As it is quite likely that this circuit will be constructed by model builders who may have relatively little electronic experience, a brief explanation of how the circuit works may be advantageous.

Opamp IC1 generates squarewave pulses by continuously charging and discharging capacitor C1. If the resistance of potentiometer P1 is increased the charge and discharge time for this capacitor increases and therefore the frequency of the oscillator decreases — this results in the

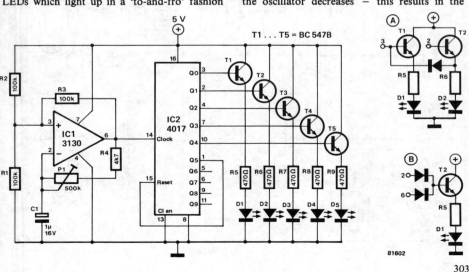

81602

LEDs being lit for longer periods.

The squarewave pulses are fed to a divide-by-ten counter, IC2. The outputs of this counter each go high in turn after every clock pulse. The previous output, which was high, now goes low and the LED connected to it, via the resistor and transistor, will go out, while the next LED in the sequence will come on. Finally, when output five goes high the counter is reset causing a new sequence to be started (LED D1 lights up).

278 'Hi-fi' siren

The title 'siren' above a circuit diagram usually implies a circuit for a two-tone or multi-tone 'horn' which sounds continuously and can be used for an alarm of one sort or another. However, the siren described here is not particularly suitable for that application, but no doubt inventive readers will find a use for it! The hi-fi siren simulates, as accurately as possible, a passing police patrol car with its siren going full blast.

What happens when a police car approaches? At first the siren is only heard very faintly. The noise increases gradually until at the moment it passes the observer the sound reaches maximum intensity. After this the noise decreases immediately while at the same time the pitch gets lower due to the 'Doppler effect'.

By examining the circuit diagram, we can see how this is accomplished electronically. The oscillators constructed around gates N1 and N2 constitute the actual two-tone siren. Initially, the base voltage of transistor T4, and thus the emitter voltage of T5, is approximately equal to the supply voltage. Therefore, no current passes through the loudspeaker. When the start button, S1, is depressed, the flipflop constructed around N3 and N4 changes state and the potential across capacitor C4 decreases slowly. This causes the emitter voltage of T5 to fall also, so that the current through the speaker will start to build up. This current is in fact switched on and off by T6 and T7 to the timing of the double oscillator transistors T6 and T7 in the rythm of the double (N1/N2), which in effect produces the required sound.

The current, and therefore the noise, continues

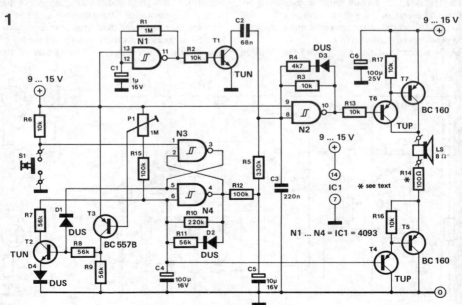

1

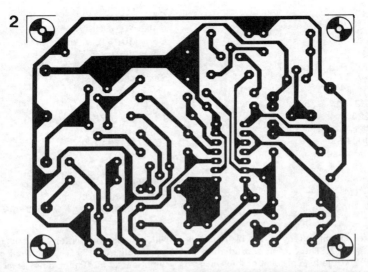

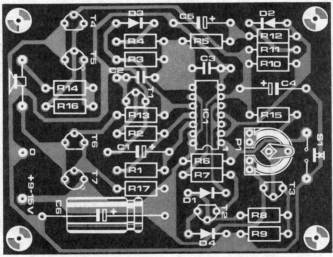

to increase gradually due to the falling voltage across C4. At a certain moment this voltage reaches the negative trigger threshold of N4, so that the flipflop is reset and the output of N4 goes high. At this particular moment the voltage on the emitter of T5 is at a minimum and the noise level is at a maximum. As the output of N4 has now gone low, the frequency of the oscillator constructed around N2 is lowered somewhat, thereby simulating the Doppler effect. Capacitor C4 will then slowly recharge up to the supply voltage level, leading to a gradual lowering of the noise level.

The circuitry around transistors T2 and T3 ensures that the noise level increases very slowly at first, but it will then speed up. This makes the sound more realistic. The resultant effect can be adjusted by means of potentiometer P1 and should be done 'by ear'. To do this, the potentiometer is turned fully clockwise, so that the wiper is at full supply voltage level. The start button is then depressed and the noise produced is listened to. The potentiometer is then turned back a little way and the pushbutton depressed once more. This procedure should be repeated until the siren sounds as realistic as possible.

Parts list

Resistors:

R1 = 1 M
R2, R3, R6, R13, R16, R17 = 10 k
R4 = 4k7
R5 = 330 k
R7, R8, R9, R11 = 56 k
R10 = 220 k
R12, R15 = 100 k
R13 = 100 Ω
P1 = 1 M preset

Capacitors:
C1 = 1µ /16 V
C2 = 68 n MKM

C3 = 220 n MKM
C4 = 100µ /16 V
C5 = 10µ /16 V
C6 = 100µ /25 V

Semiconductors:
D1...D4 = DUS
T1, T2 = TUN
T3 = BC 557B
T4, T6 = TUP
T5, T7 = BC 160
IC1 = 4093

Miscellaneous:
S1 = pushbutton
LS = loudspeaker 8 Ω /500 mW

The printed circuit board for the hi-fi siren is given in figure 2. The current consumption of the circuit is virtually dependent on the value of resistor R14. This resistor can be reduced in value to a minimum of 27 Ω if a louder siren is required. In that case the current consumption

will increase considerably, of course. When R14 has a value of 100 Ω , the total current consumption at maximum noise level is approximately 60 mA (U_B = 15 V), while at rest it amounts to only a few mA.

279 Low-noise microphone pre-amplifier

Hi-fi enthusiasts are often faced with the problem of not being able to get near enough to the object they want to record. The only solution in such a case lies in using a very sensitive, low-noise pre-amplifier combined with a good dynamic microphone. The pre-amplifiers in the usual recording equipment are normally not sensitive enough for the purpose, and produce too much noise to ensure good recording quality. It is much better to build a sepa ~te low-noise pre-

amplifier, that can be inserted in between the microphone and the recording equipment.

Of course, the available microphone will do when recording the roar of a lion. No single pre-amplifier can guarantee a linear amplification of that kind of sound and that of a nightingale at a distance of 100 yards, due to the limits of the input sensitivity. The circuit given here, however, is intended to record the nightingale, but definitely not to record a pop singer who looks

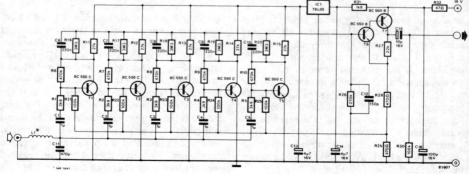

as if he is about to swallow his microphone.

Any transistor produces noise, but to combat this as effectively as possible, noise-free types from a good manufacturer should be selected. On top of that, the circuit should make optimum use of the transistor noise characteristic. It will be noticed immediately that the circuit described here contains 5 parallel stages. The noise generated by each stage can be added in the manner of a vector power, that is, as the square root of the sum of the squares of each component. As the noise of each stage is slightly out of phase, the resultant figure will be slightly lower than that of each stage. Mathematically, this reduction can be expressed as $\sqrt{n}$, so that in this case it is equal to $\sqrt{5}$, in other words, slightly less than 2.3 times. In terms of decibels it can be said that the reduction in noise amounts to 7 dB when compared with a single stage.

A further method of reducing noise is to limit the current through the transistors to a minimum. This is in fact done here, as can be seen from the 1.5 mA (stereo) value. This is even less than the 2 mA required by the voltage regulator IC1, which is included to reduce the supply voltage for the amplifier stages to 5 V. The lower power consumption produces a higher signal-to-noise ratio at the cost of considerable harmonic distortion. Local (R6 to R10) and overall (R21 to R25) feedback ensures the removal of this distortion. The circuit gives excellent results in spite of the 1% distortion which is unavoidable during recording.

What kind of results can therefore be expected from this circuit? The input sensitivity, to give an output of 60 mV, is about 0.13 mV, which is adequate for most applications. The gain of the circuit amounts to around 475 times. Audible distortion occurs with an input signal level of about 8 mV (or greater!) so that fairly strong

sound levels can be processed. The frequency response of the preamplifier, between the 3 dB points, is 20 Hz to 45 kHz, the upper limit being determined by the value of capacitor C12. The effect of L1/C11 is negligible as they are included only to prevent interference from local radio stations. Coil L1 consists of a couple of turns of copper wire through a ferrite bead, and can be omitted when there is no likelyhood of radio interference.

This design gives an improvement in signal-to-noise ratio of about 12 dB when compared with conventional designs, making it possible to record that nightingale's song from a distance of 100 m.

With the aid of this preamplifier, the enthusiast can make music recordings or outside recordings of really amazing quality. The microphone and recording equipment will naturally contribute greatly to the actual quality achieved.

As the gain of the preamplifier is dependent on the value of resistor R27, the gain can be altered by selecting a different value for this resistor. However, strictly speaking, the collector voltage of transistor T7 needs to be kept at a level of 7.5 V. Effectively, the value of R26 will also have to be altered. A smaller value for R27 means a larger value for R26. For a gain of 200, R27 should have a value of 10 kΩ : and the value of R26 should be 680 kΩ .

By incorporating a resistor in series with L1, the input impedance can be increased, but the same effect can be obtained by changing the values of R1...R5. It will be obvious that all resistors should be low-noise metal film types after having gone through all this trouble to eliminate the noise generated by the transistors.

P. de Bra

280 Extended range milli-voltmeter

A multimeter, as the name implies, is a multi-purpose measuring tool, although it has its limits. For example, its range for measuring AC in the audio band is usually inadequate, and the sensitivity, internal resistance and frequency response of the cheaper moving-coil multi-purpose instrument normally leaves quite a lot to be desired. The widerange millivoltmeter described

here closes that gap in a very simple and elegant way. The instrument can be used to measure alternating current of frequencies between 100 Hz and 500 kHz. When using MOS-FET input opamps the input impedance at all measurement ranges will amount to 10 MΩ .

At the lowest measuring voltage of 15 mV the sensitivity is such that there is a full-scale deflec-

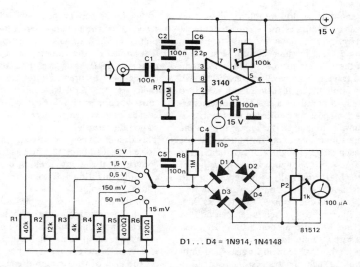

D1 ... D4 = 1N914, 1N4148

tion on the 100 μ A meter.

The opamp serves both as measurement amplifier and active rectifier. The level of amplification is determined by the switched resistors R1 to R6. With the instrument set at a particular sensitivity range, the value of a resistor can be determined simply by dividing the input voltage for a full deflection by 100 μ A. When, for example, at the measuring range of 150 mV, a 200 mV range is expected to be needed, resistor R4 should be changed to a value of 2 k.

Because the bridge rectifier diodes D1 to D4 are located in the feedback loop of the amplifier, there is compensation for the threshold voltage of the diodes, for which reason the mV scale responds in a linear fashion.

The meter is zeroed with the aid of P1 and the input short-circuited, while the measuring range is determined by P2. The latter requires a calibration voltage that can be obtained from small mains transformer with a secondary voltage of slightly less than 5 V. At this level, the voltage can be measured quite accurately with the aid of the multimeter. The calibration voltage should then be connected to the extended range milli-voltmeter set at 5 V, and the reading of the 100 μ A instrument is then adjusted, using P2, to the value of the calibration voltage. The other measuring ranges are then set simultaneously corresponding to the tolerance of the resistors R1 to R6.

When the circuit is used to extend or supplement an existing multimeter, the moving-coil part of the multimeter should be used in the 100 μ A range. The best power supply to use in that case is about 9 V, obtained from two small 9 V dry cells which will last quite a long time as the power consumption is very low.

281 Temperature alarm

This design allows a simultaneous check of a maximum of four temperatures. The individual detectors are connected to the main control unit by means of a pair of wires. When one of the detectors registers an abnormally high or low temperature, an alarm sounds. The positioning of resistor R10 determines whether the alarm is activated when the registered temperature rises above the preset temperature setting or whether it sounds when it falls below the required temperature.

When R10 is incorporated between the positive supply line and the output of IC3, the alarm will be triggered when the measured temperature exceeds that of the setting of P1. In this situation, the output of IC3 falls and the detector starts to

308

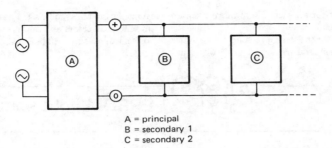

A = principal
B = secondary 1
C = secondary 2

raw a current of around 20 mA. This means that the voltage across R1 becomes greater than .6 V causing transistor T1 to conduct and the alarm to sound. This occurs because as the temperature rises the resistance of the NTC resistor (R9) decreases taking the inverting input of IC3 higher than the non-inverting input (voltage-rise). This in turn causes the output of the opamp to go low.

If resistor R10 is placed between the output of IC2 and ground, the reverse happens. In this instance, as the temperature drops the resistance of R9 increases taking the inverting input of IC3

any more were included the quiescent current would exceed that of the 'alarm current' and the design would not function correctly. In retrospect, the alarm current can not be increased as in that case the output current of the opamp would be exceeded – with detrimental results!

If another form of alarm is required, IC2 and its associated components can be omitted and the transistor can be used to control a relay or other similar device. The sensitivity of the circuit, in other words the temperature at which the device operates, can be adjusted by means of the preset potentiometer P1. It may well be advantageous

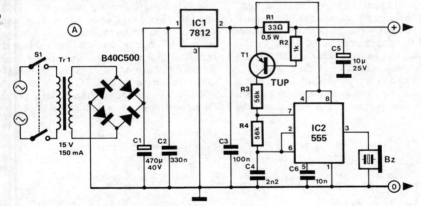

more negative than the non-inverting input. Consequently, the output of the opamp will go high and a current of approximately 20 mA will flow through resistor R10. This again causes transistor T1 in the main control unit to conduct and start the alarm oscillator, IC2.

The oscillator generates a tone of about 4 kHz which is then fed to the piezo-electric buzzer (Bz). This relatively high frequency was chosen to suit the resonant frequency of piezo elements and because it is optimal in relation to the aural sensitivity curve.

As mentioned previously, the maximum number of detector circuits that can be used is four. If

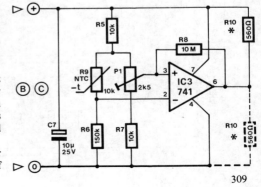

to use a multi-turn preset so that more accurate settings can be obtained.

Applications for the design include a simple fire alarm, the temperature control of two aquariums (each one requiring a maximum and minimum detector) and a temperature regulato for central heating installations.

282 EPROM light sequencer

The circuit described here is an eight channel light sequencer. The information for each channel (on or off) is contained in a 2708 type EPROM (these are coming down in price every day!). There are therefore 1024 steps before the 'program' repeats itself. It is possible to program the EPROM yourself if you have access to an EPROM programming device. Otherwise you can use an EPROM which has already been programmed for a computer. This will cause the eight lamps to turn on and off in the strangest of sequences. A test with the monitor program of the Junior Computer showed this to work very well.

The lamps are switched on or off at the 'zero-crossing' point of the mains waveform in order to avoid interference to TV or radio. The power rating of the lamps should be 200 Watts, but this can be increased to a maximum of 800 Watts if adequate heatsinks are used for the triacs.

As can be seen in the circuit diagram, the unit is controlled by the clock generator formed by N4. The oscillator frequency can be adjusted by means of potentiometer P1. The output of th clock generator drives a binary counter, IC5 which counts up from zero to 1023 in binary The outputs of IC5 are fed to the address input of the EPROM, IC6. The contents of each ad dress location are therefore read out sequen tially. A logic '1' on a data output of th EPROM will turn the corresponding lamp on vi the associated driver transistor and triac. Whe the output is logic zero, the lamp will be ex tinguished.

The supply voltage for transistors T1...T8 i only present for about 300 µ s at the zero crossing of the mains voltage. This is ac complished by the circuitry around N1...N3, T9 and T10. Thus if the base of the transistor is also high at this particular moment, the correspond ing triac will turn on and will remain on for the remainder of the half-cycle. The supply voltages for the remainder of the circuit are provided by the voltage regulators IC1...IC3.

WARNING: Mains voltages are present throughout the circuit – so BE CAREFUL!

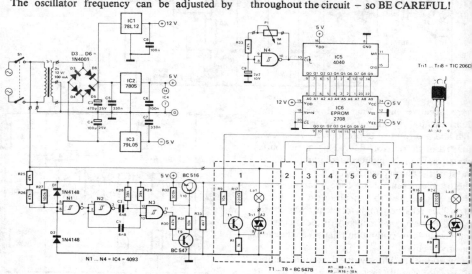

283 Fast TTL interface

: is surprising how often TTL ICs are asked to perform a difficult (if not impossible) task. It is, f course, gratifying to know that experimenters have so much confidence in the capabilities of the TTL logic family. But, on the other hand, why drive the devices to extremes when they are not likely to survive? More often than not the output of this type of IC is overloaded, or they are used, mistakenly, to drive CMOS ICs directly. In the latter case, the guaranteed active pull-up TTL output voltage (2.4 V) is lower than the minimum CMOS input voltage required to guarantee switching (3.5 V). Also, the input impedance of CMOS ICs is essentially capacitive, which means that the slew rate of the TTL output signal will suffer at high frequencies.

The upper trace in the photograph shows the effect when a TTL output is capacitively loaded (220 pF in this instance). The negative-going edges of the signal are still quite acceptable, as TTL outputs can 'sink' more current than they can 'source'. However, the output current will be reduced at the same rate at which the voltage level increases causing the positive-going edge to level off. As would be expected, CMOS ICs do not react favourably to this type of signal. This is because CMOS ICs will not switch until the input level has reached approximately half the supply level, unless the manufacturer has taken the appropriate measures to avoid this. As a result, a delay of about 40 ns will be incurred and the poor signal edge at the input is bound to lead to a far optimum edge at the output.

In the case of the lower signal shown, an effort has been made to improve the positive-going edge by including a pull-up resistor between the TTL output and the positive supply voltage. This resistor (220 Ω) will certainly improve the positive-going edge of the signal, but at the ex-

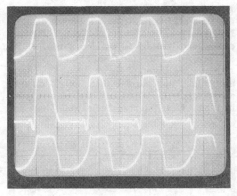

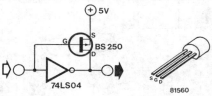

pense of the negative-going edge. The ideal solution, therefore, is to incorporate a VFET which will only operate during the positive-going section of the waveform. The middle signal shows that the amplitude will now be the same as the full supply voltage and the positive-going edge reaches its peak very rapidly despite the capacitive load.

Note: the oscilloscope in the photograph was set up as follows:

vertical deflection — 2 V/div.
horizontal deflection — 100 ns/div (in other words, the frequency of the signal on display is 4 MHz!!).

284 Automatic soldering iron switch

We all know that it is quite easy to forget to turn off the soldering iron. If you then go out of the house with other things on your mind, it is just possible to return to find a heap of smoking

rubble. This would be extremely upsetting, especially when this sort of calamity can easily be avoided. The results are not usually so dramatic, but the least you can expect is a bigger electricity bill. The circuit here will iron the problem out and will repay the effort of making it in a very short time.

The circuit operates as follows. IC1 is an oscillator divided by 2^{13} which generates a time interval of about a quarter of an hour. At the end of this time a LED flashes and a buzzer sounds. Unless S1 is pressed within 50 seconds, the circuit switches itself, and the soldering iron, off. If S1 is pressed, IC1 re-starts the 15 minute period. Although the prototype circuit behaved satisfactorily, it is just possible that 'spikes' on the mains supply line will cause the relay to pull itself back in. In this case the relay must have an

extra contact, to positively switch it off. This then requires a third pole of S1, to bridge this contact at switch on.

The switching can be done using two separate push switches which must be pressed simultaneously.

If a relay is available with an operating voltage other than 12 volts, then the circuit can be operated at the relay voltage, by changing the power supply and regulator. The supply voltage must, however, be kept between 3 and 18 volts.

M.A. Prins

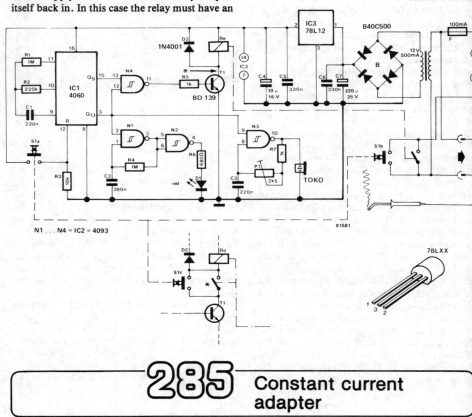

285 Constant current adapter

It is quite often the case that the electronics enthusiast requires a constant current source. When such a need does arise, for example for test purposes, it is a piece of equipment that is not usually available. However, it is not necessary to construct an entire constant current source for each application. It is sufficient to

Table

S1	I	P1 x
1	10 μ A...100μ A	10 μ A
2	100μ A...1 mA	100 μ A
3	1 mA...10 mA	1 mA
4	10 mA...100 mA	10 mA

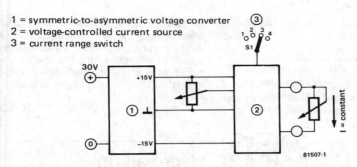

1 = symmetric-to-asymmetric voltage converter
2 = voltage-controlled current source
3 = current range switch

81507-1

ave an adapter that can be connected to an existing power supply whenever a constant current source is required.

The proposed circuit has another useful application: the asymmetric-to-symmetric power supply converter at the front end of the constant current adapter can be used separately to power an amplifier or similar circuit.

Most amateur constructors own a mains power supply with a variable output voltage of up to 30 V and a current output of around 200 mA (or greater). This supply can then be used to power the constant current adapter.

The asymmetric-to-symmetric converter consisting of IC1 and transistors T1 and T2 provides an effective output voltage of ± 15 V across the two capacitors C2 and C3. This symmetrical supply can be used separately provided the re-

quired output current is no greater than about 50 mA.

Let us now examine the constant current adapter itself in greater detail. The asymmetric-to-symmetric voltage converter is required to power the operational amplifier IC2. This opamp is used as the current source and is controlled by the potential divider consisting of potentiometer P1 and resistors R3 and R4. Potentiometer P1 can be adjusted to give an output voltage of between 1.5...15 V.

A constant current will flow through load resistor R_L, which is dependent on the voltage setting of P1 and on the range selected by switch S1. The circuit is such that, regardless of the actual range, the current through R_L is determined by the setting of P1. Transistors T3 and T4 simply form a buffer stage.

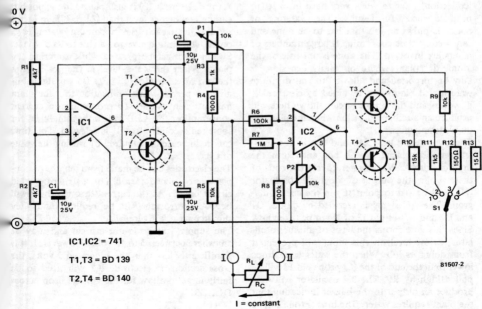

IC1,IC2 = 741

T1,T3 = BD 139

T2,T4 = BD 140

I = constant

81507-2

313

The output current of the adapter can be calculated from the formula.

$$I = \frac{0.1 \times U_{P1}}{R10 \text{ or } R11 \text{ or } R12 \text{ or } R13}$$

Potentiometer P1 should be provided with a scale from 1 to 10 so that it is easier to control the desired current. Depending on the setting of the range switch S1, the current can then be deduced with the aid of the multiplication factor given in the table below. Potentiometer P1 should be adjusted initially so that an output current of 10 μ A is obtained when S1 is in position '1' and P1 is set at minimum output.

R. Storr

286 Hydro-alarm

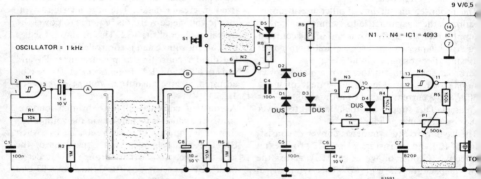

It is well known that plant growers with a large 'collection' have to work very hard in order to produce successful results. The watering of plants is only one job that has to be done and can become time consuming if large numbers of plants are involved. The same is not true of the 'domestic' plant where on many occasions it may be forgotten and allowed to run dry. The watering of plants can be aided by electronics, however, and the simple circuit shown here will produce an audible indication when the plant requires topping up.

The two electrodes (Ⓐ and Ⓒ in the illustration) are placed in the pot and form the 'hydro switch'. When water covers the ends of these probes the output of the 1 kHz oscillator (N1) will be fed to point (C) in the circuit diagram. The AC signal is rectified by diodes D1 and D2 and causes pin 13 of N4 to be taken low. Since this gate forms the basis of another oscillator, a low level on this input will prevent it from doing its job. When the water level drops lower than the end of the Ⓒ probe pin 13 will be pulled high by R9. The N4 oscillator will now produce an output to the buzzer indicating that the plant requires water. The buzzer tone can be varied by adjustment of the 500 k preset.

A third electrode Ⓑ is also placed in the pot but ending at a higher level than Ⓐ or Ⓒ, in fact it should just reach the maximum water level point. This should give you a clue to its purpose. Switch S1 must be pressed while watering the plant. When the water level in the pot reaches the end of electrode Ⓑ, LED D5 will light thus giving a precise visual indication that the plant has sufficient water. To economise on current consumption the LED will only remain lit for some ten seconds after S1 is released. This time can be increased if required by raising the value of C8.

The electrodes can be made from lengths of copper wire or etched as tracks on a strip of printed circuit board. As the current through them will be AC, corrosion will be reduced and they should have a fairly long life.

The supply voltage is not critical and may be anywhere between 5 to 15 volts. However, if it is significantly less than the suggested 9 volts, the cross section of electrode Ⓒ will need to be fairly large to allow for the voltage drop across D1...D3.

287 Automatic reset

This circuit is designed to generate a reset pulse whenever the supply voltage is switched on and, in addition, whenever there is any substantial interference 'spikes' on the power supply lines. Most digital circuits (and microprocessor systems in particular) have to be reset for a certain period after the supply voltage is initially switched on. In this instance, an active low reset pulse is generated which will remain logic zero for 30 ms after the supply is switched on. At the end of this duration the supply will be fully on.

The 'automatic reset' works as follows. The section of circuit around transistors T1 and T2 ensures that the voltage across capacitor C1 remains 0 V until the supply voltage reaches a level of 4.5 V. As soon as the supply voltage reaches this value, the transistors will stop conducting and capacitor C1 will gradually charge up via resistor R5. As a result, the voltage at point A will slowly drop from around 4.5 V to 0 V, causing the Schmitt trigger formed by N1 and N2 to be triggered and the output $\overline{RES}$ will go high. In other words, the $\overline{RES}$ output will most definitely be low for about 30 ms after switch-on until the supply voltage level has attained its correct value (+4.75 V for TTL).

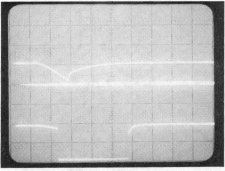

As a side-line, the circuit also allows for a reset pulse to be generated if ever the supply voltage should drop below 4.5 V for any reason. In certain computer applications this could well be vital, as such an interference spike, however short, could well erase a large section of memory! For this reason a noise generated reset pulse could well be useful, as the computer operator then knows that the program will always be started from 'square one'.

The photograph shows a characteristic form of interference spike and the reset pulse that is generated from it.

Finally, it should be noted that the Schmitt trigger need not necessarily be constructed from two inverters and two resistors. In fact, any type of Schmitt trigger will perform adequately here, such as the 74LS132 for instance.

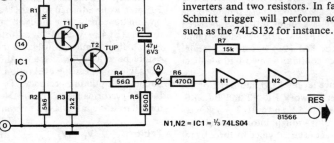

288 LED voltage monitor

A stable power supply is absolutely essential for the correct operation of computers and TTL circuits. A voltage fluctuation of 10% is certainly

not tolerable, therefore it is prudent to keep a regular check on the supply voltage level.

Because of their lack of resolution and accuracy

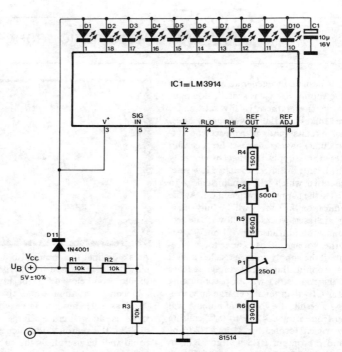

it is inadvisable to use analogue panel meters to monitor the power supply voltage. Besides this, a fluttering pointer is hardly the best choice for a warning device. The LED voltage monitor solves all these problems.

The voltage monitor is set up so that only the range between 4.5 V and 5.5 V is covered. The device used, the LM 3914, is very similar to the LM 3915. There is a slight difference between the two however: The LM 3915 has a logarithmic scale whereas the LM 3914 has a linear scale. The latter device contains a row of 10 identical 1 k Ω resistors.

The two reference levels, RLO and RHI, of the potential divider network P1, P2 and R4...R6, are set to 4.51/3 = 1.5 V and 5.41/3 = 1.8 V respectively. The '3' is brought into the calculation as the input voltage is also divided by three by resistors R1...R3. The table shows which LEDs will light for the corresponding input voltage once the circuit has been set up correctly.

For a clear warning indication it is best to use red LEDs for D1 and D10 and green ones for the rest. It may also be useful to use a different colour (orange) for D5 and D6 as an indication of the nominal voltage level.

The power supply for the circuit can be taken from the voltage to be monitored as the current

requirement is only 20 mA. Diode D11 is included to protect the circuit against reverse input polarity.

To calibrate the circuit it must be connected to an adjustable regulated power supply. The input voltage is then adjusted until a reading of 5,41 V is obtained on a digital voltmeter. Potentiometer P1 can now be adjusted so that D9 and D10 light up simultaneously. The input voltage is then set to a level of 4.61 V and P2 is adjusted so that D1 and D2 light simultaneously. As the internal resistors have a slight effect on the circuit it is advisable to repeat the calibration procedure to obtain the optimum accuracy. To ensure satisfactory performance of the LED voltage monitor, all resistors must have a tolerance of 5%.

Table	V_{CC} (V)	LED
	4.51...4.60	D1
	4.61...4.70	D2
	4.71...4.80	D3
	4.81...4.90	D4
	4.91...5.00	D5
	5.01...5.10	D6
	5.11...5.20	D7
	5.21...5.30	D8
	5.31...5.40	D9
	5.41...5.50	D10

289 Crystal oscillator... ...for low voltage supplies

It is very easy to construct a crystal oscillator using a field effect transistor. This particular circuit operates at relatively low supply voltages, from 1.5 volts upwards, and was tested with common-or-garden quartz crystals with frequencies ranging from 100 kHz to 10 MHz.

The crystal is connected between the drain and gate of the field effect transistor, T1, and operates in the parallel resonance mode. Coil L1 is included to improve the frequency range. Furthermore, it helps as an additional parallel coil for those crystals which are not particularly suited for this application and which do not feel like oscillating. Capacitor C1 is the series 'padding' capacitor for the crystal. The necessary feedback and the 180° phase shift is provided by the internal input and output capacitances of the FET. The output signal is buffered by transistor

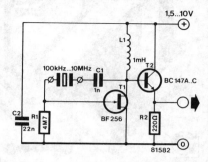

T2.

This circuit was tested with the following range of crystals: 100 kHz, 1 MHz, 4 MHz, 6 MHz, 8 MHz and 10 MHz. The circuit can be used in a variety of applications due to its low supply voltage requirements (1.5 V minimum).

290 6 to 12 volt converter

There are an amazing number of VW Beetles and Fords on the road which still operate on a 6 V battery. In such vehicles (and motorcycles) there are always problems when trying to install a modern car radio as they require a power supply of at least 10.7 V. One solution is to incorporate a 6 to 12 V converter of the type described here. This simple converter provides an output of around 700 mA and is relatively inexpensive to construct.

These two characteristics — simple and cheap — arise from the concept of the circuit which contains two integrated audio power amplifiers and does not require a transformer. The first amplifier, IC1, functions as an astable power multivibrator. The frequency of oscillation is determined by the value of capacitor C3 and is approximately 4 kHz with no load and maximally 6 kHz when a load is applied. The output signal of a second amplifier, IC2, is identical to that of

1

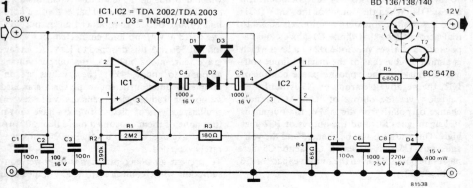

81538

317

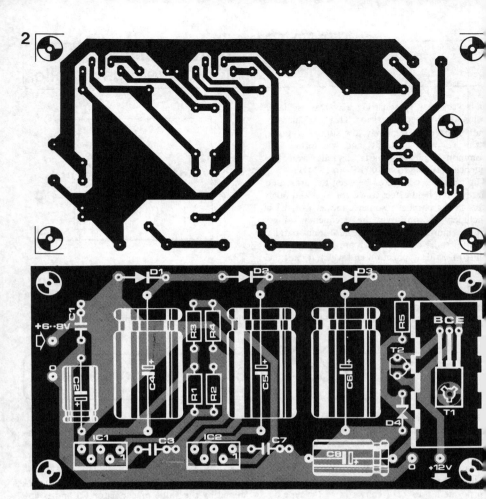

the first, albeit 180 degrees out of phase.

When the output voltage of IC1 is low, capacitor C4 charges up via diode D1 to almost full supply voltage (reduced slightly by the potential drop across D1). When the output of the AMV (IC1) becomes positive, the output voltage is added to that across C4 so that diode D1 blocks and capacitor C5 charges via diode D2 to a level which is almost double that of the original input voltage. Because of the opposite phase control of IC2, the negative electrode of C5 is until then held low via the output of IC2. At the next change of polarity of the AMV, the output of IC1 again goes low and the output of IC2 goes high. This causes C4 to be charged and the voltage across C5 to be increased. Capacitor C5 then passes its potential on to the output capacitor C6 via diode D3.

In theory, therefore, the final effect of the circuit is to treble the input voltage, but in practice C6 will only attain a somewhat lower voltage which depends on the load. Measurements taken revealed that a 6 V lead-acid battery with a nominal voltage of 7.2 V, produced an output voltage of 18 V with no load connected, but with a load of 750 mA this dropped to 12 V. At an 'average' current of 400 mA, the output voltage amounts to about 14 V. These values are undoubtedly quite sufficient to power a standard mono car radio. Measurements with several similar receivers of different makes have shown that none of them consumed more than 500 mA, and at average volume a value of 300 mA was rarely exceeded.

To prevent an unacceptable rise in power consumption when connected to a low impedance

318

Resistors:

R1 = 2M2
R2 = 390 k
R3 = 180 Ω
R4 = 68 Ω
R5 = 680 Ω

Capacitors:

C1, C3, C7 = 100 n
C2 = 100 µ /16 V
C4, C5 = 1000 µ /16 V
C6 = 1000 µ /25 V
C8 = 220 µ /16 V

Semiconductors:

T1 = BD 136/138/140
T2 = BC 547B
D1, D2, D3 = 1N5401/1N4001
D4 = 15 V/400 mW zener diode
IC1, IC2 = TDA 2002/TDA 2003

load, the converter is provided with an additional limiter stage consisting of a 15 V zener diode and a complementary Darlington circuit (transistors T1 and T2). This arrangement limites the maximum voltage to about 14,2 V. At the same time, capacitor C8 connected to the two transistors reduced the ripple of the output voltage to less than 50 mV under full load conditions. During practical trials no effect of the oscillating frequency of the converter on the quality of radio reception was noticed

The printed circuit board for the converter is shown in figure 2. Due to its small size, construction of the circuit should not pose any problems. Both IC amplifiers and transistor T1 can be kept sufficiently cool if these components are mounted (with mica washers) on a common heatsink along the longest side of the board. The heatsink should be as large as the board itself and should be mounted at 90 degrees to the board in order to guarantee an optimum heat transfer. Both IC amplifiers contain integrated protection circuitry against short circuits and thermal overload, so that the worst need not be feared if the unit is subjected to overload or overheating.

Either the TDA 2002 or the TSA 2003 can be used for the amplifiers. The TDA 2003 has the edge on the 2002 due to a few improved characteristics. The same holds true for the diodes; the 3 A diodes (1N5401) are best suited because less voltage is dropped across them. When 1N4001 types are used, a loss in output voltage of 0.5 V to 1 V should be expected.

If the values of capacitors C4, C5 and C6 are increased to 200 µ F, the maximum output current is raised by about 100 mA. For even higher output currents, two converters can be connected in parallel. In that case, the limiting stage (R5, C8, D4, T1 and T2) is omitted from the second board and a connection made between the two positive electrodes of the two C6s. Transistor T1 can then be one of the following types; BD 236, BD 238, BD 204, BD 288 or BD 438. The maximum current that can be obtained by connecting two converters in parallel is nearly doubled to about 1.3 A, therefore stereo or cassette radios can be installed in 6 V cars quite easily.

291 12 V to 6 V converter

After having described how a modern 12 V car radio can be installed in a vehicle with a 6 V system with the aid of a 6 V to 12 V converter, it may be a good idea to look at the other side of the coin — where a lower voltage is required from a 12 volt system. The most common application for this type of converter is when portable cassette recorders are to be used in the car. Many of these require a supply voltage of between 5...8 volts.

The simplest and most obvious solution is to use an integrated voltage regulator. Apart from util-

ising 6 volt types such as the 7806, it is also possible to use a 5 volt version (7805 of LM 309) and boost its output voltage by including two diodes

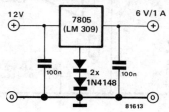

in the common lead as shown in the circuit diagram. Depending on the type of diodes used, this will produce an output voltage between 6 V and 6.5 V. The maximum output current of the types mentioned is 1 A. It is important to ensure that the regulator is sufficiently cooled by means of a suitable heatsink.

Combined radio/cassette players very often require a slightly higher voltage of 7.5 V. In this instance, either the 7808 can be used, or the 7805 with four diodes in series with the common lead.

292 Post office letter scales

No doubt, everyone is familiar with the kind of scales to be found on Post Office counters. A letter or small parcel is placed on it and the weight and the required postage can be read off it. There is no reason why this can not be accomplished electronically. Of course, some mechanical ingenuity will be required as the equipment will include some form of scale or balance mechanism. Moreover, the electronic scales should look similar to the mechanical counterpart. If the latter were not the case, no-

Table

LED	weight in g.
–	less than 60
D3	60...100
D3, D4	100...150
D3...D5	150...200
D3...D6	over 60

body would think of putting a letter on to weight it!

Let us first consider the electronic details. The quite simple circuit is shown in figure 1. It consists of two ICs and a few other components. The 9 volt supply from the battery is stabilised by an integrated voltage regulator, IC1. For this reason, the registered tariffs are reasonably independent of changing voltage supplies (a falling battery voltage). Similar to the mechanical version, the electronic scale will indicate five different rates (see table) by means of LEDs. The relevant LED will light up depending on the weight of the letter placed on the scales. The LEDs are activated by opamps A1...A4, which are connected as comparators. Potentiometers P1...P4 are used to preset the 'target' voltage at the non-inverting inputs of the comparators. The actual voltage, which is a measure of the weight of the letter is fed to the inverting inputs via the light dependent resistor (LDR), R3.

Depending on the amount of light radiated by the yellow LED, D7, actually falling on the

1

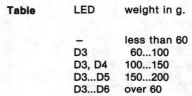

A1 ... A4 = IC2 = LM324
D1 ... D7 = LED

81505 1

Parts list

Resistors:
R1 = 56 k
R2 = 100 Ω
R3 = LDR 03
R4 = 47 Ω
R5...R8 = 330 Ω
P1...P4 = 250 k preset

Capacitors:
C1 = 10μ /10 V tantalum
C2 = 1μ /16 V tantalum

Semiconductors:
D1 = 5V1/400 mW zener diode
D2 = green LED
D3...D6 = red LED
D7 = yellow LED
IC1 = 7805
IC2 = LM 324, CA 324

Figure 1. The circuit diagram of the scales. It consists of two integrated circuits and a few extra components. LEDs D3...D6 indicate the various weights and postal charges. The opto-coupler consists of LED D7 and the LDR R3.

Figure 2. An exploded view of the scales. The tip of the ballpoint pen controls the amount of light that falls on the LDR.

Figure 3. The printed circuit board and component layout for the scales. LED D7, the LDR and the wiring are soldered to the underside of the board.

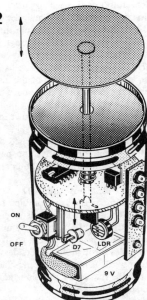

D3 = 60 ... < 100 g
D4 = 100 ... < 150 g
D5 = 150 ... < 200 g
D6 = < 200 g

81505 2

LDR, a certain voltage will appear at all four inverting inputs of the comparators. When this voltage is identical to, or greater than, that preset at the non-inverting input, the relative opamp output will go low. As the anodes of the LEDs are connected to the positive aide of the power supply, the corresponding LED will light up.

The mechanical construction of the scales (see figure 2) is reminiscent of the good old 'canned circuits' issue (December 1980). In fact, the best thing to use for this purpose is an old beer or soft drinks can. Actually, two are required. The lid of the first one (with the ring-pull) is removed and discarded. The bottom of the second one is

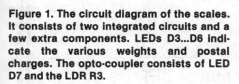

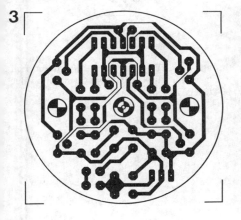

also removed (carefully) as this will be used as the lid for the first one later on, the remainder of this can can also be thrown away. A hole that will just allow a ballpoint pen to pass through it is drilled in the bottom of the undiscarded can (which is, in fact, used upside-down). The ballpoint pen is then attached to the base of the discarded can. Next, the printed circuit board is mounted in the can with sufficiently long bolts and spacers (see figures 2 and 3). The exact location of the printed circuit board should be kept so that the ballpoint pen is positioned as shown in the illustration. Obviously, the pen must be fixed into place before all the bolts are tightened up.

It should now become clear how the LED (D7), the LDR and the point of the pen combine to form the opto-coupler. At this stage it is essential that the LED and/or the LDR be positioned accurately. The ballpoint pen is then cut to size so that it just protrudes through the underside of the printed circuit board. A piece of copper-clad board is then cut to the required dimensions and glued into the end of the ballpoint.

The next operation is to drill holes in the side of the can to accommodate the LEDs, the switch (S1) and the holes whereby the preset potentiometers can be adjusted. It is probably easiest to mount the LEDs together on a small piece of Veroboard. Connections to the main board can then be made via a length of ribbon cable, which, once soldered, can be glued into place. The 9 V battery can be stuck to the side of the can with a piece of double-sided sticky tape. Obviously, the positioning of the potentiometer adjustment holes must be determined very accurately. Once everything has been packed in and all the soldering completed, the scales are ready for use.

The table shown here should be attached to the outside of the can next to the LEDs, so that the amount of postage required for the particular letter can be read off immediately. The scales are calibrated by adjusting the four trimmer potentiometers with known weights on the scales. LED D3 should light up over 60 g, D4 over 100 g, D5 over 150 g and D6 over 200 g.

K. Hense

---

293 Mains LED

The very long life span of LEDs make them eminently suitable for on/off indicators. However, their use on mains voltages has been restricted since a low operating voltage prevents their direct connection with the mains supply in the manner of a neon.

Fortunately, there is a way around this problem, the AC resistance of a capacitor can be used to limit the current. No power is lost in the capacitor at all, since the current passing through the capacitor and the voltage across it are 90° out of phase with respect to each other.

Zener diode D2, acting as an ordinary forward-biased diode in this instance, prevents excess voltage levels appearing across the LED during the negative half-cycle of the mains waveform. If the circuit is switched on during the positive half, D2 will prevent the voltage across LED D1 and R1 from rising above 2.7 V. If an ordinary diode were used here, as in the earlier circuit, the LED is likely to go to the big scrap box in the sky.

The value of C1 determines the current passing

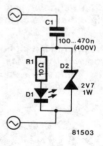

through the LED. When C1 = 100 n the current will be about 4 mA, and about 20 mA if a value of 470 n is chosen.

294 Universal digital meter

This digital meter is a great improvement on previous designs through the inclusion of an input stage containing J-FET opamps. This avoids various problems such as an unstable zero-reading. The J-FET inputs provide a very high input impedance and instead of the normal protection diodes, the circuit contains transistors connected as diodes. The transistors used have a low leakage current (1 nA).

The reason for selecting such an extensive input stage rests on two factors: The common-mode input of the 356 opamp has a range of −4 V...+4 V. The second reason is the fact that the input bias current the 356 gets away with a mere 30 pA.

The input signal is fed to IC4 via resistor R11. This IC controls the seven-segment driver (IC5) and is responsible for displaying the information once it arrives. The three position switch (S1), situated to the left of IC4 on the circuit diagram,

1

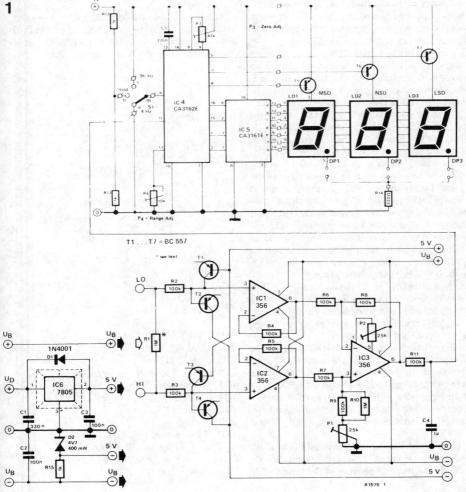

2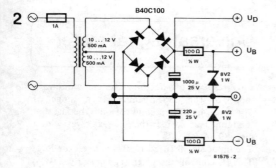

3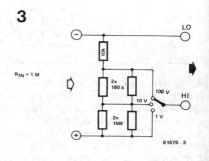

varies the sample-rate of the incoming data. In position (a) a sample is taken every quarter of a second, but in position (b) the display is 'frozen'. To display a rapidly changing input signal, the switch should be placed in position (c) in which case the sample-rate is once every 0.01 seconds and the meter responds very quickly.

Calibration of the universal digital meter is accomplished as follows: Firstly, opamp IC3 is removed and the left-hand side (circuit diagram-wise) of R11 is connected to ground. Preset potentiometer P3 is then adjusted so that the display reads 000. Opamp IC3 is then re-inserted and the earth connection removed from R11. Now, the two inputs, Hi and Lo, are connected to ground instead and preset potentiometer P2 is then adjusted to give a reading of 000 on the display. The next thing to do is to connect both the Hi and Lo inputs to a voltage supply of about 3 V and again adjust P1 to bring the display reading back to 000 (common-mode rejection). Finally, an accurate known voltage of, for example, 800 mV is connected to the input, after which preset P4 is adjusted to give the correct display of 800. During this last operation the Lo input should be connected to ground.

The power supply for the circuit is so simple that it hardly needs any description. The zener diode is included to provide transistors T2 and T4 with a slightly negative bias voltage. The power supply circuit is shown in figure 2.

An important feature of the overall design is the fact that the meter can be used in the floating or fixed mode. In the floating mode, the case of the meter (chassis) should be connected to the case of the equipment which is being tested. Also, the common-mode input voltage should, in all instances, lie somewhere between −4.0 V and +0.4 V.

In cases where the meter is operated in the fixed mode, the Lo input should be connected to ground. The input impedance of the meter, with

resistor R1 in place, is 1 M Ω. If desired, an input divider such as that shown in figure 3 can be incorporated, in which case R1 must be omitted altogether.

Resistors R2...R9 are contained in a 16 pin DIL IC package. If this particular device proves difficult to obtain, separate 100 k Ω, 1/8 W resistors with a tolerance of 1% can be used instead of the array.

Parts list

Resistors:

R1, R10 = 1 M
R2...R9 = 100 k (see text)
R11 = 10 k
R12, R13, R15 = 1 k
R14 = 220 Ω
P1, P2 = 25 k
P3 = 47 k
P4 = 10 k

Capacitors:

C1, C3, C4 = 330 n
C2 = 100 n
C5 = 270 n

Semiconductors:

T1...T7 = BC 557
D1 = 1N4001
D2 = 4V7, 400 mW zener diode
IC1...IC3 = 356
IC4 = CA 3162E
IC5 = CA 3161E
IC6 = 7805
LD1...LD3 = red FND557
        green FND537
        yellow FND547
        or: TIL 701

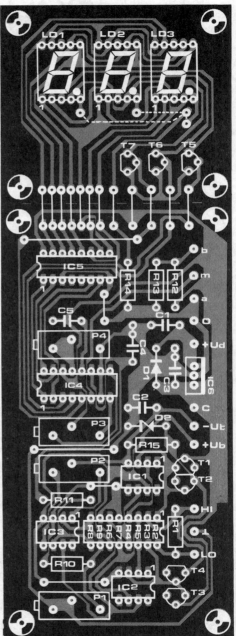

325

The musician, who does not possess 'perfect pitch', will no doubt occasionally have to use a tuning aid such as a tuning fork or an electronic 440 Hz sound generator. Low frequency 440 Hz oscillators are not ideally suited for use as 'electronic tuning forks' because of their inherent instability. For this reason, the crystal controlled oscillator described here may well offer the best solution.

Crystals with a frequency of 27.025 MHz for use in model radio control transmitters, are reasonably inexpensive and readily available. Such a crystal oscillates at a basic frequency of 9.0083 MHz, which when first divided by 5 and then by 12^{12} yields a tone with a frequency of 439.86 Hz. Ideally, a crystal with a frequency of 27.035 MHz, channel 7 of American CB transceivers, would give slightly more accurate results (440.02 Hz), but these are, as yet, not readily available in the UK!

The division by 2^{12} (= 4096) can be obtained by connecting twelve flipflops in series (IC3...IC5), while the oscillator signal is divided by 5 in IC2. Transistor T2 and the gates in IC1 serve to buf-

fer the oscillator signal from T1, and transistors T3 and T4 allow a direct connection to an 8 Ω loudspeaker. Resistor R6, indicated with an asterisk, regulates the volume of the resultant tone and can be reduced to a minimum of 22 Ω . The volume can also be increased by raising the battery voltage or by placing the speaker in a box.

If the circuit is to be made part of the Elektor Formant synthesiser, as an extra module, it can be powered from the + 15 V rail. Current consumption is somewhere in the region of 40... 50 mA.

Readers who possess a sufficiently accurate frequency counter, can try to adjust the oscillator frequency to 9.0112 MHz, using the trimmer capacitor C5. However, this may not be possible as it is slightly 'off frequency' as far as the crystal is concerned. A figure of 9.008332 is more likely. Nevertheless, without adjustment, the circuit will provide a typical tone frequency of 440 Hz with a maximum deviation of ± 0.05 Hz. This remains considerably more precise than most mechanical devices.

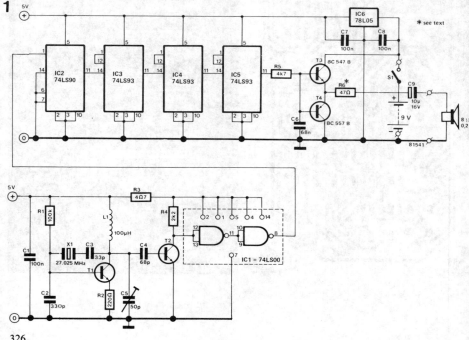

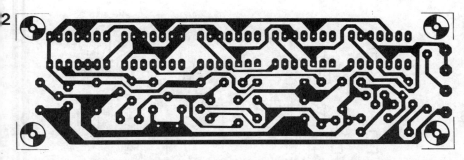

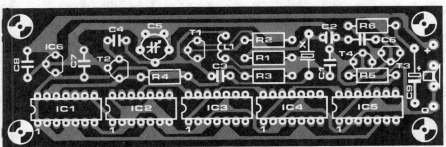

Parts list

Resistors:
R1 = 100 k
R2 = 220 Ω
R3 = 4.7 Ω
R4 = 2k2
R5 = 4k7
R6 = 47 Ω *

Capacitors:
C1, C7, C8 = 100 n
C2 = 330 p
C3 = 33 p
C4 = 68 p
C5 = 50 p trimmer
C6 = 68 n
C9 = 10 µ /16 V

Semiconductors:
T1, T2 = BF 198, BF 199, BF 494
T3 = BC 547B
T4 = BC 557B
IC1 = 74LS00
IC2 = 74LS90
IC3...IC5 = 74LS93
IC6 = 78L05

Miscellaneous:
L1 = 100 µ H
X1 = 27.025 MHz crystal (with holder)
S1 = single-pole switch
LS = 8 Ω /0.2 W loudspeaker

* see text

296 Microcompressor

Dynamic range compressors can be used in any device that requires a constant audio output level. The first example that comes to mind is the automatic record level control in cassette recorders. The compressor can also be employed, however, in such items as amateur radio equipment, discotheques, babyphones and intercom systems to ensure optimum intelligibility and to prevent any damage to amplifiers and loudspeakers. When used in combination with a

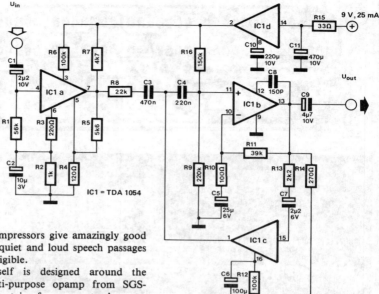

1

IC1 = TDA 1054

81513-1

microphone, compressors give amazingly good results as both quiet and loud speech passages are equally intelligible.

The circuit itself is designed around the TDA 1054 multi-purpose opamp from SGS-Ates. This IC contains four separate elements, each of which performs its own particular task. IC1a is a preamplifier which is used to boost the input signal to about 50 x (1 + R5/R4). Opamp IC1b is also used as a preamplifier, but this has a gain of 400 x (1 + R11/R10). The function of IC1d is to remove any ripple from the supply voltage, while IC1c takes care of the actual automatic level control.

A good compressor should compress the entire signal in a linear fashion, in other words, not by simply 'clipping' the top of the waveform. This can be accomplished by making the amount of level reduction dependent on the largest amplitude appearing in the input signal. To do this, the amplitude of the output signal is monitored and when this rises above a certain level, attenuation is introduced.

The attenuator, IC1c, is driven via resistor R13 and capacitor C7 and acts as a variable resistance between the junction of C3/C4 and ground. This ensures that the input to the output amplifier, IC1b, is sufficiently attenuated when the output level rises above about 1 V rms. Capacitor C7 gives the system delay time which is necessary to ensure that control is adequately fast to follow the envelope of the signal waveform, but not fast enough to respond to the waveform itself. This capacitor therefore determines the attack time of the circuit. The decay time depends on the values of capacitor C6 and resistor R12. This delay time must be much

328

longer in order to maintain a reasonably consistent sound level.

A graphic illustration of how the circuit works is shown in figure 2. The times given are valid for the component values in figure 1. The attack and decay times can be modified according to personal taste by changing the values of C7 and C6 respectively.

The input of the microcompressor is suitable for low signal levels, for instance from microphones. The input impedance is approximately 50 k . Higher input signal levels can be con-

2

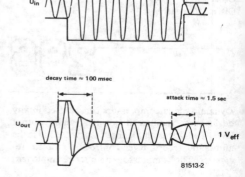

decay time ≈ 100 msec

attack time ≈ 1.5 sec

U_{in}

U_{out}

1 V_{eff}

81513-2

nected directly to resistor R8, in which case the entire circuit before R8 can be omitted.

The supply voltage can be increased to 12 V if desired, but this will mean that the rating of the electrolytic capacitors will have to be increased also.

297 Active notch or CW filter

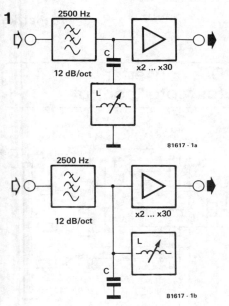

81617 - 1a

81617 - 1b

In general, the majority of low-cost shortwave receivers have poor selectivity. Usually, reception is accompanied by a number of interfering signals, or more than one transmission is heard at the same time (especially with CW transmissions, which have a very narrow bandwidth). An add-on extra for the existing inexpensive set could therefore prove very useful, particularly if a (much) more expensive one is not available (or the funds thereof).

The filter described here is an active equivalent for an LC tuned circuit and can be operated in the parallel mode (peaking function) or the series mode (notch function) as can be seen from figure 1. The filter is connected to the audio output of the receiver or, if present, the tape recorder output. The output of the filter is sufficient to drive a pair of headphones directly, provided their impedance is 600 Ω or greater.

The simulated inductor consists of the circuitry around opamps A2 and A3 (see figure 2). A 12 dB per octave filter for the input signal is provided by A1, while A4 acts as an amplifier with an adjustable gain of 2...30 times.

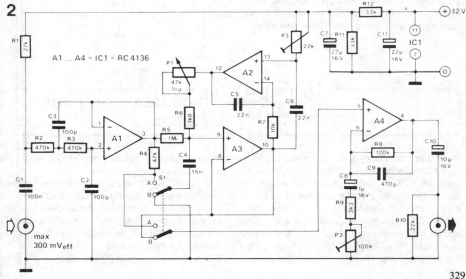

The resonant circuit can be switched between the parallel and series operating modes by means of S1. The filter can be tuned over the range 300...400 Hz by means of potentiometer P1. With switch S1 in position B, preset potentiometer P3 should be rotated to the position just prior to where the circuit starts oscillating. This calls for a precise alignment and therefore P3 should be a multi-turn type. The gain of the circuit can be adjusted by means of potentiometer P2. This can be a preset type if a fairly constant level of background noise is to be expected, otherwise a normal (volume control) potentiometer is preferred.

When the circuit is actually used, the following points must be remembered:
1) the effects of frequency drift will be pronounced
2) as the AGC circuit responds to a much wider bandwidth than that of the filter, the recovered signal could show 'alien' pumping action.

H. Pietzko

298 D/A converter for motor control

In many instances, it is quite sufficient to control motors with an on/off type action. However, if a more 'linear' control is required, the circuit given here may prove useful. The four bit magnitude comparator (4063) inputs are EX-ORed and fed to a resistive divider chain to provide an output voltage which is proportional to the difference of the comparator input values (with an accuracy of four bits). These values can be derived, for instance, from a binary counter.

The outputs of the comparator (A > B, A = B, A < B) can be used to (indirectly) turn the motor on or off and/or to reverse the polarity of the supply voltage in the case of DC motors. This kind of circuitry can be applied where varicap control is not adequate, such as for remote antenna tuning or phase-noise free VCOs.

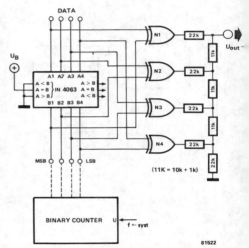

299 Frequency and phase detector

When the frequency range over which the VCO of a phase-locked loop (PLL) must operate exceeds an octave, a multiplier is no longer adequate for use as a phase detector. The circuit must, therefore, also be sensitive to frequency to avoid 'locking' when harmonics of the fundamental lock frequency are present. In many instances the 4046 CMOS PLL IC performs an extremely good job. However, it only has a maximum operating frequency of 500 kHz which can give rise to certain problems.

The circuit shown here has the above mentioned capability and behaves in a similar manner to the phase comparator (pin 13) of the 4046 PLL. The only differences being that the 4046 output is 'tri-state' and this little circuit operates at higher frequencies than the 4046.

When the input signals (1) and (2) have the same

1

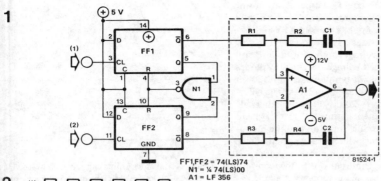

FF1,FF2 = 74(LS)74
N1 = ¼ 74(LS)00
A1 = LF 356

81524-1

2

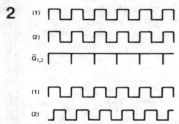

frequency and phase relationship, the two flip-flops are both reset simultaneously. Should the phase shift between the two input signals alter, the reset timing will also change. In this instance, the average voltage at the $\overline{Q}$ output of one of the flipflops will be greater than that at the other. This is clearly illustrated in the timing diagram.

The dc level at the output of the differential amplifier, A1, is used to control the VCO. The actual values of components R1...R4, C1 and C2 depend on the frequency of operation.

300 Power failure forecaster

This circuit can be extremely useful in, amongst other things, microprocessor systems. Should the main power voltage fail, the circuit will provide a logic high level at its output a short time before the supply disappears completely. This time delay, although short, can be sufficient to

take emergency measures. For instance, storing the data contained in certain of the internal processor registers into a low-power standby random access memory (battery powered).

In the circuit diagram, above the dotted line, there are two examples of 5 volt power supplies

1

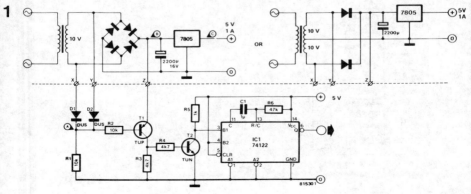

in which the circuit could be used. Also shown, are the relevant interconnections – this is why there are two sets of points marked X, Y and Z.

The circuit operates as follows: the raw smoothed supply voltage appears at point B and the raw unsmoothed voltage, rectified by diodes D1 and D2 appears at point A. As can be seen from figure 2, the voltage at point A falls below that at point B every 20 ms (at each mains half cycle). At this moment in time transistor T1, and therefore transistor T2, turns on and the monostable multivibrator will be re-triggered. Since the pulse duration of the monoflop is approximately 15 ms, the $\overline{Q}$ output will be low continuously as long as the main supply voltage is applied. However, as soon as the main voltage fails, the voltage at point A will become lower than that at point B immediately due to the

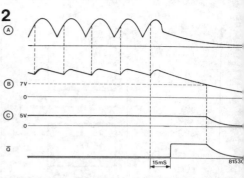

action of the smoothing capacitor. The MMV is then no longer (re-)triggered and the $\overline{Q}$ output will go high after a maximum of 15 ms. This output pulse can then be used to call an interrupt routine of the type mentioned above.

301 VHF preamp

Designing a preamp for the VHF waveband (around 100 MHz) is not always an easy matter. This circuit, however, is both relatively simple to use and is inexpensive. It has the advantage of a fairly large bandwidth (2 MHz) and good noise figure (2.5 dB). The preamp has a large dynamic range and a gain of 20 dB at a frequency of 144 MHz.

L1 and L2 are air-cored coils with an internal diameter of 6 mm and consist of 4 turns of 1 mm silverplated copper wire. L1 is tapped one turn from the earthy end, whilst L2 has a tap one turn from the end nearest R3. Ceramic types are recommended for the four 1 n capacitors.

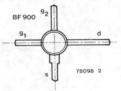

2

1

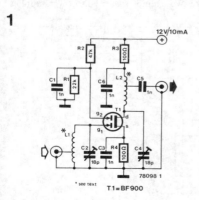

* see text

T1 = BF 900

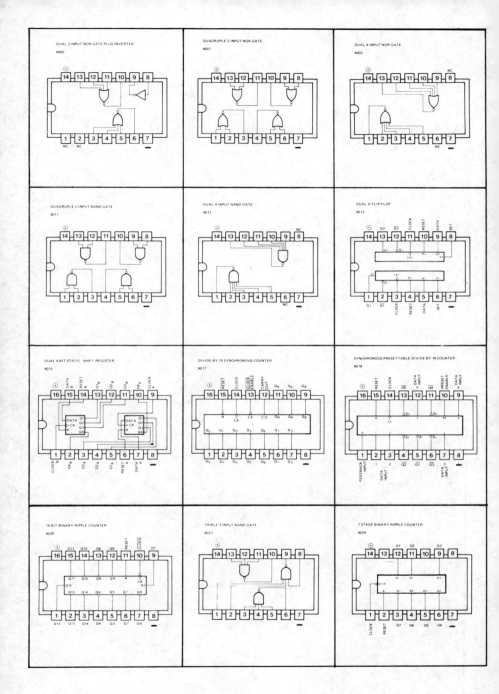

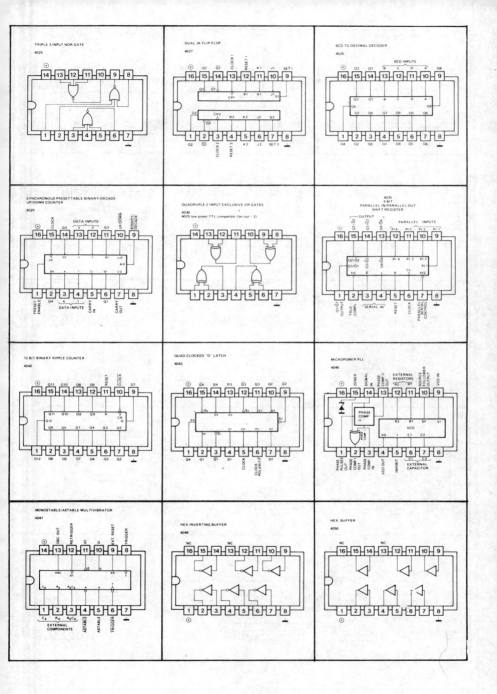

TRIPLE 3 INPUT NOR GATE
4025

DUAL JK FLIP FLOP
4027

BCD TO DECIMAL DECODER
4028

SYNCHRONOUS PRESETTABLE BINARY/DECADE
UP/DOWN COUNTER
4029

QUADRUPLE 2 INPUT EXCLUSIVE OR GATES
4030
4070 low power TTL compatible (fan out = 2)

4035
4 BIT
PARALLEL IN/PARALLEL OUT
SHIFT REGISTER

12 BIT BINARY RIPPLE COUNTER
4040

QUAD CLOCKED "D" LATCH
4042

MICROPOWER PLL
4046

MONOSTABLE/ASTABLE MULTIVIBRATOR
4047

HEX INVERTING BUFFER
4049

HEX BUFFER
4050

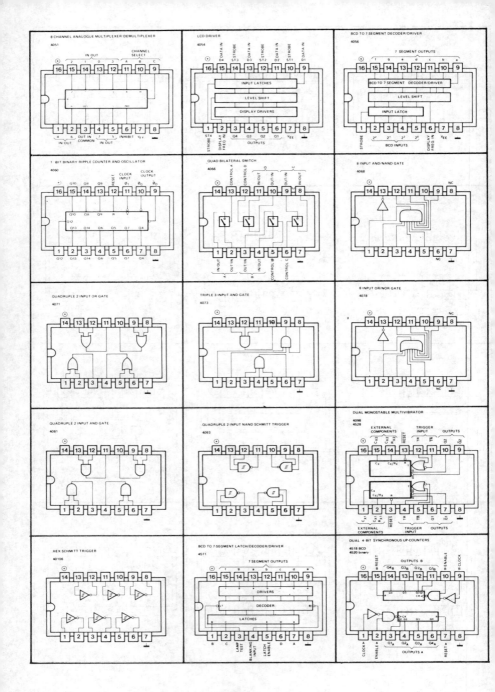

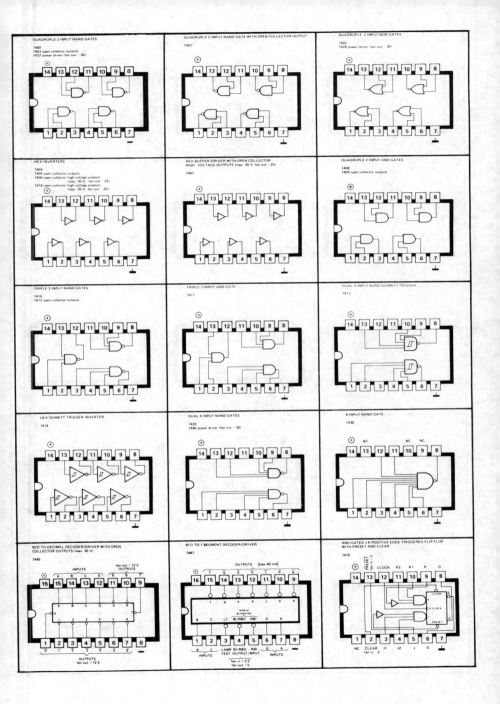

QUADRUPLE 2 INPUT NAND GATES

7400
7403 open collector outputs
7437 power driver (fan out : 30)

QUADRUPLE 2 INPUT NAND GATE WITH OPEN COLLECTOR OUTPUT

7401

QUADRUPLE 2 INPUT NOR GATES

7402
7428 power driver (fan out : 30)

HEX INVERTERS

7404
7405 open collector outputs
7406 open collector high voltage outputs
         (max. 30 V, fan out : 25)
7416 open collector high voltage outputs
         (max. 30 V, fan out : 25)

HEX BUFFER/DRIVER WITH OPEN COLLECTOR
HIGH VOLTAGE OUTPUTS (max. 30 V, fan out : 25)

7407

QUADRUPLE 2 INPUT AND GATES

7408
7409 open collector outputs

TRIPLE 3 INPUT NAND GATES

7410
7412 open collector outputs

TRIPLE 3 INPUT AND GATE

7411

DUAL 4 INPUT NAND SCHMITT TRIGGER

7413

HEX SCHMITT TRIGGER INVERTER

7414

DUAL 4 INPUT NAND GATES

7420
7440 power driver (fan out : 30)

8 INPUT NAND GATE

7430

BCD TO DECIMAL DECODER/DRIVER WITH OPEN
COLLECTOR OUTPUTS (max. 30 V)

7445

BCD TO 7 SEGMENT DECODER/DRIVER

7447

AND GATED J K POSITIVE EDGE TRIGGERED FLIP FLOP
WITH PRESET AND CLEAR

7470

337

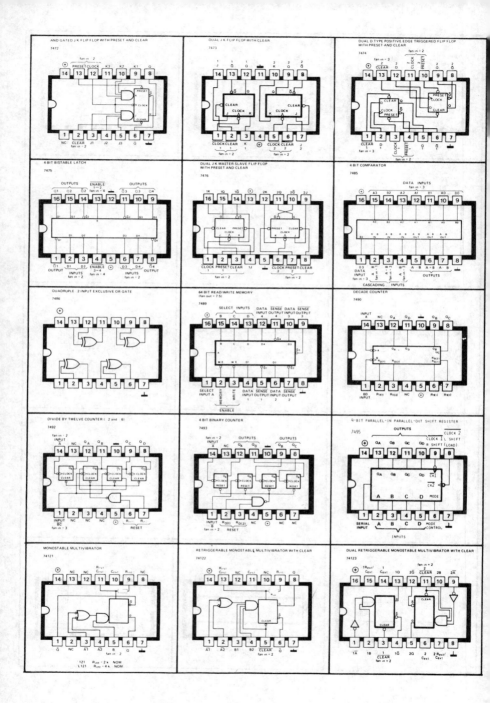

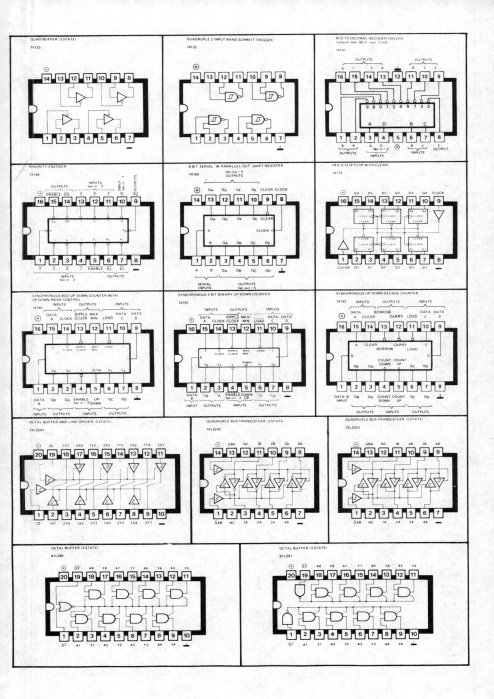

QUAD BUFFER (3 STATE)
74125

QUADRUPLE 2 INPUT NAND SCHMITT TRIGGER
74132

BCD TO DECIMAL DECODER DRIVER
(output max 60 V max 7 mA)
74141

PRIORITY ENCODER
74148

8 BIT SERIAL IN PARALLEL OUT SHIFT REGISTER
74164

HEX D FLIP FLOP WITH CLEAR
74174

SYNCHRONOUS BCD UP DOWN COUNTER WITH UP DOWN MODE CONTROL
74190

SYNCHRONOUS 4 BIT BINARY UP/DOWN COUNTER
74191

SYNCHRONOUS UP-DOWN DECADE COUNTER
74192

OCTAL BUFFER AND LINE DRIVER (3 STATE)
74LS241

QUADRUPLE BUS TRANSCEIVER (3 STATE)
74LS242

QUADRUPLE BUS TRANSCEIVER (3 STATE)
74LS243

OCTAL BUFFER (3 STATE)
81LS95

OCTAL BUFFER (3 STATE)
81LS97

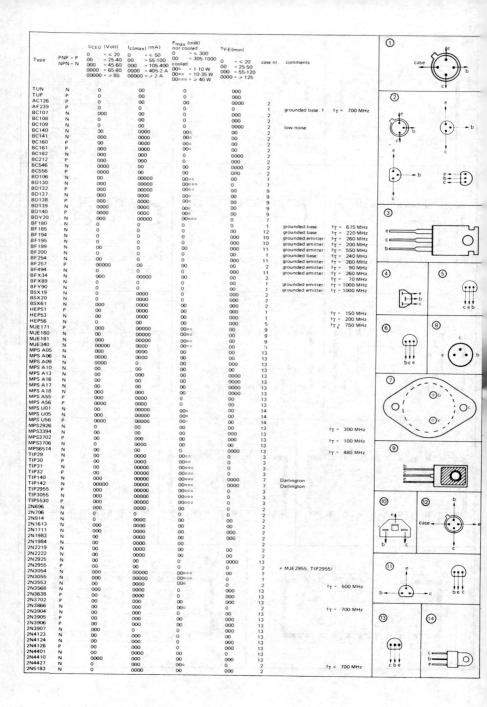

Legend:

U_{CEO} (Volt): 0 = ≤ 20 · 00 = 25-40 · 000 = 45-60 · 0000 = 65-80 · 00000 = ≥ 85

$I_{C(max)}$ (mA): 0 = ≤ 50 · 00 = 55-100 · 000 = 105-400 · 0000 = 405-2 A · 00000 = ≥ 2 A

P_{max} (mW): not cooled: 0 = ≤ 300 · 00 = 305-1000 · cooled: 00○ = 1-10 W · 00○○ = 10-35 W · 00○○○ = ≥ 40 W

h_{FE}(min): 0 = ≤ 20 · 00 = 25-50 · 000 = 55-120 · 0000 = ≥ 125

PNP = P · NPN = N

Type	PNP=P / NPN=N	U_{CEO}	$I_{C(max)}$	P_{max}	h_{FE}(min)	case nr.	comments
TUN	N	0	00	0	000		
TUP	P	0	00	0	000		
AC126	P	0	00	00	0000	2	
AF239	P	0	0	0	0	1	grounded base: f f_T = 700 MHz
BC107	N	000	00	0	000	2	
BC108	N	0	00	0	000	2	
BC109	N	0	00	0	000	2	low noise
BC140	N	30	0000	00○	00	2	
BC141	N	000	0000	00○	00	2	
BC160	P	00	0000	00○	00	2	
BC161	P	000	0000	00○	00	2	
BC182	N	000	000	0	0000	2	
BC212	P	000	000	0	0000	2	
BC546	N	0000	00	00	0000	2	
BC556	P	0000	00	00	0000	2	
BD106	N	00	00000	00○○○	00	7	
BD130	N	000	00000	00○○○	0	7	
BD132	P	000	00000	00○○○	0	7	
BD137	N	000	0000	00○	00	9	
BD138	P	000	0000	00○	00	9	
BD139	N	000	0000	00○	00	9	
BD140	P	000	0000	00○	00	9	
BDY20	N	000	00000	00○○○	0	9	
BF180	N	0	0	0	0	1	grounded base: f_T = 675 MHz
BF185	N	0	0	0	00	12	grounded base: f_T = 220 MHz
BF194	N	0	0	0	000	10	grounded emitter: f_T = 260 MHz
BF195	N	0	0	0	000	10	grounded emitter: f_T = 200 MHz
BF199	N	00	0	0	000	11	grounded emitter: f_T = 550 MHz
BF200	N	0	0	00	00	1	grounded base: f_T = 240 MHz
BF254	N	00	0	0	00	11	grounded emitter: f_T = 260 MHz
BF257	P	00000	00	00	000	11	grounded emitter: f_T = 90 MHz
BF494	N	0	0	0	00	2	grounded emitter: f_T = 260 MHz
BFX34	N	000	00000	00	00	1	grounded emitter: f_T = 70 MHz
BFX89	N	0	0	0	00	1	grounded emitter: f_T = 1000 MHz
BFY90	N	0	0	0	00	1	grounded emitter: f_T = 1000 MHz
BSX19	N	0	0000	00	000	2	
BSX20	N	0	0000	00	000	2	
BSX61	N	000	0000	00	000	2	
HEP51	P	00	0000	00	000	1	f_T = 150 MHz
HEP53	N	00	0000	00	000	1	f_T = 200 MHz
HEP56	N	00	0000	00	000	5	f_T = 750 MHz
MJE171	P	000	00000	00○	00	9	
MJE180	N	00	00000	00○	00	9	
MJE181	N	000	00000	00○	00	9	
MJE340	N	00000	0000	00○	00	9	
MPS A05	N	00	000	00	000	13	
MPS A06	N	0000	0000	00	000	13	
MPS A09	N	0000	0	00	000	13	
MPS A10	N	00	00	00	000	13	
MPS A13	N	00	000	00	0000	13	
MPS A16	N	00	00	00	000	13	
MPS A17	N	00	00	00	0000	13	
MPS A18	N	000	000	00	0000	13	
MPS A55	P	000	0000	00	00	13	
MPS A56	P	0000	0000	0	00	13	
MPS U01	N	00	00000	00○	00	14	
MPS U05	N	000	00000	00○	00	14	
MPS U56	P	000	00000	00○	00	14	
MPS2926	N	0	00	00	000	13	
MPS3394	N	00	00	00	000	13	f_T = 300 MHz
MPS3702	P	00	000	00	000	13	
MPS3706	N	0	0000	00	000	13	f_T = 100 MHz
MPS6514	N	00	00	00	0000	13	f_T = 480 MHz
TIP29	N	00	00000	00○○	0	3	
TIP30	P	00	0000	00○○	0	3	
TIP31	N	00	00000	00○○	0	3	
TIP32	P	00	00000	00○○	0	3	
TIP140	N	000	00000	00○○	0000	7	Darlington
TIP142	N	00000	00000	00○○	0000	7	Darlington
TIP2955	P	000	00000	00○○	0	3	
TIP3055	N	000	00000	00○○	0	3	
TIP5530	P	000	00000	00○○	0	3	
2N696	N	000	0000	00	0	2	
2N706	N	0	0	0	0	2	
2N914	N	0	0	0	00	2	
2N1613	N	000	0000	00	00	2	
2N1711	N	000	0000	00	00	2	
2N1983	N	00	0000	00	000	2	
2N1984	N	00	0000	00	000	2	
2N2219	N	00	0000	00	00	2	
2N2222	N	00	0000	00	00	2	
2N2925	N	00	00	00	0000	13	
2N2955	P	00	00	00	0000	13	≠ MJE2955, TIP2955!
2N3054	N	000	00000	00○○	00	7	
2N3055	N	000	00000	00○○	0	7	
2N3553	N	00	0000	00○	00	2	f_T = 500 MHz
2N3568	N	000	000	0	000	2	
2N3638	P	00	000	0	000	13	
2N3702	P	00	000	00	000	13	
2N3866	N	00	0000	00○	00	5	f_T = 700 MHz
2N3904	N	00	000	0	000	13	f_T = 700 MHz
2N3905	P	00	000	00	000	13	
2N3906	P	00	000	00	000	13	
2N3907	N	00	0	00	000	13	
2N4123	N	00	000	0	000	13	
2N4124	N	00	000	0	000	13	
2N4126	P	00	000	0	000	13	
2N4401	N	00	0000	00	000	13	
2N4410	N	0000	000	00	0	13	
2N4427	N	00	000	00	00	2	f_T = 700 MHz
2N5183	N	0	0000	00	000	2	

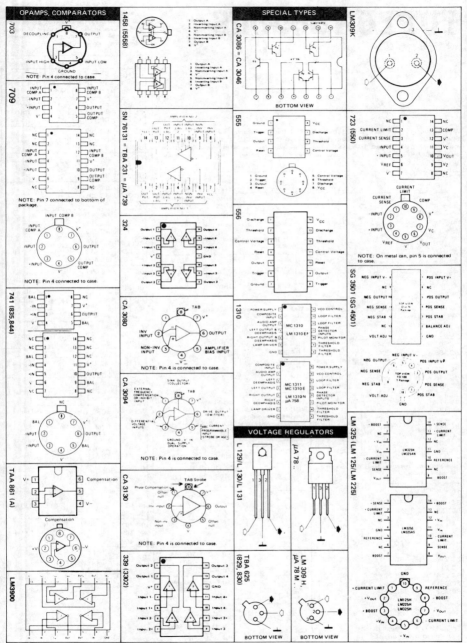

NOTE: All IC's shown top view, unless otherwise stated.

TUPTUNDUGDUS

Wherever possible in Elektor circuits, transistors and diodes are simply marked 'TUP' (Transistors, Universal PNP), 'TUN' (Transistor, Universel NPN), 'DUG' (Diode, Universal Germanium) or 'DUS' (Diode, Universal Silicon). This indicates that a large group of similar devices can be used, provided they meet the minimum specifications listed in tables 1a and 1b.

	type	U_{CEO} max	I_C max	h_{fe} min.	P_{tot} max	f_T min.
TUN	NPN	20 V	100 mA	100	100 mW	100 MHz
TUP	PNP	20 V	100 mA	100	100 mW	100 MHz

Table 1a. Minimum specifications for TUP and TUN.

Table 1b. Minimum specifications for DUS and DUG.

	type	U_R max	I_F max	I_R max	P_{tot} max	C_D max
DUS	Si	25 V	100 mA	1 μA	250 mW	5 pF
DUG	Ge	20 V	35 mA	100 μA	250 mW	10 pF

Table 2. Various transistor types that meet the TUN specifications.

TUN		
BC 107	BC 208	BC 384
BC 108	BC 209	BC 407
BC 109	BC 237	BC 408
BC 147	BC 238	BC 409
BC 148	BC 239	BC 413
BC 149	BC 317	BC 414
BC 171	BC 318	BC 547
BC 172	BC 319	BC 548
BC 173	BC 347	BC 549
BC 182	BC 348	BC 582
BC 183	BC 349	BC 583
BC 184	BC 382	BC 584
BC 207	BC 383	

Table 3. Various transistor types that meet the TUP specifications.

TUP		
BC 157	BC 253	BC 352
BC 158	BC 261	BC 415
BC 177	BC 262	BC 416
BC 178	BC 263	BC 417
BC 204	BC 307	BC 418
BC 205	BC 308	BC 419
BC 206	BC 309	BC 512
BC 212	BC 320	BC 513
BC 213	BC 321	BC 514
BC 214	BC 322	BC 557
BC 251	BC 350	BC 558
BC 252	BC 351	BC 559

The letters after the type number denote the current gain:

A: a' (β, h_{fe}) = 125-260
B: a' = 240-500
C: a' = 450-900.

Table 4. Various diodes that meet the DUS or DUG specifications.

DUS		DUG
BA 127	BA 318	OA 85
BA 217	BAX 13	OA 91
BA 218	BAY 61	OA 95
BA 221	1N914	AA 116
BA 222	1N4148	
BA 317		

Table 5. Minimum specifications for the BC107, -108, -109 and BC177, -178, -179 families (according to the Pro-Electron standard). Note that the BC179 does not necessarily meet the TUP specification ($I_{c,max}$ = 50 mA).

	NPN	PNP
	BC 107	BC 177
	BC 108	BC 178
	BC 109	BC 179
U_{ceo} max	45 V	45 V
	20 V	25 V
	20 V	20 V
U_{eb0} max	6 V	5 V
	5 V	5 V
	5 V	5 V
I_c max	100 mA	100 mA
	100 mA	100 mA
	100 mA	50 mA
P_{tot} max	300 mW	300 mW
	300 mW	300 mW
	300 mW	300 mW
f_T min.	150 MHz	130 MHz
	150 MHz	130 MHz
	150 MHz	130 MHz
F max	10 dB	10 dB
	10 dB	10 dB
	4 dB	4 dB

Table 6. Various equivalents for the BC107, -108, ... families. The data are those given by the Pro-Electron standard; individual manufacturers will sometimes give better specifications for their own products.

NPN	PNP	Case	Remarks
BC 107 BC 108 BC 109	BC 177 BC 178 BC 179		
BC 147 BC 148 BC 149	BC 157 BC 158 BC 159		P_{max} = 250 mW
BC 207 BC 208 BC 209	BC 204 BC 205 BC 206		
BC 237 BC 238 BC 239	BC 307 BC 308 BC 309		
BC 317 BC 318 BC 319	BC 320 BC 321 BC 322		I_{cmax} = 150 mA
BC 347 BC 348 BC 349	BC 350 BC 351 BC 352		
BC 407 BC 408 BC 409	BC 417 BC 418 BC 419		P_{max} = 250 mW
BC 547 BC 548 BC 549	BC 557 BC 558 BC 559		P_{max} = 500 mW
BC 167 BC 168 BC 169	BC 257 BC 258 BC 259		169/259 I_{cmax} = 50 mA
BC 171 BC 172 BC 173	BC 251 BC 252 BC 253		251...253 low noise
BC 182 BC 183 BC 184	BC 212 BC 213 BC 214		I_{cmax} = 200 mA
BC 582 BC 583 BC 584	BC 512 BC 513 BC 514		I_{cmax} = 200 mA
BC 414 BC 414 BC 414	BC 416 BC 416 BC 416		low noise
BC 413 BC 413	BC 415 BC 415		low noise
BC 382 BC 383 BC 384			
BC 437 BC 438 BC 439			P_{max} = 220 mW
BC 467 BC 468 BC 469			P_{max} = 220 mW
	BC 261 BC 262 BC 263		low noise